The Restless Landscape:
Chinese Painting of the Late Ming Period

Cover:

Cheng Chung (active ca. 1610–1644). *Landscape:* handscroll
section. Dated 1632. 11 x 160-3/4″. Collection Cheng Chi, Tokyo.

James Cahill, Editor

University Art Museum, Berkeley

The Restless Landscape:
Chinese Painting of
the Late Ming Period

Published by University Art Museum, Berkeley, 1971.
All rights reserved.
Library of Congress card catalogue number 77-171043.

This book is the culmination of a demonstration program in
museum training for art history graduate students, sponsored
by a grant from the Samuel H. Kress Foundation. This project is also supported by a grant from the National Endowment for the Arts in Washington, D.C., a Federal agency.

Introduction

Late Ming Painting

Catalogue

Acknowledgments

6

The nature of this particular exhibition and publication makes it one of the most gratifying projects in which this Museum has been involved. Because we are a University art museum, we have encouraged collaboration of all sorts between the Museum itself and the various academic departments of the University, especially and naturally with the Department of Art History.

We were therefore particularly pleased when we were awarded a grant from the Samuel H. Kress Foundation for purposes of enabling us to train graduate students in the history of art in museum scholarship by means of seminars leading to major scholarly exhibitions and publications. The seminar led by Professor James Cahill on Chinese Painting of the Late Ming Period is the first realization of this Kress-supported demonstration program, and its success, as revealed in the present exhibition and publication, is indisputable.

The project was an extremely ambitious one, and required intense devotion from Jim Cahill and his students, as well as from this Museum's staff. Everyone involved in the project is now convinced that this type of program is significant and worthwhile, and is a very concrete and feasible method of training students toward the museum profession. It also offers graduate students the opportunity to publish their own research.

Because of the great need for art historians to enter the museum profession, I am very pleased that the University Art Museum and the Department of Art History here at Berkeley have been given the opportunity to launch this joint pilot program with such notable results.

I want to express my personal gratitude to Professor Cahill, whose energy and enthusiasm for the project assured its success, and especially to the Kress Foundation for their farsightedness and generosity in recognizing the value of this type of program and hence agreeing to fund its initial stages. We are also most grateful to the National Endowment for the Arts, who made a generous grant to subsidize existing funds when the project grew even beyond its initial scope. In his Preface to this catalogue Jim Cahill thanks the many individuals and institutions without whose generous cooperation we would not have realized the exhibition or publication, and to his thanks I would like to add my own sincerest gratitude.

Peter Selz, Director, University Art Museum, Berkeley
August 1971

Preface

by James Cahill

For purchasers or borrowers of this catalogue, we have one request—or, if you will, word of advice: read it. Some of the paintings in our exhibition are simply beautiful, and can get along very well without words; but many are not simple at all, and some are (we freely admit) not beautiful. So why are they there? The simplest answer to that deceptively simple question is: since we had no illusions about possessing either infallible taste or absolute and final criteria of judgment, and since we were nine different people (myself and a seminar of eight students) with different eyes, we tried to represent as fairly as we could the different kinds of painting that the Chinese produced, and (in varying degrees) admired, in the late Ming period. And if certain of these kinds of painting evoke, especially in those encountering them for the first time, a curiosity as to what is so good about them, the second-best way to find out (the best way, of course, being to look at them for a long time) is to read what the artists and critics of the period wrote about them, and find out what kinds of people these artists were and what sort of world they lived in. We have tried to answer these questions in the introductory essays, along with providing a quick survey of the developments in painting that led up to the late Ming, a summary of the main accomplishments of the period, and discussions of particular problems such as the evidence for Western influence. If our catalogue functions as we mean it to, it will make the experience of seeing the exhibition more than the enjoyment of a group of attractive or exciting paintings; it should make it into a revelation of the qualities of a moment in human history, and not only the history of art.

The seminar out of which the exhibition grew was supported by a generous grant from the Kress Foundation; the same grant, supplemented by one from the National Endowment for the Arts, made this catalogue possible. We are extremely grateful for both, and are persuaded that no other "learning experience" could be more valuable in the training of art historians and museum specialists than this one has been. The seminar was made up of eight specialist graduate students, all able to read Chinese and carry out high-level research. As a preliminary division of responsibility, the artists and schools that make up the painting of the period were divided into eight groups (future scholars may well write of the Eight Branches of Late Ming Painting, under the illusion that this is one of those numberings the Chinese loved to make up, rather than an accident of seminar enrollment) and each member of the seminar chose, or was assigned, one of these groups. Each selected the paintings to represent that school or group (I kept only the veto power, officially, but occasionally exercised also the power of professorial persuasion), compiled the catalogue material for those paintings, and composed the essay in which they are discussed, besides contributing to the introductory essays. I plead guilty to having done a good deal of rewriting and augmenting of some of the texts, and to having added new translations and other material. Because of this and also as editor, I am responsible, if only through insufficient checking, for whatever mistakes are still present. The virtues of the text, on the other hand, are to be credited to the students; the new ideas are all theirs, my own limited store having long ago been exposed elsewhere.

By the late Ming we mean to designate the decades from around 1570 to 1644, when the dynasty fell to the Manchus, who ruled China as the Ch'ing Dynasty until 1912. (We have included a few paintings that were actually done in the early decades of the Ch'ing period, when these were by artists whose formative years were in the late Ming, and whose works continue late Ming developments.) The late Ming was scarcely one of China's golden ages; it was, on the contrary, an age of weak emperors, contending political factions, corruption, bloody purges, sudden rises and falls in fortune. It was not a period one would choose to live in, but it is one that invites study. It is especially suited to an approach that attempts to relate art to intellectual, political, and social history. In the late Ming painting world, as an unusually rich body of literature attests, issues became clearer than ever before; local schools and stylistic movements competed in paintings and contended in words; criticism and theory impinged more strongly than before on artistic creation, so that a preference for a particular master or school in the past might be used to justify the practice of a particular style in the present. This situation will be described in some detail in the introductory essays, especially the one dealing with late Ming painting theory. One way of stating the matter would be to say that styles began to function as ideas do in a lively intellectual interchange: they were conceived, evolved, developed tensions that might be resolved; they could be passionately asserted or denied, juxtaposed or combined, alluded to or elaborated. Moreover, like ideas, they carried definable implications of attitudes on larger issues. One could, by painting a picture, take a stand on some question of the cultural superiority of one locale over another, or of one period of history over another; one could either flaunt or seek to conceal one's social status, or come out in favor of tradition or the breaking of it. The very fervor with which such stands were taken belongs to a period of great diversity, potential and actual. Everything was open to question, intellectual ideas and stylistic ideas. Such dogmaticism as Tung Ch'i-ch'ang's grows in a situation where nothing is so universally accepted as not to require authoritative assertion. The parallel to the political situation in late Ming will be apparent from a reading of the account of that situation given in the last of our introductory essays.

We have many people to thank for help in preparing this exhibition and catalogue. First of all, the many lenders, both museums and private collectors, have been extremely generous in allowing us to include so many of the masterpieces of late Ming painting; our most important debt of gratitude is to them. Some who were particularly kind in showing us their paintings when we made our trip to the East, during which some of the selection was made, include Mr. and Mrs. H. C. Weng, Mr. and Mrs. C. D. Carter, Mr. J. T. Tai, Mr. Walter Hochstadter, and the staffs of The Metropolitan Museum of Art, the Princeton Art Museum, the Fogg Art Museum, the Boston Museum of Fine Arts, and the Cleveland Museum of Art. Those who gave us help in reading inscriptions and seals, and supplied valuable information, include Mr. H. C. Weng, Mr. C. C. Wang, Mr. Waikam Ho, Professor Wen Fong, and Professor Cheng Hsi. Professor Frederick Wakeman of the Depart-

8   ment of History at the University of California, Berkeley, participated in the seminar and gave invaluable guidance to our investigations of late Ming political and intellectual history which happily falls within his own field of specialization. Miss Hildegarde Fuss joined the staff of the University Art Museum just in time to take an important part in the preparation of the catalogue; having the assistance of someone with her training in Chinese language and art was an unexpected boon, but one that it is now difficult to imagine how we could have done without. Miss Lorna Price gave us many hours of her time in reading and editing all the manuscripts, and made numerous suggestions for improving the form and raising the literary level of the catalogue. I am personally grateful to the staff of the University Art Museum for cooperation and sympathy through every phase of the planning of the exhibition, particularly to the Director, Professor Peter Selz, the Curator of Exhibitions, Miss Brenda Richardson, and the Registrar, Miss Joy Feinberg. Lastly, I am grateful to my eight students for bearing up as well as they did under the pressures that attended the later stages of this project, when it began to look as though it was after all, as some had warned, too ambitious for a seminar to attempt. I hope that in retrospect, when memories of meeting (or failing to meet) deadlines have dimmed, it will seem to them as rewarding as it has to me.

Introduction

Late Ming Painting in the History of Chinese Painting

by Lucy Lo-hwa Yang

For richness and diversity few periods in Chinese painting can equal the late Ming. Numerous surviving works of this age, many of very high quality, attest to the tremendous artistic activity in the late sixteenth and early seventeenth centuries. However, with a few notable exceptions, it cannot yet be said that late Ming painting has received attention and recognition commensurate with either its historical significance or its inherent value. It has been slighted by both Chinese and Western scholars in favor of earlier Ming painting on the one hand—particularly middle Ming painters such as Shen Chou (1427–1509), T'ang Yin (1470–1523), Wen Cheng-ming (1470–1559)—and early Ch'ing painting, most notably the more individual or eccentric artists, on the other. Flanked as the late Ming seems to be by two more popular periods, it does in fact serve as a crucial link between them: it not only witnesses the end to traditions and styles whose high point lies in the earlier part of the dynasty, but also, in its more innovative and creative facets, provides a background and basis for Ch'ing painting.

The few in-depth studies that have been carried out on late Ming painting tend to be concerned primarily with leading artistic personalities, such as Tung Ch'i-ch'ang (1555–1636), Wu Pin (ca. 1568–1626), or Ch'en Hung-shou (1598–1652). This concentrated approach, limiting the scope of inquiry, has had its positive value in closing large gaps in our understanding of the art of this complex and variegated period. The approach of the organizers of the present exhibition, however, differs somewhat from those previously taken. Instead of isolating personalities, or centering our attention on principal artists, we have chosen to confront late Ming painting in all its complexity and diversity. For this purpose we have categorized the artists we include into eight groups on the basis of such determinants and variables as regional schools, stylistic allegiance, and intellectual affiliation. Some of these groups may seem more loosely assembled than others, and all are meant to represent no more than tentative and preliminary divisions. While at some points they agree with traditional Chinese classifications of schools and stylistic lineages, we have tried not to be bound by these, but to let the paintings and painters establish their own groupings. In this way, we hope to create out of the highly fragmented and unwieldy body of late Ming painting an entity more manageable and more coherent than anyone has made of it up to now. Such is our contribution to a more thorough and profound understanding of late Ming painting in the history of Chinese painting.

Background

During the middle decades of the Ming dynasty, from the late fifteenth into the early sixteenth century, landscape painting was dominated by two stylistic currents, the Che School and the Wu School. The former, which had its origin in the early fifteenth century with the artist Tai Chin (1388–1462), was centered in Hang-chou in Chekiang Province (hence the designation "Che School"), while the latter was centered in Wu-hsien, comprising what is today the city of Su-chou and its surrounding area. The geographical proximity of these two centers—they are less than a hundred miles apart—was not matched, however, by any corresponding stylistic resemblance. The Che School, a number of whose artists served in the Ming imperial painting academy, took as its models the styles of the Southern Sung Academy, most notably those of Ma Yüan and Hsia Kuei, both active in the late twelfth and early thirteenth centuries. The Wu School, in contrast, looked chiefly to the masters of the Yüan dynasty (1280–1368) for inspiration.

Che School landscapes executed during the height of the school's activity in the fifteenth century can indeed be seen to preserve, both in mood and in style, many of the features that we have come to associate with Southern Sung Academy landscape painting. The Southern Sung fondness for rendering the scenery in broad washes and brilliant brushwork continues in the Che School, along with, in some works, its interest in naturalistic depiction. Less survives of the Southern Sung concern with fleeting effects of mist and light, but certain of the earlier artists, such as the school's founder and leading exponent Tai Chin, carry on this aspect of the style as well, within the context of their time. To these qualities the Che School artists add a heightened degree of vibrancy, dazzle, and animation, all testifying to their preference for open displays of technical proficiency and for styles and means that seem closer to decoration than representation. This is particularly true of the later phases of the school, beginning in the early part of the sixteenth century. By this time, the Che School had undergone a marked degeneration, characterized by an increased stereotyping of landscape in subject and composition. This was accompanied by a conspicuous exaggeration of tonal patterns and hard and insensitive line drawing, such that the forms themselves become less substantial and less legible as three-dimensional masses. As a result, Hang-chou began to lose its hold and prominence as an artistically important center, gradually giving way to Su-chou and the Wu School.

Where the Che School artists emulated the Southern Sung, three centuries before them, the Wu School preserves a large degree of continuity with the near past, and seems to grow naturally out of the achievements of the Yüan dynasty masters and out of some early Ming artists of Su-chou who had continued that tradition. This allegiance to Yüan styles and values is admirably illustrated in the works of Shen Chou, who revitalized the Su-chou tradition and is credited with founding the Wu School. His paintings are often clearly derived from one or another of the Yüan masters, most notably Wu Chen (1280–1354), and are characterized by qualities of mildness and restraint, a conscious avoidance of anything dramatic or overtly appealing. On the whole, the Wu School artists, like their Yüan predecessors, were members of the class of scholar-painters. They regarded painting as a form of personal expression, in the same way that poetry or calligraphy can be said to serve that function, and thought of it as revealing through the medium of brush and ink something of the personality of the artist. In addition to being distinguished from Che School artists on grounds of stylistic allegiance and social position, the scholar-amateurs or literati painters, unlike their professional and academic counterparts, never painted—at least in theory—as a means of livelihood, thus managing to avoid the terrible onus of commercialism. Instead, they painted at their leisure for a small and select audience of like-minded people. As time went on, however, the taste spread, and their paintings became more popular and sought after, resulting in the semi-commercialization of the school.

Wu School painting continued to thrive into the middle of the sixteenth century under the leadership and example of Wen Cheng-ming, a pupil and protege of Shen Chou. But in the subsequent generation or two, with the painting of Wen's numerous progeny and followers, the school began to undergo a marked decline in quality. This can be seen not only in the typical composition of late Wu School works, which is characterized by an extreme elongation in proportion, such that the verticality present already in the works of Wen Cheng-ming is exaggerated to the point of absurdity, but also in the accompanying tendency to crowd the painting with minute detail confined to its surface. The end result of such manipulative measures makes late Wu School landscapes appear as tall, elaborate visual images that are organically implausible and difficult to read in terms of space and form.

Interestingly, the more or less simultaneous decline of the Che School and Wu School occurred for quite similar reasons. Neither group seems to demonstrate even the slightest interest in compositional innovation and invention, and instead continues to find satisfactory the same old compositions and forms without regard to whether they make any meaningful reference to the natural world. For late Che and Wu School artists alike, the continued reliance on long outworn formal and expressive devices surely was more a matter of convenience and habit than of a genuine, compelling fondness.

By the late sixteenth century, the situation in painting had sunk to an unprecedented low. The schools had ceased to function as the conveyors of healthy stylistic traditions, there were no such strong leaders as Tai Chin and Shen Chou, and the artistic scene was dominated by a proliferation of minor painters producing undistinguished paintings. Any serious artist faced what must have appeared to be a serious dilemma: where to go from here, how to redeem a situation that seemed almost hopeless.

It should be mentioned that for a while, around the time of Wen Cheng-ming, a viable alternative can be said to have existed in the works of Chou Ch'en (active ca. 1500–1535), T'ang Yin (1470–1523), and Ch'iu Ying (ca. 1510–1551). These three masters, while active in Su-chou, to a large extent represented a compromise between the Che and Wu Schools in that they seemed to occupy a stylistic position between the professional and literati currents. But, brilliant painters though they were in their own right, they were never able to establish any significant following. This was perhaps due to the dominant position of the Wu School, which at the time of Wen Cheng-ming enjoyed a tremendous influence and popularity. Other factors also detracted from their potential for artistic leadership, at least among the literati. One of these may have been the academic overtones associated with their obvious technical proficiency, and with the polish and finish that their works display. The literati artists—largely, no doubt, because they were incapable of it themselves—were given to disparaging such employment of technical skill. Another factor, and perhaps the most important, was the source from which their style was chiefly derived: the landscape painting of Li T'ang, an artist who was active in the early twelfth century, and who thus occupied a transitional position between Northern and Southern Sung. Li T'ang worked in the Southern Sung Academy during the early decades of that period, and such painters as Ma Yüan and Hsia Kuei were his followers. Consequently, this third current in painting, not having been continued by any good artists in the interim, was no more attractive as a potential choice than the Che and Wu Schools for any late sixteenth-century painter.

At this moment in history appears Tung Ch'i-ch'ang, famed calligrapher, painter, and statesman, and staunchly uncompromising critic of the whole history of Chinese painting. Tung Ch'i-ch'ang sought, through example and doctrine, to reinvigorate and revive landscape painting, to lift it out of the depths into which it had sunk. Fundamentally, all his efforts were aimed at restoring to landscape painting the powerful structure which he felt it had possessed in the Yüan dynasty and before, but which

had been altogether sacrificed in favor of formulaic compositions and surface interest by the late Che and Wu School artists. Toward this end, he managed to incorporate and build upon many of the ideas and principles put forward by earlier literati painters. He sought, as had the Wu School artists before him, to establish a spiritual and stylistic allegiance to the Yüan masters. But unlike the earlier Ming literati painters, who had used the past as any artist does without any set orientation, Tung consciously and dogmatically proclaimed certain styles worthy of admiration and emulation, and certain styles not. As a critic and theorist, Tung succeeded in further formulating and elaborating literati painting theory and practice. In the process, he also assured, once and for all, the continuity of the literati painting tradition. Yet equally as important, Tung, as a landscape painter, managed to provide an extensive corpus of visual material on which others could model their paintings. Because Tung Ch'i-ch'ang in his dual capacity as theorist and artist provided a way out, a viable solution to the crisis of painting in the late sixteenth century, he was greeted with great enthusiasm.

Late Ming Painting in Outline
By the beginning of the seventeenth century, the area of Sung-chiang (also known as Yün-chien) in southeastern Kiangsu Province, and the principal city within it, Hua-t'ing, had arisen as a major center of painting, rivaling and eventually even surpassing Su-chou. Moreover, although the significant developments in painting continued to be focused in this southern Yangtze River delta region, painters were no longer so concentrated in only two or three major localities, as they had been in the previous century. Other cities, too, came into prominence as centers in which interesting painting was going on. With this greater degree of geographical diversification came a corresponding fragmentation of stylistic currents into loosely formed groups, which can perhaps be considered the forerunners of the more clearly definable regional schools in the early Ch'ing period.

In Su-chou, which had been since the fourteenth century a center of artistic and literary activity, more conservative artists continued to paint landscapes in the lineage of Wen Cheng-ming. Much of their production can properly be regarded as representing a dilution or debasement of the tradition. Underlying, perhaps, a number of the changes in painting styles in early seventeenth-century Su-chou is the breakdown there of some of the ideals of literati painting. By this time, a clearly discernible tinge of commercialism had begun to intrude into artistic production. Many Su-chou artists who practiced the styles that had once been the exclusive province of the scholar-amateurs now sold their works freely, or produced paintings on commission for the ever-expanding market of the merchant class. In such transactions, paintings were indeed commodities like any other. One sign of this mercantile output is the proliferation of paintings representing views of the Su-chou region, which, if their sheer quantity is any reliable indication, must have enjoyed tremendous popularity.

Also working in Su-chou, however, were other less conservative masters who, although they likewise stemmed from the Wu School current, made more creative use of it. These others, among whom one might include Sheng Mao-yeh (active 1594–1637), Chang Hung (1577–after 1660), Shao Mi (active ca. 1620–1640), and Li Shih-ta (active early 17th century), appear to have been less burdened by the oppressive weight of the tradition, and less bound to the debased side of it. They succeeded in producing many paintings of high quality and originality. They seem to bring to Su-chou painting new stylistic features and ideas that could have sent it in a new, very promising direction. In fact, this impetus came to nothing. Although within the context of late Ming landscape painting these artists hold secure positions as innovators, their innovations did not play any significant role in the subsequent development of Chinese painting. Because this group of painters was unable for one reason or another to command any important following and thereby win a wide base of support among their contemporaries or among critics and connoisseurs of later ages, their creativity and originality remained ultimately historically ineffectual. In this sense their works represent a brilliant and valuable contribution to late Ming painting, but in terms of future development, a dead end.

For the most part the future direction of Chinese painting depended upon what was just then being formulated and given artistic expression in Sung-chiang. Although lacking any such long and distinguished history as Su-chou could boast, it had become a rich and important city, with scholars, poets, collectors, and painters among its citizens. Tung Ch'i-ch'ang had gone there in the early 1570s in order to further his studies, and because of his natural brilliance came in contact with many people of literary and artistic standing. The painter Sung Hsü (1525–1605) who was a friend of such scholar-artists as Ku Cheng-i (active ca. 1580) and Mo Shih-lung (ca. 1550–ca. 1585), was instrumental in giving Sung-chiang prominence as a center of painting in the third quarter of the sixteenth century. Sung Hsü's followers, Chao Tso (active ca. 1600–1630) and Sung Mou-chin (late 16th century), and Chao's follower Shen Shih-ch'ung (active ca. 1610–1640), continued this stylistic current, which came to be known as the Yün-chien School. The landscapes of these artists can be seen to cover a considerable range in style, and the direction of the school changes from the early period of the Sung Hsü and Sun K'o-hung, when Shen Chou was the chief model, through a period in the early seventeenth century when Chao Tso's style interacted with that of Tung Ch'i-ch'ang, to a late stage, best represented by Shen Shih-ch'ung, in which the brush drawing becomes very soft and the compositions loosely organized and diffuse.

Ku Cheng-i, Tung Ch'i-ch'ang's patron, is traditionally credited with the founding of the Hua-t'ing School. It was Tung himself, however, who made it the most powerful and influential force in late Ming painting. He and his circle reorganized, systematized, and classified the accomplishments of great masters of the past partly in order to provide a rationale for elevating the literati mode of painting to a position of preeminence. Of all past styles, the ones that most interested and affected Tung and his followers were those of the Yüan masters, in whose concern with form and structure, and with the selec-

tion, spacing, and relationship of shapes, he found a basis for giving back to landscape painting the structure and organization it had gradually lost.

Among Tung's immediate followers are Ku I-te (active 1620s–1630s) and several of the so-called "Nine Friends of Painting," including Li Liu-fang (1575–1629) and Pien Wen-yü (active ca. 1620–1670), none of whom were painters of first rank, but all of whom were significantly affected by the doctrines as well as the stylistic innovations of their mentor. This group can properly be considered as the precursor of what came to be known as the Orthodox School in the early Ch'ing period.

One of the most interesting side currents in late Ming painting lies in a clearly discernible preference among some artists for archaistic modes of depiction. In landscapes, this is exemplified in the accomplishments of those painters who revived or revitalized the Northern Sung landscape mode, the most distinguished of whom was Wu Pin (active ca. 1568–1626); in figure painting, it is seen in the works of such eminent artists as Ch'en Hung-shou (1598–1652). The former group, the landscapists, aimed at recapturing in their works the monumental compositions and awesome scenery of landscape painting of the Northern Sung period (late tenth to early twelfth century). Since the Northern Sung tradition had been largely neglected over the intervening centuries, this represents a new phenomenon in the history of Chinese painting. By this time, the landscape style of the Southern Sung Academy, which flourished in the twelfth and thirteenth centuries, had been used and ultimately discredited by the Che School artists of the early and middle Ming. Similarly, the imitators of the landscape style of Li T'ang, who belonged to a transitional age between Northern and Southern Sung, had never managed to gain any kind of foothold. Part of what Wu Pin and his associates and followers— Kao Yang (active early 17th century), Cheng Chung (active ca. 1610–1644), Wang Chien-chang (active 1628–1644) —took from Northern Sung painting was their careful, convincing manner. Such attention to realistic detail was, incidentally, precisely what Tung Ch'i-ch'ang opposed, and accounts for some of the more or less open antagonism between these two currents of landscape styles. However, while these styles had originally been used to depict nature in a realistic way, the late Ming masters used them to create fantastic and sometimes wild compositions made up of bizarre, seemingly supernatural forms. Such use of old means and techniques, but without old content and for new ends, has a clear analogy in Ch'en Hung-shou's figures, which ostensibly are modeled after T'ang or pre-T'ang figure styles, but whose strange deformities betray the absence of any intent to imitate the ancients and of any spiritual affiliation with them. An additional and very important source for such painting lay in the popular styles current in the same period, including debased imitations and forgeries of the early masters. Perhaps such combinations of archaistic use of the past and sophisticated employment of unsophisticated materials can be considered characteristic of an important segment of late Ming painting.

Several of the late Ming painters, on the basis of their sheer individuality, seem to defy classification. One of the best known and most admired of these individualists is Hsü Wei (1521–1593), whose painting is distinguished by a seemingly impetuous yet subtly controlled use of the brush. Similarly calligraphic brush-styles can be seen also in some works of Mi Wan-chung (died 1628), Wang To (1592–1652), and Tai Ming-yüeh (active ca. 1600–1656) who for this reason, and also for that of their political involvements, have been grouped together in this exhibition. These artists were active mainly in Nanking, along with Wu Pin and the others, and in differing ways also participated in the Northern Sung revival. Other artists who worked in Nanking in the last decades of the Ming, such as Hu Yü-k'un (active early 17th century) and Yün Hsiang (1586–1655), possessed different stylistic leanings, and seem to anticipate the achievements of the Nanking masters of the early Ch'ing period.

The Che School in the late Ming, while it may have seemed to be permanently eclipsed by the activity at other centers such as Su-chou and Hua-t'ing, enjoyed a short-lived comeback in the landscape paintings of Lan Ying (1585–after 1660), who has come to be designated, mainly for reasons of his local origin in Hang-chou, as the last major painter of the Che School. In his works, perhaps more than in those of any other late Ming painter, a great variety of ancient manners are employed and are basic to his achievements. If anyone can be singled out, he is the ideal exemplar for this period of an approach to painting that can perhaps properly be called art-historical. ∎

The Problem of Western Influence

by Yoko Woodson

The question of whether or not China's exposure to Western art in the late Ming period is reflected in late Ming painting has become a matter of some controversy among scholars. The phenomenon of Western influence is generally recognized in painting of the K'ang-hsi era (1662–1723) and later in the Ch'ing dynasty when such influence is clearly visible. It is less obvious in late Ming. Nevertheless, careful observation will recognize new "stylistic ideas" and motifs previously absent from Chinese painting beginning to appear in this period. We will attempt to trace some of these new features that can be seen as arising from exposure to Western art, and to suggest that the newly arrived foreign art left some mark, no matter how slight, in the late Ming period, that is to say, some decades earlier than what is generally agreed on as the beginning of "Europeanization" in Chinese painting.

Historical circumstances in the sixteenth and seventeenth centuries tell us that the Chinese during this period were increasingly exposed to European culture. The Portuguese, who established their interests in Macao and Canton, had been engaged in trade with China since the early sixteenth century. More importantly, the Jesuits began their missionary activities in China from the 1580s. One of the earliest and the most important of the missionaries was the Italian Jesuit Matteo Ricci (1552–1610), who was known as Li Ma-tou in China. He arrived in Macao in 1582 and spent several years in Nanchang and Nanking, establishing a firm base for his missionary work in these areas. In 1601 he reached Peking, where he had an audience with the Wan-li Emperor and received imperial sanction to build a church near the Hsüan-wu gate in that city.

It was natural for him and other Jesuit missionaries to rely on pictorial means to propagate Christianity. The records of Ricci and other missionaries, as well as Chinese literary sources, tell us that he and other Jesuits brought with them paintings and prints portraying the themes of Christianity, and that they continued to send requests to the Jesuit headquarters for more supplies of pictures. Such paintings and prints were effective means to introduce the Chinese to the new religion. Ricci took two paint-

ings of the Madonna and a picture of Christ as presents to the Wan-li Emperor when he had his audience in 1601.[1] He also had a large oil painting of Christ which was painted by Giovanni Nicolo in Japan,[2] where Nicolo gave lessons in Western-style painting to Japanese seminarians. The Jesuit churches were lavishly decorated with illusionistic paintings. Jacopo Niva, who was a Sino-Japanese pupil of Giovanni Nicolo in Japan, joined Ricci in 1602 and painted pictures for the churches in China.

Although the Buddhist leaders and most Chinese scholars remained anti-Catholic,[3] these colorful paintings with heavy shading, and engravings with strong effects of light and shadow, must have deeply impressed and astonished the Chinese who saw them. Chiang Shao-shu in his *Wu-sheng-shih shih* (1646) describes admiringly the paintings of Christ and of the Virgin and Child which Ricci brought with him to China: "Their eyebrows, the eyes and the folds of the garment were clear like images in a mirror. They look as if they want to move by themselves. Their solemnity and beauty is something that Chinese painters cannot treat."[4] A book written in 1634 comments on the paintings that decorated the church of Matteo Ricci by the Hsüan-wu gate in Peking: "The eyes are as if shining, and the mouths as if having voice. This is an area that Chinese painting cannot reach."[5] These illusionistic pictures from the West, of which the primary intent was to represent objects as closely as possible to visual phenomena, seem to have made a deep impression on the Chinese.

However, the question of how and to what extent Chinese painters in the late Ming period were actually influenced by these paintings and prints is more difficult to answer. At first glance, the Chinese paintings of this period may not appear to reflect any such influence. However, careful observation reveals that the painters could not have been indifferent to the newly arrived art. The shading of figures and their drapery, the coloristic treatment of forms, the dramatic total effect of chiaroscuro, deep space composition, odd and complex geological formations, as well as a variety of minor elements in some late Ming paintings have remarkable simi-

larities to corresponding features in the European paintings and prints that were in China at the time of Matteo Ricci. None of the paintings that decorated the churches has survived to our time, but some works of the pupils of Nicolo in Japan may give us a fairly good idea of what kinds of paintings the late Ming Chinese might have seen in the Jesuit churches and elsewhere.[6] The prints and books illustrated with engravings that were in China at this time have been identified recently by Michael Sullivan from Jesuit records, and some of the pictures reproduced, providing us with firmer ground for determining what works of this kind had actually reached China.[7]

As indicated by the passages from literary sources already quoted, what struck the Chinese most in the Western pictorial art was the realistic representation of human figures by heavy shading. Therefore, it is most likely that the impact of the new art was first felt by figure and portrait painters, especially the latter, whose primary purpose in painting was to render their subjects in a manner as close to the model as possible. Some of these portrait painters recognized the advantages of Western techniques of realistic representation, and ventured to learn these techniques, especially the method of shading.

Looking back on the early history of Chinese painting, we may note that there were times when the Chinese were very much interested in realistic rendering of three-dimensional forms by shading. Therefore, such shading of flesh and the folds of robes as the late Ming painters saw in the Western paintings and prints was not entirely new to the Chinese. The word *yao-t'u hua*, which can be translated "painting of concavities and convexities," was applied to a type of painting in which shading was used to create an illusion of three-dimensionality. This word appeared in literature as early as the end of the Six Dynasties period,[8] and one can witness actual examples in some of the Tun-huang cave paintings. Such shading technique was introduced to China through Buddhist paintings from Central Asia and India. The technique was practiced during the T'ang and Sung periods, in keeping with realistic tendencies in these periods. But by the later

Sung, as interest in realism diminished, the shading technique also was gradually abandoned, leaving only minor traces. By the late Ming period the state of painting had become such that Matteo Ricci (justifiably from his own point of view) commented on it as follows: "Although the Chinese love painting very much, they are behind our [Western] painters. . . . They do not know about shading. Therefore, their paintings look dead and have no life at all."[9]

In such a situation, the shading technique in Western pictures must have been astonishing to Chinese eyes. Some of them recalled that something similar had existed in their own past. Ku Ch'i-yüan in his book *K'o-tso chui-yü* (published 1618) mentions the method under the heading *yao-t'u hua:* "The European Li Ma-tou (Matteo Ricci) says that [their] painting uses the method of concavities and convexities *(yao-t'u)*. No one today [here in China] knows what this is. However, the *Chien-k'ang shih-lu* mentions that the gate of the I-ch'eng temple (in Nanking?) is painted all over with flowers done with concavities and convexities; these are said to be the work of Chang Seng-yu. These flowers are done in a technique brought from India, in red (cinnabar) and blue-and-green pigments. When one sees them from a distance, the eye is fooled into seeing concavities and convexities, but when seen closer they prove to be flat. . . . Thus we know that Westerners had this technique long ago, and that Chang Seng-yu already used it (in China). . . ."[10]

It is difficult to know whether any recollection of such use of shading in the dim past was in the minds of artists who adopted this technique in the late Ming, or whether it was entirely inspired by contacts with European pictures; the fact that a millenium had passed since the time of Chang Seng-yu makes the latter possibility seem more plausible, and we can understand Ku Ch'i-yüan's words as reflecting the usual Chinese preference for finding precedents in their past rather than for recognizing true innovations or adoptions from non-Chinese sources. In a similar way, Chinese critics would evoke the "boneless" method of the T'ang period and earlier to explain the appearance in the late Ming of painting done in color only, without outlines.

In any case, the practice of shading spread among late Ming painters. One of the earliest to use it was the Fukienese portraitist Tseng Ch'ing (1568–1610). Chiang Shao-shu's account of him, quoted elsewhere, makes it clear that Tseng was interested in producing realistic portraits by shading. The source of this shading technique is almost certainly to be found in Western paintings and prints. Originally trained in Fukien, and so exposed to influences through the trade with Europeans taking place in the southern coastal ports, Tseng was later (in 1595 and 1599) active in Nanking, where he must have had opportunities to see the Occidental paintings and prints. Moreover, he is said to have used a pigment called "Western red" which was an animal substance introduced by Ricci.[11]

An example of Tseng Ch'ing's painting that agrees with such descriptions in contemporary literature is the seated portrait in a landscape setting, dated 1639 (cat. no. 80). The flesh parts, especially the face, are done carefully with light shading in a tone slightly darker than the basic flesh color; in the face this is used on the sides of the cheeks and on the eyelids. The bony areas just below the eyebrows and on the cheeks are slightly highlit. Lines in darker color around the eyes and the mouth indicate the sagging skin and muscles of an old man. In some features, such as the linear emphasis, the portrait does not differ strikingly from conventional ancestor portraits of the Ming period, which were rendered strictly with lines and no shadows. But those portraits had never been taken seriously by the Chinese as works of art; they were purely functional ancestral images. Tseng Ch'ing's portraits, on the other hand, were not drawn simply to serve as symbolic images of ancestors, but were meant as vivid records of the subject's personality. The portrayal of the old man in our painting is realistic to a degree that might well have excited Chiang Shao-shu to comment that Tseng's figures look "as if alive," and shows the personality of the subject with a power of characterization that must have come from many years of experience as a portraitist.

Tseng Ch'ing adopted the new technique, then, into traditional portrait painting and raised it to the level

of an art. He founded a school of realistic portraiture and influenced not only the painters of his native place, P'u-tien in Fukien, but also painters in other areas. One of the portraitists influenced by him was his direct pupil Hsieh Pin, active around 1650. The handscroll representing "A Landscape with Scholars" in the Ching Yüan Chai Collection, dated 1648 (cat. no. 81), is a cooperative work of Lan Ying, who did the landscape, and Hsieh Pin, who painted the figures. Shading in slightly darker color is used around the eyes of the figures, although it is not as obvious as in the portrait by Tseng Ch'ing. Unlike the generalized figures that were commonly placed in landscape paintings, the figures here are strongly characterized and given equal importance with the landscape.

Although such painters as Tseng Ch'ing and Hsieh Pin must have been inspired and stimulated by the new Western paintings and prints in creating more realistic portraits, their attitude can still be called eclectic, in that they took the technique of shading from the Western pictures and subordinated it to the linear tradition of Chinese painting. The new method was so perfectly blended with the styles and techniques of their own tradition that superficial observation may not recognize such influence. The same pattern can be observed in some late Ming landscape paintings, in which the traces of Western influence are even more subtle. For landscapists, it was the heavily shaded forms and strong contrast of light and dark in the Western pictures, especially prints, that were most impressive.

One of the painters who was interested in lighting is Chao Tso, a native of Sung-chiang. His paintings often exhibit strong effects of light and dark in surface pattern, as well as convincingly three-dimensional forms rendered by shading. Moreover, his particular way of using light and dark seems to indicate an almost correct understanding of the mechanism by which a single light source creates lighter and darker sides on a solid form. The hand-scroll in the Ching Yüan Chai Collection, dated 1609–1610 (cat. no. 28) illustrates this point clearly. Some mountains, especially distant ones, are divided vertically into darker and lighter halves. Since mountains treated in this way occur many times in the scroll, the viewer can clearly locate the light source, although there is not absolute consistency—overhanging cliffs are not darkened as much as they properly should be.

Such concern with quasi-naturalistic lighting had been absent from Chinese painting for centuries. The source of light had occasionally been vaguely indicated, and light and dark patterning had been created in a rather abstract manner, without much reference to actual visual phenomena. Sometimes it was used to distinguish one "fold" of a mountain from the next in a pattern of alternating light and dark. Even the works of the eleventh-century landscapist Kuo Hsi, the most concerned with effects of light among early painters whose work survives, do not show any single source of light, although he seems to have understood how sunlight produces areas of light and dark on a rounded form.[12] His paintings seem to contain multiple light sources; light is all over, spread through the composition in an abstract manner, applied as if naturalistically to individual forms but not to the whole.

The understanding of a single light source in Chao Tso's painting is thus entirely new in Chinese painting, but it had, of course, been an important principle in European pictorial art, especially after the Renaissance. In fact, the method of dividing a mountain vertically into lighter and darker sides was often used in a more or less schematic fashion as a means of showing a source of light in Western pictures at this time, and Chao Tso's mountains have a striking similarity to those seen in Western prints that are known to have been in China.[13] The sudden appearance of this understanding, and the mechanism of working from a visual phenomenon to a faithful rendering of it by pictorial means, in Chao Tso's painting cannot easily be explained except by supposing that he had seen some such model and learned the principle from it.

Ku Ch'i-yüan, in his book *K'o-tso chui-yü*, which we have mentioned already, quotes Matteo Ricci's explanation of the rendering of light and shadow in European painting: "Any person's face, when he faces the light straight on, will be bright and white. When he turns sidewards, then the side toward the light is white; but on the side not turned toward the light, the eyes, ears, nose, mouth, and other recessed parts all have dark shapes."[14] The principle was only applied by Matteo Ricci to figures, but can easily be observed in the mountains in Chao Tso's painting.

If Chao Tso was interested in naturalistic rendering of light and dark, and the scientific approach of the Western pictures, the Nanking artists, especially Wu Pin, seemed to be interested in a general impression of fantasy and oddity, with complex and dynamic geological formations and dramatic contrast of dark and light, which they found in some of the European prints. Involved as he was in the Northern Sung landscape tradition, which he and others were reviving at this time, Wu Pin must have seen affinities between that tradition and the European prints: strong contrasts of light and dark, repeated turret-like mountains, rough textures of rocks created by strong shading, deep recession into space along winding paths and streams, and hard-edged clouds covering parts of the peaks. Wu Pin absorbed certain "stylistic ideas" from the new art and combined them with the Northern Sung style. His fantastic landscape manner, which he created from the end of the sixteenth century, may be seen as the natural and fruitful product of the assimilation of these two styles.

The illusionistic tendencies anticipated in most impressive form in works of Wu Pin, were continued by later Nanking painters such as Fan Ch'i, Tsou Che, and Yeh Hsin, at last reaching a climax in the works of Kung Hsien (died 1689). These illusionistic tendencies, shared by the Nanking artists, arise out of their acquaintance with the tradition of Northern Sung painting and their frequent opportunities to observe Western prints in the Nanking area, although the problem of whether such later artists as Kung Hsien knew the prints first-hand or through second-hand derivation is less clear.

Besides the relatively obvious manifestations of Western influence in Chinese painting that we have discussed, there are a few other new developments in the period that may well be due to exposure to the new art. We refer to cases of artists who seem to be breaking away from the traditional uses of color and of space composition.

Like illusionistic shading, color was an essential part of the means of expression and of naturalistic rendering of forms in Western painting. In Chinese painting, it had never been given the same importance, either for expressive or for representational value. Tints of color were likely to be applied sparsely to a few elements that the artist was emphasizing. The sky was not treated in actual color, but was left neutral. Even in the "green-and-blue" manner of painting, where color was a dominant element in expression, it was still used in an abstract fashion; it was spread evenly within the ink outlines, without modulation, shading, or highlights. Colors were always bound to objects delineated by ink lines; forms filled in with colors stood out against a neutral ground.

However, in the early decades of the seventeenth century, following directly the coming of Western painting, we see a significant change in the employment of color in works by such painters as Hsiang Sheng-mo, Ku Ning-yüan, Chang Hung, and Lan Ying, as well as others not represented in this exhibition. The range is still typically limited to a few colors: blue, green, yellow-orange, and brown, sometimes touches of red. But these colors are now laid on more loosely and tend to fill broader areas. They are not always bounded by ink outlines; they sometimes flow over them, or are applied without any outlines. Sometimes they were not flat, but were used with heavy shading or highlights.

An obvious example that exhibits the new coloristic approach is the hanging scroll representing a winter landscape by Lan Ying, painted in Wang Wei manner, dated 1638 (cat. no. 63). The rocks and cliffs, though delineated by lines, are rendered in color with smooth shading. Most noteworthy are the tree trunks. Their brown color is applied with dry, rough, undefined strokes, without much linear drawing. The sides of the trunks are heavily shaded, and the central areas are highlighted with orange, indicating their bulging cylindricality. Except for a few strokes in dark color to indicate some rough texture, the three-dimensionality of the twisting trees is achieved through purely coloristic means, similar to those used in oil painting. Contrasting to these tree trunks, roughly treated but strikingly three-dimensional, are the twigs and leaves, still drawn carefully in lines and filled in with colors, in a traditional way.

A similar treatment, but even more consciously and carefully done, can be seen in the huge tree in one of the album leaves by Hsiang Sheng-mo, dated 1649 (cat. no. 11-F). A huge bare tree stands against a blue mountain and a sky colored with the red glow of sunset. It is rendered in many overlapping undefined strokes of brown, without much linear drawing. The bulging center of the trunk is left unpainted, functioning as an area of highlight. The darker-colored dots are carefully and regularly applied to render the rough texture of the trunk. While some branches in the front are outlined, those behind are rendered in strokes of greyish brown, without outlines at all. The slight modulation of color tones remarkably expresses the overlapping branches in three-dimensional space.

In addition to the coloristic treatment of the tree in this leaf, we may note an attempt to fill the space with colors: the blue background mountain, the green grassy land, and most of all, the sunset glow in the sky, painted in broad washes of red and blue. As mentioned before, the sky in Chinese paintings had ordinarily been left neutral, and was only rarely given its proper color; the use of red in the sky of Hsiang Sheng-mo's leaf, while it may look commonplace enough to Western eyes, is remarkable in the context of Chinese painting.[15]

The Western treatment of space and the use of linear perspective seem to have been adopted into Chinese painting only in a later period. But in the late Ming there are already some signs of departures from the typical Chinese space treatment: high viewpoints begin to lower to eye level and tend to be fixed, with a minimum shift in angle of view; uncharacteristically flat and continuous recessions along ground planes are to be seen.

In the leaf representing a winter landscape by Hsiang Sheng-mo, for instance (cat. no. 11-H), the scene is shown from eye level and there is no shifting of view point. (It should be noted that the sky is again indicated in the red of a sunset glow.) Another interesting example is the "Scholars Gazing at Reflections of the Moon" (cat. no. 71) by an unrecorded artist named Ch'en Ch'üan. Although the tall form of the hanging scroll is retained, there is no imposing mountain; the space is filled with wide stretches of water and strikingly flat land. Although there is still some shifting of viewpoint from the foreground to the middle, the focus is more or less fixed in the middle ground. The illusion of deep space is enhanced by the tree groups, slightly diminishing in height as they recede into depth, and by the diagonally placed bridge, which is in itself treated in pseudo-linear perspective, and with upper and lower sides visible. The same bridge will reappear, somewhat schematized, in works of Kung Hsien.

A curious motif in this picture is the reflection (or reflections) of the moon. Multiple reflections of the moon from a single, fixed vantage point are obviously scientifically impossible, but even the depiction of a reflection of an object in the water is something new to Chinese painting. It also appears, even more strikingly, in a painting by Wu Pin, some decades earlier.[16]

As we have seen, many new motifs and features of style appear in paintings of this period, features that cannot easily be adduced in earlier Chinese painting. If these were isolated occurrences, one might take them for accidental or truly innovative achievements of the Chinese artists. But the cumulative evidence they present to us, along with their coincidence with the coming of European art and the close correspondences to be observed between them and the European pictures, is enough to persuade us that significant departures from earlier Chinese practice were already taking place by the late Ming, and that we cannot account for these departures without recognizing the importance of influences from Western art.

However, we would be mistaken if we expected to find a truly "Europeanized" painting as we do at a later period, in the Ch'ing dynasty. What we see in the late Ming is an experimental phase, in which the Chinese painters had only just felt an impact of the West, were inspired or stimulated by it, and experimented with various fresh possibilities, using new techniques and "stylistic ideas" in the context of a purely Chinese tradition and style. Thus, the paintings at first glance may not seem unusual at all, until we realize that they contain features that were unknown in China before this time, or had not been seen since the T'ang and Sung periods.

Perhaps the influence in this early stage was not such as to leave crucial marks on the history of Chinese painting. But the venturesome urge toward fantasy, and the keen attitude of objectivity toward natural phenomena and painting, which some late Ming painters received from Western pictorial art, were to be transmitted to the Individualists in the early Ch'ing dynasty. Their flowering is best exemplified in the works of such artists as Kung Hsien, which make up a separate stylistic current from that of the truly Europeanized painting of later times as represented in the works of Chiao Ping-ch'en and Leng Mei at the end of the seventeenth century, and the imitators of Giuseppe Castiglione in the eighteenth. ∎

Notes

[1]Tei Nishimura, "The 'Mother and Child' (Etching) Issued by the Society of Jesus of Japan," *Bijutsu Kenkyu* (September 1937), p. 16. [2]Quoted by Tei Nishimura, "Paintings of 'Society of Jesus' in Japan and Those of Western Style at the end of the Ming Dynasty," *Bijutsu Kenkyu* (January 1940), p. 15. [3]John Fairbank and Ssu-yü Teng, *China's Response to the West*, Cambridge, 1954, p. 14. [4]Michael Sullivan mentions that the painting of Christ described by Chiang Shao-shu in *Wu-sheng-shih shih* was the work of Giovanni Nicolo. See Sullivan, "Some Possible Sources of European Influence on Late Ming and Early Ch'ing Painting," Paper for the International Symposium on Chinese Painting, Taipei, 1970, p. 1. [5]Liu T'ung and Yü I-cheng, *Ti-ching ching-wu*, 1634, chüan IV. This book is devoted to the historical description of famous places in Peking and its environs. [6]For a detailed account of Sino-Japanese relations in the late Ming period, see Tei Nishimura, "Painting of 'Society of Jesus' in Japan and Those of Western Style at the end of the Ming Dynasty," *op. cit.;* and M. Sullivan, *op. cit.*, pp. 1–2, 4. [7]M. Sullivan, *op. cit.*, pls. 1–5. For a preliminary attempt to relate these

18 to late Ming paintings, especially landscapes, see James Cahill, "Wu Pin and His Landscape Paintings," Paper for the Taipei symposium (see note 4). [8]Yoshiho Yonezawa, "Chugoku kinsei kaiga to seiyo gaho (1)," *Kokka*, 685, p. 92. [9]Quoted by Y. Yonezawa, *op. cit.*, p. 91. See also Paul Pelliot, "La peinture et la gravure européennes en chine au temps de Mathieu Ricci," *T'oung Pao*, 1920–1921, p. 6. [10]Ku Ch'i-yüan, *K'o-tso chui-yü*, 1618, chüan V, p. 20. [11]Yoshiho Yonezawa, *Painting in the Ming Dynasty*, Tokyo, 1956, p. 91. [12]James Cahill, "The Early Styles of Kung Hsien," *Oriental Art* (Spring 1970), p. 62; see also "Some Rocks in Early Chinese Painting," *Archives of the Chinese Art Society of America* XVI (1962), pp. 84–85. [13]For example, compare Chao Tso's mountain (cat. no. 28) with plate 3 in Sullivan's article cited above. [14]*K'o-tso chui-yü*, chüan VI, p. 24a. [15]Compare the sky in this leaf by Hsiang Sheng-mo with that of "Four Cities" which was painted in Japan by a Jesuit artist around 1590 (for a color plate, see Yoshitomo Okamoto, *Nanban Bijutsu*, Tokyo, 1966, pl. 19). [16]Leaf no. 8 in the album, "Record of the New Year's Holidays," Palace Museum, Taipei (MA 28).

The Achievements of Late Ming Painters

by Elizabeth Fulder

Of all Chinese painting, that of the late Ming remains the most difficult to characterize. In scanning the period, we discover a reason that will largely serve to explain why this is so: the most salient feature of the late Ming's artistic consciousness is expressed in contradictory, or better, counterpositional attitudes. There was, for example, a continual striving for innovation by artists of the period, yet it was dependence on earlier traditional structures that most often carried the painters through. Again, while the late Ming exploited the principles of abstraction, it led no revolt against the long-established principles of using natural forms as subject matter. Considered historically, it was at the same time a determiner of directions for the Ch'ing Dynasty and a terminus for the decadent academicism of the preceding generation.

In approaching late Ming painting, it is tempting to focus upon the counterpositions, the dualisms, the inconsistencies of the period, or to be diverted, as many scholars are, by a dominating interest in the personality, theories, and works of Tung Ch'i-ch'ang. The painting of the period can only be understood, however, if we understand the assumptions by which the major painters operated and about which the paintings of the period are organized. The period exhibits such a complexity of styles that the general nature of its trends can perhaps best be appraised by declaring tradition and innovation to be the ground-clearing issues.

It is important to bear in mind that aesthetic attitudes in the Ming were mixed, impure, and therefore hard to disentangle. In consequence, the two issues, tradition and innovation, frequently overlap and interact. A single painting by Wu Pin, for example, might mix structural affiliations with the Northern Sung, abstractly innovative treatment of space, and self-consciously specialized and fantastic forms. It is obvious that the late Ming contains many hazards for the historian.

Tradition
The late Ming attitude toward the long-established traditions of Chinese painting is the point at which this discussion must be opened. Painters of the period faced an old artistic problem: should they lose the chance for change by remaining too traditional, or should they lose the chance for communication by changing too radically? The answer evolved by late Ming to this problem was to encompass the entire field; thus, the range includes, at one extreme, painters truculently traditional in approach, such as some of the late Su-chou artists, and at the other, artists such as Tung Ch'i-ch'ang who—at least in their paintings—evinced little nostalgia for the past.

This may seem too obvious an answer to an old problem to merit describing it as a particular attitude, but it is a different kind of obviousness in the late Ming. The difference is caused by two closely related circumstances. The traditional amateur and professional painting styles, originally derived from the Yüan and the Southern Sung, had become over-ripe, fossilized through sheer over-use by the late sixteenth century. Only a few stand-pats could still employ them without embarrassment. The second circumstance is sociological. The amateur painters began to lose their traditional aversion to selling their works in the late Ming, and the professional painters began to work in styles more closely related to those of the amateurs. These factors, together with the profusion of painting centers, led to the blurring of the classical amateur-professional distinction which had previously represented separate styles and aesthetic attitudes. In consequence, the structural and stylistic choices, previously limited by the painter's position in the professional or amateur lineage, proliferated. The old range of possibilities—opting for either neo-classical extensions of Southern Sung or Yüan styles, professional or amateur—was enlarged, and the painters were compelled toward a broader tolerance of new ideas and inventions, and new uses of the past. Indeed, the impression persists when looking at late Ming painting that one of its crucial distinctions, as well as one of its crucial problems, was the apparent consciousness of the search for formal solutions.

It is not puzzling, then, but perfectly appropriate that some artists, because of their birth and upbringing in some area with an artistic history and tradition of its own, chose to continue that local tradition. Su-chou painters sought fresh ideas in the Wu School tradition of Wen Cheng-ming or the professional tradition of Ch'iu Ying and T'ang Yin, while the professional painters who gravitated to Nanking chose the more conservative traditions of that area as inspiration. Other painters, such as Tung Ch'i-ch'ang and Lan Ying, attempted to return to the real roots of the amateur and professional traditions and build new styles on these. Still others, such as Ch'en Hung-shou and Wu Pin, stimulated by the need for an organizing form for their own inventions, rediscovered older traditions that had long remained in disuse. At the same time, many painters—and this includes to some degree all the best painters of the late Ming, many of them members of the above groups as well—followed the mandates of their own imaginations.

The second group of painters mentioned above directs our attention to Tung Ch'i-ch'ang. Tung is a consistently unlosable figure in the late Ming. He always gets in the way when one is looking for other artists, because he was a painter of excellence and a theorist of much prominence and influence who was concerned with the same general problems as less articulate painters of his day. The late Ming formulations of the relationship of their painting to the past, and to the future as well, often center about Tung's theories, which attempted not only to clarify and systematize the history of Chinese painting, but more importantly, consciously to bring abstracted structural principles back into the forefront of artistic concerns. In his admiration and sympathy for the aesthetic values of the Yüan amateurs he was aligned with the Wu School painters of the earlier Ming. But in his articulation of the need for a return to Yüan formal and structural originality and conviction, rather than variations and repetitions of their old forms, Tung set himself apart from the followers of the Wu School and also assured himself a larger and more durable influence.

Both Tung's paintings and his theories, although to an extent his practice does not always follow his preachment, were in fact more traditional than much of his contemporaries' efforts, if only in the sense that they had much more in common with the true tradition of amateur painting than any other works at the time. Tung Ch'i-ch'ang's style will come under closer scrutiny in the later discussion of abstraction. It remains to affirm here that his importance as a theorist lies in his obvious critical intelligence. His plea was one for criticism, for the rational imagination, as urgent now as it was then.

In fact, other painters in the late Ming had ideas very similar in essential respects to some of those that underlie Tung's statements, but their statements are diffused in their paintings and are therefore less accessible. The professional painters in Nanking, for example, although radically different —even opposed—in attitude, style, and social and artistic status from the amateur-intellectuals centered around Tung Ch'i-ch'ang in Hua-t'ing, arrived at a similar diagnosis of the artistic problems of their age, and proposed profound structural cures likewise rooted in past principles.

The subject matter, in their case a fantastic and bizarre combination of unstable shapes and irrational spaces, was different from Tung Ch'i-ch'ang's, and the forms needed to unify, solidify, and relate these complex fantasies were of another, relatively unexploited, professional tradition—the Northern Sung. This simpler, more immediately impressive and more monumental type of landscape structure was firm ground, and more important, it was accessible ground. Its fresh wholesome air and mountain crags had remained relatively unexplored in the intervening centuries and provided a solid and traditional foundation for the very personal innovations of such painters as Wu Pin.

The grafting of new manners onto old structures has also to do with Ch'en Hung-shou, the most original and talented figure painter of the late Ming. In his case, however, the neo-classic obligation is not to the Yüan or to the Northern Sung, but to a still earlier style considered to be that of the Six Dynasties period. Taking the elegant and subtle structures, subjects, lines, and costumes of a thousand years earlier, he imposes upon them certain ironical distortions and exaggerations (perhaps

caught up in the popular art of his day) which extend the references and thereby enrich the style.

A convenient example of still another use of earlier traditions is found in Lan Ying's work. What distinguishes him from most of his contemporaries is his wide-ranging adaptation of a variety of old manners. He did not seek general principles with which to organize a distinct personal style, as did Tung Ch'i-ch'ang, Wu Pin, or Ch'en Hung-shou. Neither is his work an eclectic mixture of old and new, but rather an ever-changing series of ingenious and slightly schematized variations in a variety of traditional manners.

In summary, it was integral to the late Ming's attitude toward tradition that the artist got the best of both worlds by using a known, yet previously little-used superstructure, at the same time extending it with innovative ideas, not just in brushwork or superficial variations of the design, but innovation involving a total relationship between all the parts.

Innovation
A consideration of tradition in the late Ming leads directly to the late Ming's attitude toward innovation. The two issues lie naturally on the same creative level, but innovation extends in the opposite direction from tradition. It is important to establish the precise distinction between painters who use old structural configurations upon which to base contemporary elaborations (e.g., Wu Pin) and those more innovative painters who achieved a greater degree of interpenetration between new surfaces and new structures such as Tung Ch'i-ch'ang. (As will be demonstrated later, this is not true of either of these artists in all cases; in fact, the categories may often be reversed.) The theme of innovation is pursued on two levels. The first is dominated by abstract principles, the second by more romantic elements of fantasy.

Abstraction
Tung Ch'i-ch'ang's theories suggest that one seek in natural forms, or in well-constructed old paintings, a principle for the organization of landscape compositions. This search led him to a rediscovery of

the natural relationship between surface texture and the structural organization of the forms underlying it, a principle which seemed to have been forgotten in many paintings of the mid-sixteenth century. In Tung's paintings, however, in addition to a new and coherent bond between texture and form, based on what was apparently a principle of naturalism, one discovers shapes and relationships of a manifestly abstracted kind. Space, mountains, rocks, and trees are separate and ideal entities combined in careful constructions which act not according to the dictates of nature, but according to the dictates of Tung Ch'i-ch'ang's art. Spatial inconsistencies, unnaturally darkened or illuminated surfaces do not negate the value of the paintings as landscape, but rather increase their value as art by expanding the possibilities of new links between forms.

Tung was not alone in the rediscovery of an interdependence between the surface and the coherent organization of more solid forms in a painting. Chao Tso, Ch'en Hung-shou, Sheng Mao-yeh, and Wu Pin, for example, all make new and varied attempts in their landscape paintings to re-inform the surfaces through shading, faceting, or the interweaving of textures. These painters all concern themselves with a new, more penetrating and more abstract morphology which contrasts significantly with the essentially decorative surface textures and brush conventions of most mid-sixteenth century paintings.

The treatment of space in late Ming paintings follows the same abstract dictates. Tung Ch'i-ch'ang will often shift the horizon abruptly in the middle of a composition; Wu Pin often establishes ambiguous and shifting relationships between planes; Shao Mi may neglect individual spatial relationships entirely and then set the whole landscape thus constructed into an atmosphere of mist and clouds. This new employment of space as a true and independent formal element, which the previous generation failed to acknowledge, was an original contribution of the late Ming painters.

Brushwork was also an area in which late Ming painters found opportunity for abstraction. In the works of many painters it becomes an almost independent component of the design (Cheng Chung; Sheng Mao-yeh; Chao Tso). Personal variations for expressive purposes are wider than before, and eccentricities are encouraged (Hsü Wei; Lan Ying).

The attention to brushwork and its concomitant abstractions was an idea inherited from the literati tradition of the Yüan. However, none of the painters before the late Ming carried these abstract principles as deeply into the larger structures of landscape as did Tung Ch'i-ch'ang. Under his influence, the next generation, painters of the early Ch'ing dynasty —in the concrete and unsentimental landscapes of Hung-jen or the Four Wangs, for example—deal even more successfully and systematically with some of his favorite notions than did his contemporaries.

As important and pervasive as the idea of abstracted forms and relationships was to the organizational efforts of late Ming painters, every painter still remained preoccupied with natural forms, even if only as a basis for their departures from natural relationships. The subject matter, no matter how unreal the connections, the shapes, or the textures, no matter how inventive the compositions, remained rooted in reality—trees, mountains, streams, figures.

Some painters, to be sure, emphasized the realistic aspects of their subjects more heavily; others played upon the contrasts between realistically conceived details and more bizarre surrounding forms. Chang Hung, for example, in some of his works revitalized the conventionalized and schematized textures of Wu School trees and surfaces by making them more specifically descriptive of certain places or certain types of natural terrain and forms. Cheng Chung painted carefully detailed and observed figures, animals, and architecture within a more abstracted composition. Even Wu Pin paid meticulous attention to architectural forms and the drawing of foliage, taking special advantage of their contrasts with the fantastic environment.

During this period there is also a revival of portraiture of the most realistic kind. In addition such

painters as Ch'en Hung-shou mix realistic details and careful observation of natural forms with an exaggerated distortion and archaizing of drapery or proportional relationships. The juxtaposition and contrast of this kind of realistic detail and natural relationships with an inconsistent, abstracted and often bizarre use of space and form is what distinguishes both landscape and figure painting of the late Ming from the more timid naturalism of the early Wu School on the one hand, and the serious and systematic abstractions of natural forms in the early Ch'ing period on the other.

Fantasy
The second key to innovation in the late Ming is the element of fantasy. The bizarre, the fantastic, the romantic image forms a part of the answer to the problem of a worn tradition, and also opens up new areas for artistic exploration. These stimuli to the imagination, however, do not come to formal focus easily. They require strong, simple organizing principles because the material is complex and personal and not necessarily combined in principle with its own system of organization, as is abstraction. Such romantic, lyrical, intuitive, and mistily defined orders as those of Shao Mi or Sheng Mao-yeh's album leaves work beautifully in small scale where they can pursue vivid sensuous detail and simple orders, but they require stronger organizations to lithify them into hanging scrolls.

One new organizing form used in several ways by some of the more romantic painters of the late Ming demonstrates a fresh compositional principle. It orders and aligns smaller, more complex forms abstractly against a simpler, more powerful shape whose outline encompasses the rhythmically articulated details of the rest. Shao Mi's album uses this compositional device in one of its most original manners; its floating scenes, with their pleasing eccentricity of form, lack any significant obligations to the past.

Fantasy in late Ming painting is seen carried to its extreme in the paintings of such Nanking artists as Wu Pin. His fantasy was muscle; he was a solid weight-lifter, a little full-bodied, but his paintings have a tension which arises from interrelationships

closely argued. He finds solutions to his organizing problems in the clear dominating forms, limited spatial recession, and meticulously detailed surfaces of Northern Sung landscapes. The careful ecology of these structures underlies the greatest achievements of Wu Pin.

A radical temperamental difference seems to separate those innovators dominated by abstract ideas rather than more romantic notions. The romantic orders are usually more accessible, more charming than the serious and searching conceptions of the abstractionists. Emotions or commotions operating in mist or private fantasy will always remain marginal at communication. One can read them as emotive fantasies and even then the denser meanings might be missed. Early Ch'ing painters could only note they were there and pass on to the firmer ground of Tung Ch'i-ch'ang, where there were charted ways to exploit abstraction. From the viewpoint of the Ch'ing, or the West, it is Tung's ideas and paintings, more than those of the romantics, which shine in a prophetic light. Science teaches us that the measure of a solution is not in questions answered, but in questions discovered, new ground laid open.

For the late Ming period, further development of traditional painting was difficult, except as the final refinement of a failing tradition or as development into abstraction. What emerges most curiously is the fact that Tung Ch'i-ch'ang, who pointed the most fruitful new course, took his bearings more strongly than any of his contemporaries from traditional theory.

From our point of view, his vision appears to have been a limited one: in his paintings, he assumes, lies the answer to the problems of tradition and innovation when in fact they have barely defined the question. Facing as we do the hard certainties of Cage and Pollock we might be tempted to think that Tung feared to take the decisive step into abstraction. But for every radical change of forms, one must wonder what worse forms might take their place. The problem was an ancient one in Chinese painting, and is painfully enough a modern one as well. ∎

Late Ming Painting Theory

by Mae Anna Quan Pang

Theories on painting, both as philosophy and as a kind of literature, had a special place in the lively intellectual life of the late Ming. Those who engaged in discussions and wrote essays on painting were scholars, or literati, who as often as not assumed multiple roles as amateur painters, collectors, connoisseurs, art critics, art historians. Some of them, in addition, were active in the political world, holding posts in the civil service; others chose leisurely lives as cultivated gentlemen in retirement; many moved from one sphere to the other. Some struggled unsuccessfully to pass the examinations that were the entry to an official career; others did not bother to try. And some of these scholars were deeply involved in such pursuits as literature, philosophy, and religion.

In casual writings that often took the form of inscriptions on paintings, these scholars expressed their opinions on paintings they had seen, or those in their own collections. Within the literati (or scholar-amateur) school of painting and its associated writings, there had always existed a diversity of views, and sometimes sharp disagreements on the relative evaluation of paintings of certain periods and masters of the past, as well as of contemporary works. Late Ming scholars were especially uninhibited in expressing their opinions and in taking strong stands on artistic issues. Particular paintings and quotations from past writings on painting were referred to in support of arguments; so did theory impinge, more than usually, upon practice. As heirs to a long-lasting culture, these scholars were very historically minded, aware of the rich and complex history of painting in China and of their own positions within it. They were thus very much concerned with contemporary painting, and their reactions to it were the principal stimulus in the formulation of their ideas on painting.

It was easy enough for these scholars to reject the craftsmanlike approach to painting, in which techniques, rules, and established methods were to be mastered, and skillful workmanship was the standard for evaluation. However, the situation was complicated by some painters who took advantage of this anti-technical orientation and went to the opposite extreme of total freedom from the rules. Such excesses evoked reactions against their careless and sloppy work. For example, Wang K'en-t'ang (who took his *chin-shih* degree in 1589), says: "Painters of nowadays do not know the difference between light and heavy touch (i.e., do not know how to use the brush), and yet they despise and abandon the rules of using ink. 'Trusting their hands,' they just daub and smear. What [kind of painting] is this?"[1] Hsieh Chao-chih writing around 1600 says: "People nowadays give rein to their inclinations and take their 'mind' as teacher, so that their paintings are rendered in a careless and haphazard manner. They often use the pretext of seeing the expression of *i* (conception) as the end [of painting]."[2]

The scholars reacted negatively as well to another approach, the slavish imitation of the manners of early masters, a practice which had taken hold in painting in the early Ming period. When asked whether such earlier Ming artists as Shen Chou, Wen Cheng-ming, and T'ang Yin had "captured the brush-conceptions of the ancients," Tung Ch'i-ch'ang replied, "The leading masters of recent times haven't produced a single stroke that doesn't resemble the ancients. But in not having any that *don't* resemble, they have none that *do* resemble. You could speak of this as lacking [the art of] painting."[3] In the same vein Fan Yün-lin, who took his *chin-shih* degree in 1595, said of the painters of his time who followed the Wen Cheng-ming tradition: "Among them are some who choose to imitate some famous master, but the only one they know is Wen Cheng-ming. They manage a slight resemblance. But with all their copying, they only capture the 'skin' of his external form, without getting anything of his spirit and principle."[4]

In their effort to correct a stagnant situation in painting, scholars in late Ming felt compelled to seek a new creative approach—a way of working within some kind of order or framework, but without limiting the individual's creative freedom.

The Painter as Cultivated Scholar

Late Ming writers were intent on establishing a non-constricting discipline for painting. They believed that the artist should be endowed with the attributes of the cultivated scholar. Their criteria were no doubt intended, in large part, to bolster their own claims to superiority over those uncultivated painters who were tainted with a "craftsman's approach," as well as to exclude those who painted carelessly or hastily.

A phrase still important in the vocabulary of late Ming painting theory was *ch'i-yün sheng-tung*, "spirit-resonance engendering movement," which had originated more than a millenium earlier as the first of Hsieh Ho's Six Laws of Painting. Through the intervening centuries it had been held as a somewhat vaguely understood but nonetheless supreme desideratum. Late Ming theorists continued to believe that its presence in painting depended upon a corresponding quality in the artist, and that he was born with it, endowed by heaven.

However, as Tung Ch'i-ch'ang pointed out, this quality could also to some degree be acquired, if one "studied ten thousand volumes, travelled ten thousand miles, and freed one's mind from worldly cares."[5] Other writers, such as Li Jih-hua (1565–1636) agreed that such cultural saturation was an absolute necessity for a good painter. Painting was not an isolated activity, he insisted; the artist must be well-read and learned, with a broad knowledge of events past and present, engaged in a variety of cultural pursuits, imbued with antiquarian interests, and freed from worldly cares.[6] Fan Yün-lin, himself a scholar from Su-chou, criticized the commercial painters of that city for "not knowing a single character."[7]

Calligraphy, another of the proper pursuits of the scholar-gentleman, was sometimes regarded as "identical" with painting. T'u Lung, a writer who took his *chin-shih* degree in 1577, commented that calligraphy and painting should be looked at (and, by implication, judged) in the same way.[8] Li Jih-hua said that one must be good in calligraphy in order to know how to use the brush in painting,[9] and Tung Ch'i-ch'ang advised scholars to apply the techniques of calligraphy to painting so as to be free of the pernicious ways of professional painters who were, at least in theory, illiterate or semi-literate.[10] T'ang Chih-ch'i (1579–1651) singled out landscape painting especially as a proper pursuit for one's leisure time, and likened it to the *ts'ao* ("grass" or draft) and *hsing* (running) forms of script, in that it should be neither labored nor restricted by rules.[11]

Calligraphy, a discipline that every scholar could master, and virtually all did, thus became a satisfactory substitute for the specialized technical training of the craftsman painter. The formal qualities of brush movement, design, and texture that the literati captured in calligraphy could be imparted to painting.

Some writers introduced another requirement for the good painter: he must have seen genuine works by great masters of the past. Li Jih-hua commented that in his time some unconventional people worked hard on painting but did not succeed in it, because they had not seen enough genuine paintings by old masters to nourish their minds.[12] T'ang Chih-ch'i expressed a similar opinion, saying: "People of today have not seen many genuine works of the ancients; although they speak of painting, they do not understand it."[13] Even Lan Ying (1585–after 1660) himself a professional artist, remarked that one had to study the brush-and-ink of the ancients to learn how to paint. He complained that very few reliable works from the hands of the old masters were to be seen.[14] The uncultivated painter was thus set apart from, and far below, the cultivated one.

The Works of the Old Masters
This emphasis on familiarity with the surviving works of the ancient masters inevitably gave rise to the question of how one might learn from them without falling into the vice of mechanical imitation. The first to resolve this problem satisfactorily was Tung Ch'i-ch'ang. Complaining that recent artists had been imitating the works of the old masters slavishly, he distinguished between *lin-mo*, direct copying of another painting, and *shen-hui*, a "spiritual communion" with the earlier work and its author. He illustrated his point by citing the followers of Tung Yüan: "Chü-jan followed Tung Yüan; Mi Fu followed Tung Yüan; Huang Kung-

wang followed Tung Yüan; Ni Tsan followed Tung Yüan. Each produced something quite different from all the others. When a common painter copies, what he turns out is identical with his model. How can he, working in this way, expect to have any influence on others?"[15] By spiritual communion, he meant an intuitive understanding of the work of the ancient master. One was then supposed to create one's own style, as Tung Yüan's distinguished followers had done, by changing or transforming *(pien)* what one intuitively understood. In another passage, Tung further explained his point: "Those who study the works of the masters of the past and cannot transform them are as if they were fenced or walled in. They are far removed from the works of the old masters because they imitate them too closely [i.e., imitate their external appearance]."[16] In these statements Tung emphasizes the "self" and "individuality" of the painter, which were held to be instrumental in his attaining to a new manner of painting.

These ideas expressed by Tung Ch'i-ch'ang seem to have echoed throughout the writings of younger commentators on painting, who tended to define them more clearly, adding other ideas of their own. Among them was Li Liu-fang (1575–1629), who explained that the purpose of learning from the ancient masters was not to seek for *ssu* or formlikeness, i.e., exact visual correspondence with their work.[17] T'ang Chih-ch'i held a similar view, and explained it in greater detail. He began by pointing out that the copying of old models had been recommended already in Hsieh Ho's Sixth Law, and became the "short-cut" *(chieh-ching)* or fast way for painters to learn their art. It is easy to do direct copies *(lin-mo)*, T'ang said, but difficult to transmit the *shen-ch'i*, or spirit, of the master's work. The correct way to copy was to take as one's basis the conception *(i)* of the master's work, not its external form *(chi)*. He added that when a vulgar person tries, every brush stroke ends up being the same as in the original painting.[18]

Yün Hsiang (1586–1655), an artist active in Nanking at the very end of Ming, also had some interesting ideas on *pien*. He also stressed that the purpose of this "change" was not to achieve *ssu* but to transmit the *shen* of the work of the master. He used as an analogy the way elements in nature are transformed into different states and yet remain as single, unchanging substances: mountains are transformed into such transient aspects as "laughing, dripping (moist), adorned, sleeping," and yet remain the same mountains; water is transformed into ice and yet remains water; the sun and moon take on the five colors, and yet remain the same sun and moon; shadow is transformed into light, but light and shadow are the same.[19]

Fan Yün-lin and Yüan Hung-tao (1568–1610) are two others who discuss the question of which aspects of the work of old masters one should pursue. Fan maintains that in following the manner of a certain master, one should go beyond the study of his works alone, and trace the origin of his style in earlier works that *he* may have followed. When one follows Wen Cheng-ming, for example, one should go back to the Sung and Yüan masters whom Wen learned from. In this way, one will avoid obtaining only the "skin" or outward appearance of his style, and will catch its *shen-li*, or spirit and principle. Fan recognized that studying the masters of the past would enable one to understand better the prevalent styles of his own period, freeing one at the same time from slavish imitation and enabling one to originate his own style.[20] Fan's point, simply stated, is that one can define his own position in a tradition of painting, and his relationships to other artists, whether dependent or independent, only when he is fully aware of that tradition and of the achievements of those other artists.

Yüan Hung-tao from Su-chou was one of the leaders of the Kung-an School of literary theory, which engaged in an anti-revivalist movement in literature. He was a close friend of Tung Ch'i-ch'ang, who was deeply influenced by him. Yüan Hung-tao stressed the necessity of studying the creative aspect of the master one is following. In imitating the poetic style of Li T'ang, he commented, "One should take the *hsin* (heart, or mind) of Li T'ang, the part that is *not* derived from Han, Wei, or Six Dynasties poetry, but is Li T'ang's own, as one's *fa*

24

(method, or model); this is the true *fa*."[21] He also suggested that in following the old masters, one should be flexible and learn from them in a way that is in accordance with one's own needs and circumstances. If it will lead to success in one's painting, one should not hesitate to follow the old masters by, however strange it might seem at first, doing the exact *opposite* of what they did. This is far better than to imitate them directly and fail to succeed.[22]

The work or style that is followed is thus only the means to a creative end, and the person who is learning from it is the real "master." Li Liu-fang pointed out that the Yüan painters Ni Tsan, Huang Kung-wang, Wu Chen, and Kao K'o-kung all followed the works of various ancient masters, and yet remained themselves.[23]

Nature and Art
One was supposed to take nature as one's teacher. Tung Ch'i-ch'ang commented: "A painter who models himself after the ancient masters is on the right track. But to advance, he must model himself after *heaven and earth*."[24] And elsewhere he expresses the same thought using a different term for nature: "Painters first take the ancients as their teachers, and then take Creation (*tsao-wu*) as their teacher."[25] Doing so, he says in another passage, will keep imposters—those who paint willfully and carelessly—from mixing in their midst.[26] Tung advised the painter to observe, early in the morning, the changing appearance of clouds and mists, which resemble closely the mountains in paintings, and to study trees in nature. After much observation, and when there is total accord between the form, the mind, and the hand, and each forgets the others' separate existence, the spirit of the landscape will be transmitted.[27]

Various writers advance different reasons why one should learn from nature. Yüan Hung-tao stresses the necessity of trusting one's own experience: "A good painter learns from objects and not [just] from people...a good poet learns from the myriad forms of nature, and not [just] from his predecessors."[28] For T'ang Chih-ch'i and Shen Hao (a painter and

theorist active 1630–1650), it was *because* the ancient masters had based their art on nature that one should do the same.[29] Nature for them was the actual mountains and streams of the natural world. T'ang also uses the term *tzu-jan*, a word meaning "spontaneity" or "self-generating" which is commonly used for nature—which is, as he says, "the most ancient and natural of all."[30] Before one can achieve the highest goal of capturing the *shih*, or force, of a myriad miles in a single foot of painting, he says, one must give close attention to the phenomena of the physical world, and thereby understand the methods of the ancients. Most of all, such absorption of nature will free one from the restrictions and conventions of current styles, and of the "touch of vulgarity" of the professional painter.[31] Thus, the natural world was a source of both inspiration and freedom.

Learning from nature, however, did not mean reproducing its outward appearances in one's painting. For Tung Ch'i-ch'ang, looking at natural scenery became a subjective experience in which the scenery was viewed through a veil of painting, or art history. Once while traveling to the West Lake by boat, he was fond of recounting, he opened the curtain of the boat window and saw an "ink-play" by Mi Fu, which awakened him to awareness of Mi's method of painting mountains and mists.[32] Tung recognized in strange clouds resemblances to snow-covered mountains in paintings by Kuo Hsi, and remarked that the old critics were correct in saying that Kuo Hsi's mountains resembled clouds.[33] When he saw rain-swept peaks in a storm, he thought of dark ink.[34] This interchangeability of painting and nature, within his experience, even allowed relative evaluations: he once said, in looking at an actual scene and a Mi Fu handscroll, that Mi's painting was like "something left over" (*sheng-wu*),[35] and on another occasion made this pronouncement: "Painting is not the equal of mountains-and-water for the wonder of scenery; but mountains-and-water are not the equal of painting for the sheer marvels of brush-and-ink."[36]

Painting was often compared to nature in the aspect of creativity; for example, Li Jih-hua said that the

brushwork of Huang Kung-wang, in its power of transformation, competed with the wonders (*shen-ch'i*) of Creation (*ts'ao-hua*).[37] Hsü Ch'in, writing around 1630, said that nothing equals landscape painting in its capacity to compete with the creative force in nature.[38] Tung Ch'i-ch'ang, who saw the artist as an individual who possessed this potential for creativity, wrote: "The Way of painting is to be found in the painter who controls the universe with his own hands." Wherever he looks, Tung says, the artist sees *sheng-chi*, the motivating force of life, or the incipient and activating force that creates and transforms.

As Tung saw it, the ones who create in this way are the amateur artists, who "take refuge and pleasure in painting." An additional benefit arising from this approach, Tung believed, is that they were likely to lead longer lives. He gives examples of scholar-amateur painters, such as Huang Kung-wang (the first, he says, to "take pleasure in painting," who accordingly lived to the age of eighty-five), and the Ming masters Shen Chou (who lived to eighty-two) and Wen Cheng-ming (who died at eighty-nine). On the other side are those professionals, or misguided amateurs, who "meticulously and carefully delineate" in their paintings, and who are thus the slaves of Creation (*ts'ao-wu*) in striving for clear, exact definitions of things as they appear; they lack *sheng-chi*, and thus have poorer prospects of longevity. For instance, the archetypal craftsman-artist, for Tung, was Ch'iu Ying (ca. 1510–1551), who lived only into his early forties; and Chao Meng-fu (1254–1322) who, although an amateur artist, was sometimes charged with collaboration for having served the Mongol rulers, lived only to sixty-eight. Tung recognized that these two were not equal in quality, but both, for him, belonged to the class of the *practiced*—those who worked to perfect their techniques, and took a craftsman's approach to painting. Tung himself, it should be noted, lived to be eighty-one.[39]

The Mind of the Artist
The final authority in learning, and in creation, was the mind. As Yüan Hung-tao put it, "A good scholar learns from his mind and not [just] from the *Tao*."[40]

This concept of complete freedom for the mind, within the non-constricting framework of nature and the old masters as sources, can be traced, as Wai-kam Ho has done in a recent study, through Tung Ch'i-ch'ang to the late sixteenth-century iconoclast Li Chih (*chin-shih* in 1552), who influenced Tung strongly, and beyond him to the philosophical fountainhead of the whole T'ai-chou School in the metaphysics of Lu Hsiang-shan (1139–1192) and Wang Yang-ming (1472–1528). According to this school of Neo-Confucianism, "the universe exists only in one's mind," and similarly, "all truth exists only within the mind." The mind thus forms a single body, or substance, with heaven and earth, or all things. Therefore, to learn from nature is to learn from one's mind; to return to the past is to return to one's own mind. The process of learning is one of reconstructing the laws of nature or of the old masters' paintings; this process is carried out in accordance with one's free will, and is accomplished through communication with nature or the great paintings of the past. "The moment of truth ... came at the instant of communication and interaction between the painter and his subject, or to be more precise, at the instant of the formation and projection of the painter's mind-image." In other words, the process of reconstructing the laws of nature or art is at the same time a creative process leading to self-expression for the painter. When one has grasped and become master of these laws, "through the 'sudden awakening' to one's innate perception and sensibility, then the barrier between imitation and originality no longer exists."[41] This awakening triggers and inspires one to create paintings in one's own style.

Tung Ch'i-ch'ang compared such painters as Tung Yüan, Chü-jan, and Mi Fu to those who enter the realm of Buddhahood at a single stroke. These representatives of the creative "sudden awakening" were contrasted with the unfortunate Ch'iu-Ying, who again serves to represent those who worked painstakingly and succeeded only after a long period of concentration and effort. Such hard work, directed toward meeting externally imposed standards rather than internal motivations, was presumably what ruined his chance for longevity.[42]

The Art Historical Approach to Creation
From the early Ming period, the history of painting had commonly been formulated as a unilinear, evolutionary development, in which both figure and landscape painting were included. Tung Ch'i-ch'ang, in his epoch-making reformulation, concentrated on landscape, which he saw as developing in two separate, parallel currents, both having their origins in painting of the T'ang dynasty. He called these the Northern and Southern Schools. His distinction, as he pointed out, had nothing to do with where the artist was born or worked; it was based rather on the distinction between the two approaches outlined above: the "sudden awakening" of the creative approach, likened to the "sudden enlightenment" of the Southern School of Ch'an Buddhism, and the "gradual awakening" of the craftsman's approach, which is comparable to the "gradual enlightenment" of the Northern School of Ch'an. Tung Yüan, Chü-jan, and Mi Fu are listed in the Southern School along with its reputed founder, Wang Wei, who is credited with the creation of a landscape mode that broke away from the traditional combination of fine outlining and even washes of color. Those painters who practiced the more academic, detailed, and colorful "blue-and-green" mode of landscape such as Li Ssu-hsün and Chao Po-chü, as well as Southern Sung Academy masters such as Ma Yüan and Hsia Kuei, make up the Northern School.[43] Although Tung does not actually include Ming period followers of these traditions such as Ch'iu Ying[44] and Tai Chin and the Che School painters in his list, his comments on them in other contexts make it clear that they belonged to the "Northern" camp.[45] It is clear also from various passages in his writings that he considered this current of painting to be in a stage of decline,[46] and he advised painters not to practice it.[47]

This oversimplified division of the history of painting has some basis in fact, but there are many points at which it is of questionable validity; this is not the place to discuss them in detail. The real significance of Tung's rewriting of the past lay in the pseudo-historical basis it gave to his distinction between the two approaches to painting discussed above, the intuitive "sudden awakening" of his Southern

School and the painstaking "gradual awakening" of his Northern School. In a general way these were identified, respectively, with the traditions of the scholar-amateurs and the professionals; we know this from the close correspondence between Tung's list of literati painters and his enumeration of Southern School artists.[48] From the Sung and earlier masters mentioned above, the Southern School continued through the Four Great Masters of the Yüan dynasty and the leading Wu School masters, Shen Chou and Wen Cheng-ming, in the Ming,[49] culminating, of course, in Tung himself.

Tung's new formulation was eagerly taken up and elaborated by younger writers, who worked out the distinction between the two "schools" in greater detail. They are not consistent in the lists of artists they assign to one or the other, nor was Tung himself consistent in his lists of Southern School masters and scholar-artists. Their aim was not so much to establish these lineages firmly and in detail as it was to illustrate with historical examples their general theories and provide precedents, whether real or purported, for contemporary practice. Tung's younger friend Ch'en Chi-ju (1558–1639), for example, carried Tung's distinction more clearly into the area of style, describing the "Li School" (the Northern School of Li Ssu-hsün) as "stiff and meticulous, lacking the scholarly spirit"—this last virtually a truism, since the scholar-artists all belonged to the opposition—and the "Wang School" (the Southern School of Wang Wei) as "pure and harmonious, placid and free."[50] Hsü Ch'in carried the distinction into the recent past, listing the painters of the Che School, Tai Chin (1388–1462) and his followers, in the Northern School, and recognizing that this current of painting had long ago entered the stage of decline. In the Southern School he included the same Su-chou masters as Tung had, i.e., Shen Chou and Wen Cheng-ming.[51] Shen Hao similarly identified the Che and Wu with the Northern and Southern Schools, and stated more explicitly Tung's implicit identification of these with the amateur and professional currents. Wang Wei's "literary" style of painting (Wang was of course a great poet) he saw as "lofty and elegant in composition, subtle and placid in expression." Li Ssu-hsün he regarded as the founder of the professional *(hang-chia)* tradition, characterizing his painting as having "strange and steep" [mountains?], impetuous and hard [brushstrokes], wavering and sweeping." The characterization would in fact apply better to the works of the later Che School artists than to Li Ssu-hsün's stylistic tradition; in Shen's mind, the distinction was probably not clear. This lineage, he said, would soon fall into the vice of "wildfox Ch'an," a term for the excessive and undisciplined branch of Ch'an Buddhism, and the succession would "fall into dust." [52] It was surely the somewhat forcedly wild and undisciplined painting of some of the late Che School masters that he had in mind.

In viewing the history of painting in terms of two different approaches, the theory of the Northern and Southern Schools attempted, among other things, to resolve the controversy concerning the relative merits of Sung and Yüan painting, which had become rather heated in the second half of the sixteenth century. [53] Defending Sung were Kao Lien (active ca. 1572) and T'u Lung *(chin-shih* in 1577), both from Chekiang and therefore perhaps influenced somewhat by local loyalty to the painting tradition of that region. What they were reacting against was probably the strong preference for the Yüan masters among the scholar-amateur artists of the Hua-t'ing circle. By the late Ming, Sung versus Yüan had come to be mixed up with Che School versus Wu School, and professionals versus amateurs. Kao Lien and T'u Lung argue against those who criticize Sung painting as academic, too skillful, lacking in inspiration. They defend the Southern Sung Academy masters Li T'ang, Liu Sung-nien, Ma Yüan, and Hsia Kuei as "reaching the ultimate in refined workmanship;" these were the very artists on whose work the Che School styles were chiefly based. Underlying their arguments was a unilinear, evolutionary view of the history of painting. They even maintained that the styles of the Yüan masters were derived from those of Sung — Huang Kung-wang, for instance, took his style from Li T'ang and Hsia Kuei. [54]

Chan Ching-feng (active ca. 1591), a follower of Wang Shih-chen (1526–1590) still saw the develop-

ment of painting as a series of epochal changes, or transformations *(i-pien)*; the Southern Sung Academy styles represent one, the Four Great Masters of the Yüan another. He too criticized those who exalt Yüan over Sung. [55] This was the period when Tung Ch'i-ch'ang, Ku Cheng-i, Mo Shih-lung, and other Hua-t'ing scholar-artists were doing just that, and they were surely the ones whom Chan and others of his persuasion attacked.

Tung's theory of the Northern and Southern Schools put these discussions into a new framework by seeing the development of painting as two separate, parallel currents. The Southern Sung Academy masters were not dismissed from historical importance, but were regarded as leading figures in the Northern School. Earlier Sung artists whom Tung and his circle could admire, such as Li Ch'eng and Fan K'uan, were placed (somewhat anomalously) in the Southern School, and regarded as part of the lineage leading to the Yüan masters. [56]

While the Northern and Southern Schools theory was accepted more or less uncritically by many other writers, along with the preference for the Southern School artists implicit in the formulation of it, a few artists and writers remained unconvinced. Yün Hsiang says that he takes elements of style freely from both "Schools," and even from the styles of Ma Yüan and Hsia Kuei, adapting them to his needs; he says it is "comparable to the Northern and Southern roads to Ch'ang-an — both get there; we only have to make sure we don't get lost." [57] Ch'en Hung-shou, writing in 1652, blamed Ma Yüan and Hsia Kuei for having discredited the whole "Northern" lineage; he praises Li Ssu-hsün and Chao Po-chü, both key figures in Tung's Northern School. [58] Wang To and other painters of that Nanking circle, as we will see in the chapter devoted to them, criticize the archetypal Yüan amateur, Ni Tsan, and praise the Northern Sung masters; artists such as Wu Pin, not so articulate, reveal the same leaning in their stylistic practice.

These issues in the evaluation of old painting were entwined with the issues of opposing local schools in late Ming painting itself. According to Shen Hao,

the Hua-t'ing group championed Tung Yüan, while the Su-chou group preferred Chao Meng-fu, especially as represented in his more conservative works in Sung-derived styles. (Tung Ch'i-ch'ang's belittlement of Chao may have been, then, a blow directed at the Su-chou faction.) Each condemned the stylistic degeneration of the other, and spoke of correcting styles that had become corrupted. This they proposed to do by imitating *other* old styles, which would somehow have a salutary effect on the evils of current practice. In the end, the sheer complexity and ponderousness of this historical structure, and its paralyzing effect on artists who tried to find their way through it and find themselves places in it, probably had much to do with stimulating the new, creative impulses in late Ming painting. Shen Hao finally advocates not concerning oneself with lineages and schools at all: "*Do not bother* with Tung Yüan or Chao Meng-fu, with Hua-t'ing or Su-chou, with imitation or correcting corrupt practices; walk alone and be contented with yourself." [59] The early Ch'ing Individualists were to do just that; the supreme proponent of independence, both in theory and practice, was of course Tao-chi.

Principles and Techniques of Painting
The writings on painting of this period, like the painting itself, deal principally with landscape. Hsieh Chao-chih complains that people of his day seldom depicted figure subjects or illustrated narratives, and that paintings of flowers and birds were looked down upon. As for paintings of Taoist and Buddhist subjects, they "were not one in a hundred." [60]

Writings on landscape are concerned mainly with principles of composition and techniques of using brush and ink, rather than with the aspects and moods of the real landscape of nature. Again, this corresponds to the direction that painting was taking. Tung Ch'i-ch'ang's writings, for instance, reveal the same concerns that underlie his paintings. The modes of formal construction that he found in the works of the Yüan masters, especially Huang Kung-wang, and which he developed in his own works, he articulated in his theoretical writings; some passages from these will be quoted in the chapter that deals with him as an artist. From Huang he took the method of conceiving the entire landscape as a unified framework which is then proportioned into component parts; these in turn are proportioned into still smaller units. This method he calls "proportioning and uniting" *(fen ho).*[61] Also derived from Huang was the method of giving both three-dimensionality and momentum, or motivating force *(shih),* to terrain forms by first outlining and then applying texture strokes *(ts'un)* to the forms.[62] Intensifying this dynamic quality is a "rising and falling" movement in the distant mountains. A forest of trees should also have this "rising and falling" movement,[63] while the individual trees should turn and bend.[64] All these points are anticipated in Huang Kung-wang's own essay on landscape painting, *Hua shan-shui chüeh.*[65] In fact, the general tendency to treat elements of landscape in terms of their formal properties and compositional function, rather than their individual interest and value, may be noted already in Huang's essay, for example when he speaks of trees being used to fill empty spaces, or of their aspects of "looking upward and downward, facing forward or back, dark and light, dense and sparse."[66]

Tung's contemporary and fellow townsman Chao Tso (active ca. 1610–1630) writes of this same *shih* as the principal desideratum in painting. For him, all elements of landscape have *shih*—mountains, forests, rocks. The winding and turning, rising and falling movements must be connected into a single continuous movement that runs through the whole composition and unites it. One should plan the composition, he advises, by drawing lightly with a semidry brush, to arrange the forms and their movements *(hsing shih);* only after this can one begin painting. If this method is followed, the *hsing shih* of the scenery will appear "as if accomplished in a single breath."[67]

Also important in these discussions, and elements in Tung's theoretical apparatus, are the qualities of substantiality *(shih)* and insubstantiality *(hsü),* which refer to density or sparsity of brushwork, and the compositional balance between solid mass and void.[68] T'ang Chih-ch'i notes that small paintings are best suited to exhibit insubstantiality, and that the more of it they have, the more extraordinary they are. Large paintings should give a feeling of insubstantiality within substantiality.[69]

Techniques of using brush and ink were widely discussed. Huang Kung-wang had written of "having ink" and "having brush" to refer to, respectively, painting in which the brushstrokes were blurred and those in which they were distinct.[70] Tung Ch'i-ch'ang thought of "brush" and "ink" somewhat differently; for him, painting in outlines without texture strokes were "lacking in brush," while those with texture strokes but without sufficient separation in tones and "light and heavy, frontal and backward-facing, light and dark" were "lacking in ink."[71] The texture strokes were evidently considered to define the structure of the forms, and the ink gradations to give them bulk. For Ku Ning-yüan, "lacking brush and lacking ink" were the faults of using "astringent" (dry and rough) ink for the initial drawing (and covering this up with wet strokes in a fuzzy manner). One should instead, "first establish the sinews and bones, and then gradually add the flesh."[72] If the ink is put on too dry, Ku says, breath-resonance *(ch'i-yün)* will be lacking; but if one consciously seeks for breath-resonance, then the ink washes will become excessive and overflowing. If the ink is applied too richly and moistly, on the other hand, then pattern and order will be lacking; but if one consciously seeks for pattern and order, the result will be stiff, "carved painting" *(k'o-hua).*[73]

The techniques of applying ink were discussed with endless elaborations by different writers. T'ang Chih-ch'i differentiates between what he calls tender or young *(nun)* ink and old *(lao)* ink; this refers not to the ink itself but to the manner of using it.[74] He writes further of the method of overlaying ink *(chi mo),* dark on light or light on dark and says that the Sung and Yüan masters would do this in seven or eight layers.[75] Yün Hsiang speaks of ink as manifesting the "five colors," or performing the functions of color.[76]

The most systematic presentation of this technical vocabulary is in a work by Wang K'o-yü written around 1643, which classifies and defines terms relating to ink, brushwork, conventions for depicting trees and rocks, and so forth.[77] Such systematization culminates in the famous *Mustard Seed Garden Manual of Painting (Chieh-tzu-yüan hua-chuan),* the first part of which, dealing with landscape, was published in 1670.

In the face of all this insistence on following rules in composition and disciplines in the use of brush and ink, the stress that some writers, notably Ku Ning-yüan, place on achieving an effect of awkwardness or a "primitive quality" *(cho)* in order to avoid a "professional air" in one's paintings[78] may seem paradoxical. The point is that the artist should have mastered these disciplines—some of which he possessed already through the practice of calligraphy—to the point where they do not inhibit his painting, as do the stricter canons and conventions of the professional artist, but only strengthen it, allowing him to work creatively in his individual style.

Conclusion
In a period when individuality and creativity were exalted in many areas of intellectual and artistic life, theoretical writings on painting were produced in unprecedented volume and complexity. Tung Ch'i-ch'ang's new creative approach to painting, which lifted it out of stagnation, was set forth in writings that reconciled innovation and creativity with a firm base in tradition.[79] He found freedom by establishing order; and behind his order was a controlled view of history, expressed in his theory of the Northern and Southern Schools. The past was thus a source of inspiration; but it was also, once Tung had marked in it a canonical lineage of masters worthy of imitation, a source of orthodoxy, with a potential for stifling the very creativity that Tung advocated. That potential was to be realized in the early Ch'ing Orthodox School masters, who narrowed the scope of acceptable styles and compositions to the point where a certain monotony set in and the school declined, to be raised again to greatness only by Wang Yüan-ch'i, who carried still further Tung's abstract manipulations of form. Meanwhile, in reaction to the Orthodox masters and to those who misread the Northern and Southern

Schools theory as factual history rather than as a functional formulation, the Individualist masters of the early Ch'ing again advocated, and practiced, a creative approach. In this they are akin to Tung Ch'i-ch'ang, and follow the way he opened, at the same time that they are deliberately breaking free of the order that he imposed on painting. ∎

Notes

[1]Wang K'en-t'ang, *Yü-kang-chai pi-chu*, quoted in Yü Chien-hua (ed.), *Chung-kuo hua-lun lei-pien*, Peking, 1957 (hereafter *CKHLLP)*, Vol. II, p. 750. [2]Hsieh Chao-chih, *Wu-tsa-tsu*, circa 1600 (Shanghai edition of 1959), p. 196. [3]Yüan Hung-tao, *Yüan Chung-lang chi*, circa 1600, quoted in *CKHLLP*, Vol. I, p. 129. [4]Fan Yün-lin, *Shu-liao-kuan chi*, circa 1600, quoted in *CKHLLP*, Vol. I, p. 126. [5]Tung Ch'i-ch'ang, *Hua-chih*, in *Jung-t'ai pieh-chi*, compiled by his grandson Tung T'ing. Preface by Ch'en Chi-ju dated 1630 (Taipei edition of 1968), chüan 6, p. 1b. [6]Li Jih-hua, *Chu-lan mo-chün t'i-yü*, compiled by Chiang Yüan-tou. *Mei-shu ts'ung-shu* edition (hereafter *MSTS*), Part II, Vol. 2, pp. 260, 269, 274–275, *Tz'u-t'ao-hsüan tsa-cho* quoted in *CKHLLP*, Vol. I, pp. 131, 132, 134. [7]Fan Yün-lin, *op. cit.*, p. 126. [8]T'u Lung, *K'ao-p'an yü-shih*, chüan 2, p. 33, in *I-shu ts'ung-pien*, Taipei, 1966 (hereafter *ISTP*), Part I, Vol. 28. [9] Li Jih-hua, *Tz'u-t'ao-hsuan tsa-cho*, quoted in *CKHLLP*, Vol. I, p. 131. [10]Tung Ch'i-ch'ang, *Hua-chih*, in *Jung-t'ai pieh-chi*, chüan 6, pp. 3a–b. [11]T'ang Chih-ch'i, *Hui-shih wei-yen* in *MSTS*, Part 5, Vol. 6, pp. 119–120. [12]Li Jih-hua, *Chu-lan mo-chün t'i-yü*, pp. 268–269. [13]T'ang Chih-ch'i, *Hui-shih wei-yen* in *MSTS*, Part V, Vol. 6, pp. 149–150. [14]Lan Ying, quoted in *CKHLLP*, Vol. II, p. 777. [15]Tung Ch'i-ch'ang, *Hua-ch'an-shih sui-pi*, compiled in 1720 by Yang Wu-pu, *ISTP* edition, p. 44. Also see *Hua-chih*, chüan 6, p. 6a. [16]Tung Ch'i-ch'ang, *Hua-chih*, chüan 6, p. 19b. [17]Li Liu-fang, quoted in *CKHLLP*, Vol. II, p. 751. [18]T'ang Chih-ch'i, *Hui-shih wei-yen*, p. 126. [19]Yün Hsiang, quoted in Ch'en Tsuan (ed.), *Yü-chi shan-fang hua wai-lu* (mid-18th century), in *MSTS*, Part I, Vol. 8, pp. 147–148. [20]Fan Yün-lin, *op. cit.*, p. 126. [21]Yüan Hung-tao, p. 129. [22]Ibid. [23]Li Liu-fang, *op. cit.*, p. 751. [24]Tung Ch'i-ch'ang, *Hua-chih*, chüan 6, pp. 10a–b. [25]Ibid., 38b–39a. [26]Ibid., p. 48b. [27]Ibid., pp. 10a–b. Also see Li Jih-hua, *Tz'u-t'ao-hsüan tsa-cho*, p. 756; and T'ang Chih-ch'i, *op. cit.*, pp. 123–124. [28]Yüan Hung-tao, *Yüan Chung-lang ch'üan-chi*, Hong Kong, 1950, p. 9. [29]T'ang Chih-ch'i, *op. cit.*, pp. 128–129. Shen Hao, *Hua-chu* (circa 1640) in *MSTS*, Part I, Vol. 6, p. 37. [30]T'ang Chih-ch'i, *op. cit.*, pp. 123–124. [31]Ibid., p. 122. [32]Tung Ch'i-ch'ang, *Hua-chih*, chüan 6, pp. 3a, 35a–b. [33]Ibid., pp. 35b–36a. [34]Ibid., p. 54b, with date 1610 mentioned. [35]Ibid., p. 35b. [36]Ibid., p. 5a. [37]Li Jih-hua, *Tz'u-t'ao-hsüan tsa-cho*, p. 756. [38]Hsü Ch'in, *Ming-hua lu*, colophon dated 1673, in *MSTS*, Part III, Vol. 7, p. 36. [39]Tung Ch'i-ch'ang, *Hua-chih*, chüan 6, pp. 5b–6a. [40]Yüan Hung-tao, *op. cit.*, p. 129. [41]Ho Wai-kam, "Tung Ch'i-ch'ang's New Orthodoxy and the Southern School Theory," Symposium paper, Princeton University, 1969, pp. 13–15. [42]Tung Ch'i-ch'ang, *Hua-chih*, chüan 6, pp. 50a–b. [43]Ibid., chüan 6, p. 6b. The translation here is from the slightly variant text in Tung Ch'i-ch'ang, *Lun-hua so-yen* included in Cheng Ch'ao-tsung, *Mei-yu-ko wen-yü* (completed in 1627), p. 255. A copy of this text was kindly provided to us by Mr. Wai-kam Ho. [44]Ibid., chüan 6, pp. 50a–b. Ch'iu Ying is regarded as belonging to the school of Li Ssu-hsün, along with Chao Po-chü and Chao Po-su. [45]Ibid., chüan 6, pp. 4a–b. He implicitly criticizes the Che School followers as sweet, perverse, vulgar, and pernicious. Chao Meng-fu (from Chekiang) is implicitly grouped with the Che School. See also chüan 6, pp. 46a and 48a, where the later Su-chou artists fall under criticism. [46]Ibid., chüan 6, pp. 6b, 4a–b; he states that the Che School with Tai Chin as leader will soon be extinguished. [47]Ibid., chüan 6, pp. 50a–b; after he turned 50 in 1605, Tung realized that the Li School (Li Ssu-hsün, Chao Po-chü, Chao Po-su, and Ch'iu Ying) should not be practiced. In another passage (chüan 6, p. 4b) he says that Ma Yüan, Hsia Kuei, Li T'ang, and Liu Sung-nien should not be followed either. [48]Ibid., chüan 6, p. 4b. [49]Ibid., chüan 6, p. 6b. [50]Ch'en Chi-ju, quoted from Chang Ch'ou (1577–1633), *Ch'ing-ho shu-hua fang* (preface 1616) in *CKHLLP*, Vol. II, p. 754. [51]Hsu Ch'in, *op. cit.*, pp. 36–37. [52]Shen Hao, *op. cit.*, p. 29. Although the Che School followers are enumerated and Wen and Shen of the Wu School are mentioned, the followers of Wen and Shen are not included. [53]Ho Wai-kam, *op. cit.*, p. 3, dates the Northern and Southern theory as probably not earlier than 1588. It is probably not later than 1605, on the other hand, since Tung states that after turning fifty (in 1605) he first realized that the Li Ssu-hsün tradition of landscape should not be followed; in this passage he uses the concepts of sudden and gradual enlightenment (*Hua-chih*, chüan 6, pp. 50a–b). [54]T'u Lung, *op. cit.*, p. 32. Kao Lien, *Yen-hsien ch'ing-shang ch'ien* in *MSTS*, Part III, Vol. 10, pp. 180–187. There is no evidence in their writings that they were aware of the concept of the Northern and Southern Schools; their defenses of Sung, and attacks on the partisans of Yüan, may antedate the publication of that theory. The unilinear view of painting history underlying their writings is similar to that of Wang Shih-chen (1526–1590); see *CKHLLP*, Vol. I, pp. 116–117. The same can be said of the writings of Wang's follower Chan Ching-feng (see following note). [55]Chan Ching-feng, *Tung-t'u hsüan-lan pien*, late 16th century, in *MSTS*, Part V, Vol. 1, pp. 47–48, 78, 183, 110–111. [56]Tung Ch'i-ch'ang, *Hua-chih*, chüan 6, p. 4b. [57]Yün Hsiang, *op. cit.*, p. 142. [58]Ch'en Hung-shou, quoted in *Yü-chi shan-fang hua wai-lu*, in *MSTS*, Part I, Vol. 8, pp. 134–135. [59]Shen Hao, *op. cit.*, p. 31. [60]Hsieh Chao-chih, *op. cit.*, pp. 196–197. [61]Tung Ch'i-ch'ang, *Hua-chih*, chüan 6, pp. 9a–b. Also *Hua-ch'an-shih sui-pi*, *ISTP* edition, p. 36. [62]*Hua-ch'an-shih sui-pi*, pp. 39, 35. [63]*Hua-chih*, chüan 6, p. 11b. [64]*Hua-ch'an-shih sui-pi*, p. 36. [65]Huang Kung-wang, *Hsieh shan-shui chüeh*, in T'ao Ts'ung-i, *Nan-ts'un cho-keng lu*, Preface 1366 (Peking edition of 1959), pp. 94–97. [66]Ibid., p. 94. [67]Chao Tso, *Lun-hua*, quoted in Ch'in Tsu-Yung, *Hua-hsüeh hsin-yin*, preface 1856 (Shanghai edition of 1918), chüan 3, pp. 12b, 13a. [68]Tung Ch'i-ch'ang, *Hua-ch'an-shih sui-pi*, p. 36. [69]T'ang Chih-ch'i, pp. 124–125. [70]Huang Kung-wang, *op. cit.*, p. 95. [71]Tung Ch'i-ch'ang, *Hua-chih*, chüan 6, pp. 11a–b. [72]Ku Ning-yüan, *Hua yin* (late 16th century) in *MSTS*, Part I, Vol. 4, pp. 19–20. [73]Ibid., p. 21. [74]T'ang Chih-ch'i, *op. cit.*, p. 126. [75]Ibid., pp. 131–132. Already foreshadowed in Huang Kung-wang, *op. cit.*, pp. 94, 97. [76]Yun Hsiang, *op. cit.*, p. 148. [77]Wang K'o-yu, *Shan-hu-wang hua-lu*, preface 1643, in *MSTS*, Part II, Vol. 1, pp. 240–250. [78]Ku Ning-yüan, *op. cit.*, p. 20. [79]The idea of creating within tradition by means of transformation is stated by Tung in the form of a question: "How could one abandon the methods of the ancients and create [wholly] anew?" See *Hua-ch'an-shih sui-pi*, pp. 35–36.

Real and Ideal: Intellectual Solutions in the Late Ming

by Patricia Berger

The late Ming is dynamically consistent though its solutions to intellectual and social problems are seemingly heterogeneous. Most of the innovators of the era were responding to an environment of social disintegration. While it is difficult to establish causal links between such diverse areas of intellectual endeavor as moral and ethical philosophy and aesthetic theory, they can be seen as analogous in their reactions to the discrepancies existing between tradition and fact. An examination of one might therefore elucidate the set of pressures brought to bear on the other.

The most influential philosopher of the Ming dynasty was Wang Yang-ming, whose School of the Mind (Hsin-hsüeh) developed in opposition to that of the Sung Neo-Confucian philosopher Chu Hsi. Chu Hsi's approach to Confucian doctrine was accepted as orthodox by the time of Wang Yang-ming. He asserted that the extension of knowledge was attained through the investigation of things, an objective approach to the multitudinous phenomena which the idealist Wang Yang-ming took as an analytical *elaboratio ad absurdum*. Wang said: "What Chu Hsi meant by the investigation of things is 'to investigate the principle (li)[1] in things to the utmost as we come in contact with them.'[2] To investigate the principles in things as we come in contact with them means to look into each individual thing for its so-called definite principles. This means to apply one's mind (hsin) to each individual thing and look for principles in it. This is to divide the mind and principle into two."[3] While Chu Hsi believed that each thing contained its own principle and was consequently worthy of investigation, Wang Yang-ming felt that principle was prior in the mind and was superimposed as a grid over neutral nature. He did not recognize the duality of the perceiver and the perceived but believed that all things were contained in the mind. Things, then, were equivalent to the event of perception and had no active existence outside the mind.[4] Wang Yang-ming's position served to eliminate any conflict between real and ideal structures since, in his view, the order of nature was not inherent in nature itself, but proceeded from the mind. Things were as they seemed.

Wang Yang-ming opposed the elaboration and glorification of detail by Chu Hsi's followers as "trifling with things and losing one's purpose in life."[5] He advocated instead the investigation of one's own mind and the extension of the mind's principle to all things. His primary interest, then, was in structure rather than detail, a theoretical position he shared with artists of the late Ming. Among this group was Tung Ch'i-ch'ang, who said, expressing his annoyance at the interest in detail among landscape painters of the late Ming, "Nowadays people pile up small bits to make a large mountain; this is one of the worst mistakes. An ancient master made only three or four large divisions and accomplished the whole composition. Although within these divisions there are many small details, the principal thing is to grasp the momentum of the design."[6]

That Tung Ch'i-ch'ang's approach to the painting of the landscape was structural rather than anecdotal is clear in his own diagrammatic and self-assertive compositions. He paid little attention to the sort of detail that would link his subjects to specific natural phenomena, but concentrated on the articulation of generalized forms. The method (fa) of painting consisted of the integrated grouping of these forms, which had been drawn from an orthodox artistic tradition. Independent of time and place and removed from their historical contexts, they were seen as distilled essences, as ideal answers to the representation of categories of visual events. As Tung said: "There are some who say: 'One should form an individual style in painting trees.' This is not right. For example, in painting willows, one should follow the manner of Chao Ch'ien-li, in painting pines, of Ma Ho-chih, dry trees, of Li Ch'eng. Such are unchanging principles through the ages."[7]

Tung espoused a set of principles borne by an orthodox artistic tradition, believing that the reality of brush and ink was not inferior to, but only separate from, that of nature. His artistic tradition, however, he defined himself in order to provide ballast for his formalist attitude. His Northern and Southern Schools of painters are artificial constructions having nothing to do with the actual geographical distribution of painters through history, although his

choice of terms reflects the fact that rivalries between schools during his day were usually based on local origin. The terms themselves were taken from Ch'an (Zen) Buddhism, which had also been divided, after a doctrinal dispute, into Northern and Southern Schools. While the Northern School conceived of the attainment of enlightenment as a gradual process, the Southern School saw it as a sudden awakening. Applying this dogmatic opposition to painting, Tung said that the Southern School painter was one who "entered the land of the Tathagata Buddha in a single stroke" while the Northern School painter "became a Bodhisattva only after a long and meritorious record of hardship."[8] The artists Tung placed in the Southern School, beginning with Wang Wei (699–759) and ending, of course, with himself, were not interested, as he saw it, in the fine rendition of detail so much as in the broader possibilities of composition. The artists in his Northern School, beginning with Li Ssu-hsün (651–716) and his son Li Chao-tao, originators of the blue-green style and the ultimate ancestors (in Tung's eyes) of the Che School painters, saw compositional structure, Tung felt, as an eventual outcome of the juxtaposition of innumerable finely rendered details. While these artists took composition as inevitable and therefore not variable, Ma Yüan and Hsia Kuei, two painters of the Southern Sung (but included by Tung in his Northern School), assumed a paradigmatic composition which they elaborated but little. For the painters of the Northern School, the possibilities of structure were not so fascinating as those of decoration and mood.

Wang Yang-ming, with his emphasis on the unity of principle and mind, did not conceive of reality as static. Innate knowledge (liang-chih), the "original substance of the mind,"[9] the principle of right and wrong,[10] a basic concept of Wang's idealism, was only knowable in association with an activating event. Nature and mind, then, were interdependent, since nature depended on mind for structure or order, but mind on nature for stimulation. Wang's neutral nature is also given moral value by the mind of the perceiver. For Wang, "the original substance of the mind is none other than the principle of nature and is never out of accord with propriety (li)." [11] As a consequence, there is no conflict between what is true and what is desirable or proper. In a like manner, Tung Ch'i'ch'ang and other literati painters accepted what Victoria Contag has termed the "second reality" [12] of generalized and traditional type-forms, believing them to represent the "unchanging principles through the ages." For them, the use of what would seem to be static and overworked type-forms became, in fact, a dynamic and spiritual communion of artist and tradition. Typeforms served as activating events for the elucidation of true order. The traditions of brush and ink could convey a subtle order not immediately apparent in the myriad forms of the natural landscape. As Tung Ch'i-ch'ang said: "If one considers the uniqueness of the scenery, then a painting is not the equal of real landscape. But if one considers the essential subtlety of brush and ink, then the real landscape can never equal painting." [13]

Both Wang Yang-ming and Tung Ch'i-ch'ang concerned themselves with establishing the norms of proper behavior. While much of Wang's writing is individualistic ("Your innate knowledge is your standard"), [14] he advocated that "people overcome their selfishness and recover that which is common to the substance of the minds of all men." [15] By emphasizing the unity of all minds, he also placed the individual securely within the society of other men. In his essay "Pulling up the Root and Stopping up the Source" [16] he describes life during the time of the legendary rulers Yao and Shun: "There was no distinction between the self and the other, or between the self and things. It is like the body of a person. The eyes see, the ears hear, the hands hold, and the feet walk, all fulfilling the function of the body. The eyes are not ashamed of their not being able to hear. When the ears hear something the eyes will direct their attention to it. The feet are not ashamed that they are not able to grasp. When a hand feels for something, the feet will move forward." [17] Here Wang Yang-ming provides a broad model for social interaction which allows all people to function naturally according to their abilities, united by the common substance of the mind. Wang sees society as structured by virtue [18] and as a system of relationships which all serve to support the commonwealth.

A number of Wang Yang-ming's followers in the sixteenth and seventeenth centuries were also concerned with breaking down the barriers between self and society. Living during a time of social upheaval, these philosophers tried to redefine society so as to encompass people who had hitherto been regarded as socially marginal. Several of these philosophers were avowedly popularistic, advocating radical restructurings of traditional beliefs and hierarchies.

Among them was Wang Ken, founder of the T'ai-chou School. He lived from about 1483 to 1540. He was the son of a saltmaker who educated himself in the classics and determined to become a sage after visiting the tomb of Confucius. Later he became a student of Wang Yang-ming. [19] Though he differs from Wang Yang-ming in emphasizing the physical self (shen) rather than the mind (hsin), he continues Wang Yang-ming's analogy of the body and society, arguing that the preservation of the physical self is necessary for the preservation of society. [20] He defends self-love as the equivalent of love for society, saying:

> If I only know how to preserve myself and do not know how to love other men, then I will surely seek to satisfy only myself, pursue my own selfish gain, and harm others, whereupon they will retaliate and my self can no longer be preserved. If I cannot preserve myself, how can I preserve the world, the state and the households? This comes from the habit of thinking only in terms of one's own class and not knowing the fundamentals. If I only know how to love others and do not know how to love myself, then it will come to my body being cooked alive or the flesh being sliced off my thighs, or to throwing away my life or killing myself, and then myself cannot be preserved. And if myself cannot be preserved, with what shall I preserve my prince and my fathers? [21]

It would seem that Wang Ken recommended the most egalitarian and egocentric of societies; but instead, he merely wished to restructure a society that had previously excluded himself and others like him. He began touring the countryside as a preacher and rapidly achieved widespread popularity. As his movement grew, it developed a local and regional organization. Leadership was determined by per-

sonal transmission of the teaching by Wang Ken himself. In every sense, he had become the center of a new, orthodox hierarchy.

Ho Hsin-yin, who lived from 1517 to 1579, was another philosopher of the T'ai-chou School. He was a scholar who passed the provincial examination but who discarded his official career after hearing the teachings of Wang Ken. He, like Wang Ken, seems to have wished to find freedom for the individual within the forms of society, but a society redefined in terms of universal equality. He first attempted to establish a utopian commune (based on the idea in the Great Learning that the family is the foundation of the state) called the Collective Harmony Hall within which life was to be anti-individualistic, cooperative and egalitarian, but regulated in every detail. The commune failed, not internally, but because of government pressure. Ho was arrested, but after his release lectured and gathered a large following. [22]

Ho was especially interested in redefining the relationships between men. He wished to transcend the limits of family loyalties and so he concentrated on the relationship of friend to friend. He said, "Humanity regards all as one's own kind…The kinship between father and son is not the only kinship; kinship extends to all worthy of one's kindness—to all creatures that have blood and breath." [23] Ho, then, did not assert any radical independence of society, but just a radical restructuring of it.

Li Chih, who lived from 1527 to 1602, is considered the greatest radical of the Ming dynasty. Raised as a Moslem in the Chin-chiang district of Chuan-chou in Fukien province, he received a classical education but failed to attain his chin-shih degree. [24] After a period of routine government assignments, he felt he had discovered the Way and later was exposed to the Diamond Sutra of the Prajñāpāramitā literature (Vajracchedika Prajñāpāramitā). He became convinced of the unity of the Three Teachings (Confucianism, Taoism, and Buddhism) and in 1588 became a Ch'an monk. [25] Officially, however, he was not licensed as a monk, nor did he keep the monastic discipline. He began writing fervent defenses of the theory of the identity of the Three Teachings and violent attacks on traditional Confucian literature and traditional historical heroes. In 1590, he published his *Fen-shu (A Book for Burning)* and in 1600 his *Ts'ang-shu (A Book for Hiding)*.[26] Both were scathing indictments of historical heroes and of the Confucian administration.[27] Both books were proscribed in 1602. Li Chih was arrested and his books were burned. He committed suicide soon afterward in Peking.[28]

Li Chih's role as a social reformer is clear. A hero-worshipper himself, he attacked historical personages held dear by Confucians, reversing time-honored decisions in dozens of cases. Like Ho Hsin-yin, he re-evaluated the five Confucian relations, emphasizing the male-female relationship and the broader relationships of teacher to student and ruler to minister. Also like Ho Hsin-yin, he tried to clarify the complexities of social structure. His conscious separation from secular society and from familial ties by his token adoption of the monkish role seems to have served the purpose less of giving him entree into the religious life than of positioning him as a detached though fervent observer of a decaying society.

Opposed in spirit though not in intent to the T'ai-chou School was the Tung-lin Academy in Wu-hsi, Kiangsu Province. The Tung-lin Academy reached its height of fame during the reign of the Emperor Shen-tsung (1572–1620), better known by his reign title Wan-li.[29] The Wan-li Emperor is charged by the official Ming history, the *Ming shih*, with responsibility for the downfall of the dynasty. During his reign, partisan struggles took place between the "pure set" or "righteous circle," Confucian officials who tried to uphold moral standards at court through directed criticism, and their antagonists, certain corrupt and opportunistic officials at court, especially in the Nei-ko or Grand Secretariat. The Nei-ko had been instituted by the first Ming emperor, T'ai-tsu, and was meant to replace the Chung-shu-sheng or Imperial Chancellory. T'ai-tsu had eliminated the Chung-shu-sheng because his minister Hu Wei-yung had conspired against the throne. Therefore, T'ai-tsu made reinstitution of the Chung-

shu-sheng illegal for any of his successors. Anyone advocating its restoration was to be executed.[30] After T'ai-tsu's death, however, the Nei-ko rushed to fill the administrative void. Soon the Nei-ko differed from the old Chung-shu-sheng in name only. Grand Secretaries like Chang Chü-cheng, whose administration occupied the first ten years of Shen-tsung's reign, ruled the Empire as Prime Ministers or Imperial Chancellors had once done, but without any constitutional controls.

The criticism made by the "pure set" was not restricted to particular officials in the Nei-ko. Many objected to the power which had come to be concentrated in the Nei-ko and demanded that this body be reduced to its original stature. They felt that rule by the Nei-ko involved the danger of arbitrary and despotic power being exercised through non-constitutional means. Their objections earned them the wrath of some of the most powerful politicians in the country.

One of the main figures in the struggles against the despotism of the Nei-ko was Ku Hsien-ch'eng who reopened the Tung-lin Academy in 1604.[31] Ku Hsien-ch'eng and his friends were convinced that the prevailing evils were due to a lack of public spirit among the educated classes. Therefore, in contrast to the followers of Wang Yang-ming, Ku and his friends stressed the social duties of the gentry as the leading group in the community. The Tung-lin scholars did not speculate on, nor did they wish to change, the fundamental and traditional structures of society, yet soon they became the rallying point for the "pure set," and the movement of political activity which was centered there developed into organized agitation against any and all groups guilty of moral laxity. This political agitation was based on a sense of outrage against the immoralities of the government, and it continued until the Academy was bloodily purged by the eunuch Wei Chung-hsien in 1625.[32] Despite its radical political stance with respect to the prevailing government, the Tung-lin Academy was a bastion of conservative Confucianism. The Academy's philosophical position was derived from that of Chu Hsi and, in fact, the charter of the Academy, written at its

reopening in 1604, harks back to Chu Hsi's *Rules of the Pai-lu Tung*, a famous academy in Kiangsu. Especially reminiscent is the inclusion of the Four Essentials, that is, to know nature, to have a firm objective which consists of emulating the sages, to respect the classics and to have the right motives.[33] Moreover, the Tung-lin scholars emphasized the necessity for morally defensible action in all phases of life. Like many moderates of the School of Wang Yang-ming, the Tung-lin scholars argued against the moral subjectivism of the radical followers of Wang. In his *Notebooks (Hsiao-hsin-chai cha-chi)* Ku Hsien-ch'eng argued against philosophical affiliation with Wang Yang-ming. He said:

> The danger of following Chu Hsi is inhibition; that of following Wang Yang-ming is dissolution. For the inhibited, there are things that he does not do; for the dissolute, there is nothing that he does not do. Inhibitions are repugnant to human nature; it is therefore easy to take advantage of this natural repugnance and emancipate ourselves from them. Dissolution is gratifying to human feelings; it is therefore difficult to go against their current and repress it. Once, Confucius, discussing abuses concerning ritual said, "In ritual, it is better to be simple than elaborate." Accordingly, with regard to the dangers in study one must also say, it is better to be inhibited than dissolute.[34]

The Tung-lin scholars felt that a traditionally accepted moral stance had to be taken on every issue. Thus, the Academy took violent exception to the radical followers of Wang Yang-ming, believing that they desired heterodox individualism exclusive of the forms of society. Instead, the philosophers of the School of the Mind desired only a clarification of traditional forms which they felt had been elaborated to the point of obscurity by the followers of Chu Hsi. While Wang Yang-ming himself tried to justify the necessity for a heterogeneous, stratified society, his followers, mostly men alienated from the mainstream of culture, saw that traditional society could not accommodate the social disintegration that accompanied the end of the dynasty. Even Wang Yang-ming realized that structures from earlier times could not be fitted to the present.[35] Thus, to avoid conflict between real and ideal structures, these philosophers redefined the ideal norms of society, simplifying them and making them more

32 comprehensive. This popularizing tendency was shared by a number of painters at the end of the Ming, most notably Ch'en Hung-shou. By directing their attention to popular topics but rendering them with a subtle and sophisticated brush, they widened their appeal to include people formerly excluded from the rarified world of art appreciation. The Tung-lin scholars, noticing the same failure of reality to meet their expectations, reacted with political activism. They tried to change reality so it would fit into a traditionally ideal structure, one that would support a literati ethic of privileged individualism.

Tung Ch'i-ch'ang and other literati painters found yet another solution. They created a sequestered and exclusivist enclave whose reality was a carefully constructed, thoroughly justified set of norms. These they defined so as to enclose themselves safely within an orthodox tradition, a tradition that served to keep out the discordant confusion of the outside world. ■

Notes

[1]*Li,* usually translated as "principle," has been rendered by Professor Peter Boodberg as "infrastructure," a translation he derives from the fact that the character originally meant the veins or flaw lines in jade. The notion of structure will be useful later on. [2]Chu Hsi in his *Ta-hsueh chang-chu,* chüan V. [3]Wang Yang-ming, *Ch'uan-hsi lu,* translated by Wing-tsit Chan, *(Instructions for Practical Living and other Neo-Confucian Writings)* New York and London, 1963, section 135. [4]*Ibid.,* section 6. [5]*Ibid.,* section 135. [6]Tung Ch'i-ch'ang, *Hua-ch'an-shih sui-pi,* chüan II. [7]*Ibid.* [8]Tung Ch'i-ch'ang, *Jung-t'ai pi-chi,* chüan IV. Translated by Wen Fong, "Tung Ch'i-ch'ang and the Orthodox Theory of Painting," National Palace Museum Quarterly, 2.3 (Jan. 1968), 1. [9]Wang Yang-ming, *Ch'uan-hsi lu (Instructions for Practical Living),* section 152. [10]*Ibid.,* section 206. [11]*Ibid.,* section 122. [12]Victoria Contag, "The Unique Characteristics of Chinese Landscape Paintings," *Archives of the Chinese Art Society of America,* Vol. 19, 55. As Contag notes, the term "second reality" *(erh-shih)* is her translation of a term used by Hsün-tzu. [13]Tung Ch'i-ch'ang, *Jung-t'ai pi-chi,* chüan IV. Translated by Wen Fong, "Tung Ch'i-ch'ang and the Orthodox Theory of Painting," 6. [14]Wang Yang-ming, *Ch'uan-hsi lu (Instructions for Practical Living),* section 206. [15]*Ibid.,* section 142. [16]*Ibid.,* sections 142 and 143. [17]*Ibid.,* section 142. [18]*Ibid.,* section 142. [19]William Theodore de Bary, "Individualism and Humanitarianism in Late Ming Thought," in *Self and Society in Ming Thought,* 159ff. [20]Mary Douglas, in her "Social Preconditions of Enthusiasm and Heterodoxy," *Symposium, Forms of Symbolic Action, Proceedings of the 1969 Annual Spring Meeting of the American Ethnological Society,* has developed a theory of orthodoxy which supports Wang's anti-individualism with respect to society. She says: "…Philosophical controversies about the relationship of spirit to matter or mind to body can be interpreted as exchanges of condensed statements about the relation of society to the individual. The body or flesh, in these arguments, represents society, mind and spirit represent the individual. To insist on the superiority of spiritual over material elements is to insist on the liberties of the individual and to imply a political program for freeing him from social constraints. In the contrary view, to declare that spirit works through matter, that spiritual values are made effective through material acts, that the body and mind are separate but intimately united, all this necessary emphasis on the mingling of spirit and matter implies that the individual is by nature subordinate to society and finds his freedom within its forms." In this view, an emphasis on the body implies an emphasis on society. In the same manner, Wang Yang-ming used the body as a metaphor for society (see above, note 17). Douglas' quote from p. 69 of her article. [21]Wang Ken, *Ming-chih pao-shen lun,* in *Wang Hsin-chai hsien-sheng chi,* chüan III, translated in part by de Bary, "Individualism and Humanitarianism," p. 165. [22]De Bary, "Individualism and Humanitarianism," p. 180. [23]*Ibid.,* 184. [24]*Ibid.,* 188. [25]*Ibid.,* 190. [26]*Ibid.,* 192–193. [27]It is interesting to note here that Li Chih, upon meeting that consummate Confucian official Tung Ch'i-ch'ang, declared that he wanted Tung to be his bosom friend for life. See Nelson Wu, "Apathy in Government and Fervor in Art," in *Confucian Personalities,* Arthur Wright, editor, 280. [28]De Bary, "Individualism and Humanitarianism," 193. [29]Heinrich Busch, "The Tung-lin Shu-yüan and its Political and Philosophical Significance," *Monumenta Serica* (1949–1955), 42ff. Information on the Tung-lin Academy is also readily available in Charles Hucker, "The Tung-lin Movement of the Late Ming Period," in *Chinese Thought and Institutions,* John Fairbank, editor, 132–162. [30]Busch, "The Tung-lin Shu-yüan," 14. [31]*Ibid.,* 34. [32]*Ibid.,* 57ff. [33]*Ibid.,* 35. [34]Ku Hsien-ch'eng, *Hsiao-hsin-chai cha-chi,* (his notebooks kept from 1594 to his death in 1612) as quoted and translated by Busch, "The Tung-lin Shu-yüan," 100. [35]Wang Yang-ming, *Ch'uan-hsi lu, (Instructions for Practical Living),* section 142.

Regional, Economic, and Social Factors in Late Ming Painting[1]

by Marsha Smith

Historical approaches to late Ming painting, in order to simplify a complex situation, have grouped artists according to the artistic centers in which they were active. This solution is supported by the distinct cultural personalities that the late Ming art centers appear to have possessed, which were necessarily of consequence to the art produced in them. The cultural personalities of these centers, Nanking, Su-chou, and Sung-chiang, were determined by the historic, geographic, and economic situation of each, and were further affected in varying ways by the dominant social and political factors of the time.

Peking was the political capital of late Ming China. It would be logical to assume that due to the concentration of wealth and influence in such a city, it would also have been the cultural capital, but this does not seem to have been the case. The days of the geographical coincidence of political and cultural expression in a single capital city had ended with the passing of the Southern Sung court at Hang-chou. By the sixteenth century the cultural focus of China was clearly located in the Su-chou area, encompassing Su-chou as the capital, the neighboring area of Sung-chiang, and the small town of Chia-ting.

The split between the center of political and administrative activity and the center of cultural expression had begun in the preceding dynasty, the Yüan (1271–1368). During that period China was ruled by foreigners who had invaded from the north, the Mongols. The Mongols made their capital at Peking, in the far north of China proper, physically isolated from the southern centers in which artists and intellectuals had concentrated during the preceding Southern Sung period. In the face of foreign domination at the capital, Chinese loyalist intellectuals sought refuge elsewhere. Many chose Su-chou, to the south of the Yangtze River, a city which had been a center of strong Chinese resistance to the Mongols. Su-chou's cultural pedigree was already impressive by the Yüan period, with such notables as Ku K'ai-chih, Su Tung-po, and Mi Fei in its past. By the end of the dynasty it was a well-established cultural center. Located in Su-chou and Sung-chiang were two of the most important literary circles, and these cities shared many of the great masters of late Yüan painting.

Su-chou also attracted many intellectuals and literary figures when in 1356 it became the site of Chang Shih-ch'eng's attempt to restore Chinese rule to China. However, this revolt was not the one to succeed. Instead, Chu Yüan-chang in 1368 established the Ming dynasty at Nanking and took the reign title Hung-wu. At this time there was no major shift of intellectual and cultural activity away from Su-chou to Nanking. One reason no doubt was related to the new emperor's suspicions of the intellectuals who had supported his rival for power in Su-chou.

Nanking's day of glory in the cultural history of China had passed centuries earlier, during the Six Dynasties period (222–589 A.D.). It is said that in later centuries Nanking retained the flavor of antiquity. In its short reflorescence under Hung-wu, it was extensively rebuilt. However, its real cultural re-awakening was not until the late Ming. The cultural differences between Nanking on the one hand and Su-chou on the other should not be overstressed, for they were geographically quite close. While it never really offered rivalry, there was a great deal of interchange facilitated by the extensive waterways that honey-combed the whole region. Nanking participated in the general cultural predominance of this southern area over the north and Peking.

Nanking's day, even as a political capital, was short. In 1421 the third emperor of the Ming, whose reign title was Yung-lo, returned the capital to the north, to Peking, leaving Nanking as a subsidiary capital. Peking was once again the administrative and ceremonial heart of China, although now under Chinese rule. But there was still no return to the coincidence of art and power in one capital, as there had been in the Sung. This is not to say that the early Ming courts did not patronize the arts, for they did. In re-establishing the Ming, the early rulers wished to bring back the national glories of the Sung, and one way in which they did this was the reinstitution of imperial patronage of the courtly artistic tradition.

However, artists who took part in this revival did not have an easy time of it, and those who worked under the dictates of the first emperor, in particular, did so at risk to life and limb. Yung-lo also organized academic painters at the capital, but the high point of court art in the Ming was under Emperor Hsüan-tsung, who attempted to recreate the artistic milieu of the famous Sung court of the Emperor Hui-tsung. It should be noted that even the art directly associated with the courts did not necessarily center on Peking; many of the court artists seem to have worked chiefly in the secondary capital at Nanking.

In spite of the efforts of the Ming emperors, neither of the Ming courts was able to draw the best artists of the Sung-derived courtly traditions permanently away from their old centers, and the real flowering of Ming academic art occurred in the old Southern Sung capital itself, Hang-chou. This was, of course, in the Che (Chekiang) School of painters. Therefore, before the sixteenth century, Su-chou was rivaled only by Hang-chou, with the court-associated art on the periphery. And by the middle of the sixteenth century, the brilliance of Hang-chou and academic painting in general was almost completely eclipsed, leaving the literati artistic traditions of the Su-chou area preeminent. The artistic circles of Su-chou were only upstaged by nearby Sung-chiang during the late Ming with the emergence of the unique personality of Tung Ch'i-ch'ang.

One other geographical area figures prominently in accounts of late Ming painting, that of the southeastern seacoast. The province of Fukien, due to its position on the coast, was very important to international trade. Some trade with the Portuguese, largely clandestine, seems to have been going on by the early sixteenth century. As noted in a previous essay, this contact has raised questions about the possibility of some Western influence on artists such as Wu Pin and Tseng Ch'ing who came from Fukien. Fukien was a wealthy, prosperous, and culturally advanced area, but it seems to have exported its most interesting artists, notably to Nanking, and the area itself did not grow into a major center of painting that drew artists to it.

The cultural importance of Su-chou and its neighbors must also be related to economic factors. They are located in Chiang-nan, the very fertile region south of the Yangtze River which is among China's best rice, tea, and fruit growing regions. The history of the economic growth of the area goes back to the T'ang and Sung dynasties. During the Yüan, Su-chou was not only an intellectual refuge, but a center of economic activity and the most prosperous city in China.

The Ming as a whole was a period of remarkable economic expansion, with the growth of industries and crafts and the development of domestic and international trade. The sixteenth century in particular witnessed an increase in population, agricultural production, commerce, and wealth, especially in the southern areas. The steady improvement in conditions in the Chiang-nan area was to a large degree propelled by its industries, particularly the weaving and dyeing of silk and other textiles. The Ming court attached great significance to silk as a symbol of distinction as well as for its utilitarian functions. The fame of the silk from Su-chou goes back to the days when that city created the finest silks for the Southern Sung court. Also important to the court was cotton cloth, and Sung-chiang became in late Ming a center for its production.

Cotton and silk were only part of what was supplied to the capital at Peking from the Chiang-nan region and the south. The economic backwardness of the north forced the capital at Peking to rely almost totally on southern sources for everything. Connecting the south to Peking was the Grand Canal. It ran from Hang-chou via the secondary capital at Nanking to Peking. Cities located along this canal flourished. A continual flow of grain and palace supplies traveled essentially in one direction, to the north, on this canal. Maintained at Nanking were about 2,000 ships dedicated to meeting the needs of the capital city.

While Peking appears to have been not only culturally secondary but also an economic parasite, those roles that it did play, in addition to the political, were important and fill out the economic picture, besides throwing into relief the roles of the cities to the south. In addition to performing utilitarian functions, Peking was also a stage for the display of national grandeur, a center for ceremonies and the ritual focal point of the country. The court confirmed its authority through displays of wealth and elaborate pageantry. As a symbol of supremacy, it was entitled to extravagance. For example, from the late fifteenth century until the end of the dynasty in 1644, the number of palace eunuchs alone grew from 10,000 to 70,000. The court continually required more and more massive inputs of resources of every kind.

The growth of the independent power of the southern provinces is easily seen in view of this growing dependence of Peking. Where the earlier Ming emperors Hung-wu and Yung-lo almost ruled by martial law, by the late Ming power of the land lay in the economic-base areas. When Su-chou spoke, as in the anti-eunuch uprising in 1626, Peking listened.

Interwoven with the history and economy of the centers is another dimension which directly relates to art and its production. This is the social dimension, the nature of the society, its demands and its rewards. Wealth in Ming China was not an automatic entrée to power and position. Wealth had to be transmuted into official status, and this was done through the examination system. Scholars proceeded through a series of examinations largely on Confucian subjects, and took various degrees. Their continued success ultimately took them to the capital, Peking, for the examination which, if passed, allowed them to hold the highest positions in the elaborate Chinese ruling bureaucracy. Many of these scholars might also be landowners or sons of landowners; but wealthy landowners were not automatically members of the elite until they, too, had proven themselves at the examinations. It is of course true that wealth made easier the securing of these degrees, as it allowed the scholar to sustain himself and have the opportunities for the serious study that was required.

To a very limited extent, there were ways to by-pass the examination system in the late Ming. A few lower degrees could be purchased. However, these degrees, while they carried some of the privileges of rank, were recognized as being purchased, and did not lead to high office holding. The higher degrees which made the bearer eligible to hold office were limited to those who succeeded at the examinations, the genuine scholars. The possibilities for inheriting rank were also very limited, and succeeding generations usually had to reclaim their rights and privileges through the system.

It does seem that in the later Ming, possibilities for dramatic rises from poverty-stricken backgrounds to positions of wealth and power were less than they had been earlier in the dynasty. However, much upward social mobility was still possible. As a consequence, and because membership in ruling classes was not hereditarily stable, officialdom was seldom a homogeneous group, but rather a varied society.

Social mobility was assisted in the Ming by the lack of effective legal restraints on it. Indeed, it was even encouraged, as there were no restrictions on the numbers of lower degrees given. It was also aided by the emphasis on schools, which had begun early in the dynasty with the emperor's recommendation that schools be set up in every county and prefecture and by the growth of private academies in the sixteenth century. Improvements in printing in the sixteenth century also facilitated study for the examinations by making available, even to indigent scholars, the necessary books.

The life of Tung Ch'i-ch'ang can be used to exemplify the potentials for social mobility that existed in the Ming. He was a fourth-generation commoner, and although he had wealthy relatives he received no assistance from them. He fled to Sung-chiang from his native Shanghai upon becoming subject to corvee labor, a type of land tax, on his three-odd acres of poor land. As a student in the prefectural school at Hua-t'ing, the seat of Sung-chiang, he was partially supported in his studies by the government. From this beginning, Tung Ch'i-ch'ang rose through the examination system to the attainment of the final degree in Peking and held some of the highest positions in the country.

Ming society was not simply made up of officials and commoners, or landed and non-landed classes. Another important group, and a source of potential officials, was the rising middle class which had acquired fortunes through commerce. In addition to being able to purchase lower degrees, members of this class could give their sons the education necessary for passing the examinations. Peasants had suffered relatively little from legal discrimination, and were traditionally entitled to take the examinations. The agrarian and Confucian outlook of China had always seen nobility in the life's work of both the farmer and the scholar. Merchants were a different matter. From the point of view of the literati, the merchant's life was spent in the exploitation of the labors of others. The profit-making and self-seeking associated with the merchant class was regarded contemptuously. This attitude, it should be noted, extended to those painters who painted for money. Professionalism in art was considered vulgar by the amateur literati-bureaucrat artists. But vulgar or not, the merchant class prospered, and the most serious discriminatory laws which had once existed against them were removed by late Ming times. Official positions were open to them, giving further dimension to the complex social makeup of the bureaucracy.

In the rich merchant families, the more promising members were encouraged to prepare for the examinations, become degree holders, and take office. Many of the other members, however, would take up the avocations of the elite and become bibliophiles, art connoisseurs, or patrons of scholars and artists. They were in part driven by a sense of social inferiority to imitate the scholars and officials. Art was among the possessions of the scholar-officials, who were frequently not only connoisseurs and collectors, but also painters themselves. In their eagerness to join these elite circles, rich merchants often became the victims of forgers of art and curios.

Official status in the Ming, although it carried wealth and power with it, was not necessarily the gateway to everlasting prosperity and well-being. Particularly in the late Ming, the privileges of official status were accompanied by such complex and dangerous

political intrigues that office holding, particularly high office holding in Peking, was not always the most judicious course of action. The fate that befell the artist-official Huang Tao-chou (1585–1646) illustrates this point. Another example of social mobility, Huang Tao-chou came from a poor family in Fukien. In 1622 he took the highest academic degree and was admitted into the Han-lin Academy of scholars. Due to his political stances, notably his opposition to the powerful eunuchs, he more than once lost his position. In 1640 he was accused of a hostile political act, flogged, and imprisoned. In 1642 he was banished. His post-1644 Ming loyalist involvement led to his execution. Another late Ming artist and official, Chang Jui-t'u (active ca. 1620–1645), who was also from Fukien, took a different political stand, pro-eunuch, and wound up stripped of honors and condemned by history.

One alternative to such participation, that of foregoing social status and position and remaining a commoner, had its drawbacks also. For example, commoners did without such of the literati's prerogatives as certain garments, sedan chairs, etc. They paid more taxes and were not exempt from labor service, or from such corporeal punishments as beating with bamboo, as were the literati. Commoners were also subject to official whims, some of which were designed to humiliate. A famous example is the story of Shen Chou (1427–1509), the great Wu School master, who when confronted with the demeaning order to paint a mural chose to execute it with dignity.

Between the two extremes were various half-way measures, designed to procure the benefits of officialdom while attempting to avoid its dangers. One such system was employed by Tung Ch'i-ch'ang, and involved periodic and strategic retirement from the tensions of the capital. Another means was to take only the lower degrees, thereby securing the privileges, but not making oneself available for official appointment. Ch'en Chi-ju, a close friend of Tung Ch'i-ch'ang, chose this means of evasion. He took his first degree at the age of twenty-one, then gave up an official career for a home in the hills and a living earned by private tutoring, writing books of

a popular nature, and composing birthday congratulations and epitaphs.

Ch'en Chi-ju's chosen manner of support again raises the question of professionalism. To what degree was the turning of one's scholarly abilities, such as writing and painting, into means of livelihood regarded as turning professional, and under what circumstances? Official status did bring with it wealth sufficient to allow for the literary and artistic activity of officials to be amateur in nature, but the line between the art produced for intimate circles of friends and art for profit was actually not so clear. For example, consider the scathing indictment of that one-time literati bastion, Su-chou, written around 1600 by Fan Yün-lin: "The men of Su-chou can't recognize a single character and haven't seen a single genuine work by an ancient master…they smear and daub on a mountain, a stream, a plant, a tree, then hang it in the market place and exchange it for a peck of rice" (quoted in Yü Chien-hua, *Chung-kuo hua-lun lei-pien*, I, 126). How literally this statement can be taken is questionable. Various forms of exchange were possible, the prearranged giving and returning of gifts, and so on. The blurring of distinction between the amateur and professional in art can be related to the general blurring of status in the late Ming between commoners and the elite. Simple class distinctions were impossible to draw. Examples have been found of many Su-chou and Sung-chiang officials and their families who were also engaged in the vulgarities of trade.

Political involvement was but one way in which the fortunes of an official family might be reversed. As noted before, membership in the elite was only in a very limited way hereditary. Without institutional means of self-perpetuation, and with the necessity for each generation to reaffirm the family position through the examinations, there were drastic fluctuations in family fortunes. Some of the participation in the less acceptable commercial side of life, such as turning art to profit, was related to these fluctuations. It seems frequently to have been the case that the younger generations, accustomed to wealth and comfort, turned away from the trials of the examination system to take up elitest hobbies and spend the family money. It was not only these succeeding generations who indulged in hobbies. With the tremendous increase in leisure in the Ming, officials and merchants alike had the time and money for expensive pastimes such as collecting books and art. However, expensive pastimes, particularly when practiced by those who were pursuing neither careers in commerce nor official degrees but only riding on the family fortunes, tended to drain these fortunes seriously and to have decided consequences for future generations of the family.

One of the most noticeable effects of the potential for downward social movement was the frequent change in the ownership of famous libraries and art collections. Art does not seem normally to have stayed in the possession of a single family over a long period of time, thereby to be kept from the rest of the world. Downward social movement caused by political disaster, as it affected art collections, might be illustrated by the case of the unpopular Yen Sung and his son Yen Shih-fan. These two, regarded historically as villains, amassed an impressive collection of books and art. When they finally fell out of favor with the emperor in 1565, their property was confiscated and the paintings inventoried by Wen Chia, the son of Wen Cheng-ming. The catalogue he compiled appeared under the title, *Record of Heaven's Reducing the Ice Mountain to Water (T'ien shui ping-shan lu)*.

The case of the famous collector Hsiang Yüan-pien is interesting in that he managed to pursue his passion for collecting while never taking an official position, and without disrupting the family fortunes. When his brother was successful in the examinations and Hsiang Yüan-pien failed, he turned to collecting art. He was reportedly very able at authentication and obsessed with questions of price. These traits, and the successful maintenance of the family fortune, might be related to the fact that the family kept a pawnshop. Mixtures of the scholarly and commercial life were not unknown, and provided an alternative to the dissipation of wealth. Although not respectable in purely ideological terms, such compromises allowed for the maintenance of the expensive and nonofficial scholarly life.

Several generalizations may be made in summarizing the importance of these social factors to late Ming art. The demand for art in this period was large and varied. The practice of art and the collection of art were common parts of the equipment of the scholar, and were marks of social status. The growth of wealth and leisure, and the increase in the number of people who had both, stimulated the production of art. Also, works of art were often forced back into circulation by reversals of fortune, caused by various factors. And finally, the distinctions between purely professional and purely amateur art became unclear, as did the class distinctions upon which they were based.

The diverse social possibilities that affected the creation and consumption of art, considered together with certain historical and economic factors, permit some characterization of the great art centers, Nanking, Su-chou, and Sung-chiang, in the late Ming. Nanking, due to its geographical position on the Grand Canal in the prosperous Chiang-nan region, participated in the urban growth, increased commerce, and wealth of the sixteenth century. It reached a cultural and intellectual high point in the late Ming and was famous as an affluent center of leisure, inhabited by large numbers of artists, writers, and collectors. Its historical position gave it a unique character. When the court moved to Peking in 1421, Nanking became the secondary capital in which was installed a duplicate of the Peking administrative structure, complete with all the departments and ministries, with subordinate bureaus and functionaries. This drew to the city members of the official class who came from all over the country and from a variety of social backgrounds. Nanking offered them a particular kind of refuge. It allowed the Confucian scholar to execute his duties to the state, enjoy the benefits of high position, and still be outside the main political arena with its attendant dangers at Peking. The offices in Nanking also had reduced staffs and reduced duties, and so offered a considerable leisure for their holders to enjoy the finer things of life. Even the army headquarters was duplicated in Nanking, and in the later years the army personnel had little to do and passed much of their time with drinking parties and scenic tours.

The influx of officials from other parts of the country into Nanking also affected the art circles of the city. It is true that Nanking participated in the larger cultural richness of the Chiang-nan area and it had its share of local literati who rejected the official life, such as the artist Hu Yü-k'un. There were also painters such as Ch'en Hung-shou who made up a significant but non-official part of the life of the city. However, more important historically were the artists who were drawn to Nanking by the court, for the reasons noted above.

Except for devitalized remnants of the courtly traditions of painting, Nanking did not meet these artists with a strong and singular artistic outlook of its own, and no distinct artistic school is associated with it in the late Ming. The picture of the city that emerges is one that finds superimposed upon the antique flavor of the Six Dynasties period, and imbued with the beautiful setting, the diversity brought by the continually changing officialdom at the court. Nanking was perhaps the most complex and cosmopolitan of all the late Ming centers.

Su-chou still possessed in the late Ming its particular literati-oriented artistic and intellectual outlook, which it had carried on basically uninterrupted from the Yüan period. The city was industrially important, and participated in the general economic growth of the area, with the additional advantage of its location on the Grand Canal. While not a center of national political activity, it was nevertheless of vital political importance to the whole country through its economic role. The information available about Su-chou imparts the sense of a city self-sufficient economically and politically, quite unlike either of the capitals.

The scenic beauties of Su-chou, which was encircled and intersected by canals and bridges, and was famous for its gardens, attracted many traveling scholars. Yet it cannot be compared to Nanking as a magnet for talent. It was more self-sufficient in its culture, as it was in economics and politics. It is tempting to see this as a causal factor in the stagnation of artistic currents in Su-chou at the end of the Ming period. The artists included in this exhibition who were active in Su-chou were all natives, and inherited its particular intellectual and scholarly outlook. They also appear not to have participated in official life, remaining instead in Su-chou to live and work.

These circumstances may help to explain the accusations of professionalism that were leveled at the painters of Su-chou. First, we can easily imagine that the affluent society of the city, with its rising middle class, created a very large demand for works of art, partly as status symbols. Second, it is reasonable to suppose that artists of scholarly backgrounds, in order to maintain a livelihood while not holding official position, found professionalism to be a necessity.

Sung-chiang was bound to Su-chou by close ties that were cultural and artistic as well as geographic and economic. Like Su-chou, and unlike Nanking, it had perpetuated from the Yüan period a literati-oriented cultural outlook and artistic tradition. However, by the late Ming a sense of competition had developed between Su-chou and Sung-chiang. Attempts to create alliances of literary and philosophical societies between the two centers failed because of the strength of this rivalry. In painting, Sung-chiang was set apart from Su-chou at this time by the emergence of a group of artists who took a new direction. The focus of this group was the singular personality of Tung Ch'i-ch'ang. He had arrived in Sung-chiang as a young man, and worked and lived there for the rest of his life, except for the time he spent at the courts as a high official. Where the Su-chou artists for the most part did not participate in officialdom, and the artists of Nanking were more closely tied to the court than to their home provinces, Tung Ch'i-ch'ang seems to have divided his time between the two alternatives.

Tung Ch'i-ch'ang shared the established and dominant artistic attitudes of Sung-chiang. Yet his commitment in art was to a larger view. His horizons were broader than those of either Su-chou or Sung-chiang. As shrewdly as he played the political game, with an eye to the larger trends while allowing for carefully timed retreats, he played the artistic game

by looking beyond the traditions of his home while relying upon them. In an extremely oversimplified view of the situation, Tung Ch'i-ch'ang can be seen to have had the best of all possible worlds. Added to his genius were the solidity of the traditions of Sung-chiang and the stimulating diversity and contacts of his life at court. ■

Notes
[1] This article is drawn largely from the following sources:
(1) Chen Chih-mai, "Hsiang Yüan-pien," in *Draft Ming Biographies*, no. 3, New York, 1965; (2) John Hay, "A Chin-ling Album" (unpublished manuscript, Princeton University); (3) Ho Ping-ti, *The Ladder of Success in Imperial China*, New York, 1962; (4) Ray Huang, *The Grand Canal During the Ming Dynasty*, Doctoral dissertation, University of Michigan, 1964; (5) Arthur Hummel, editor, *Eminent Chinese of the Ch'ing Period*, Washington, D.C., 1943–1944; (6) Li Chu-tsing, "The Development of Painting in Soochow During the Yüan Dynasty," Paper for the International Symposium on Chinese Painting, Taipei, 1970; and (7) Frederick Mote, "The Transformation of Nanking," Paper for the Conference on Urban Society in Traditional China, Portsmouth, New Hampshire, 1968.

Political Culture and Aesthetic Activity

by Judith Whitbeck

The period that spanned the reigns of Emperor Shen-tsung (1572–1620), his son, and his two grand-sons (1620–1644) witnessed striking innovations in both painting and political action. Often painting was valued as a means of stepping out of the routine of bureaucratic service or of expressing attitudes toward human life and its significance. Many literati painters held bureaucratic office; among them were Tung Ch'i-ch'ang, Li Jih-hua, Tsou Chih-lin, Mi Wan-chung, Chang Jui-t'u, Wang To, and Huang Tao-chou. Other painters, in particular Hsü Wei and Ch'en Hung-shou, spent their prime adult years repeatedly failing the civil service examinations which provided the only entree to civil office. Several professional painters, including Wu Pin, served the government as calligrapher-secretaries. Painters in all these categories were involved in the political life of their time. Even those painters—literati or professional—who remained outside of government service could not completely ignore politics, for political controversy became increasingly intense and widespread during the later part of the Wan-li period (1572–1620) and this pattern continued through the T'ien-ch'i (1620–1627) and Ch'ung-chen (1627–1644) periods.

It was not uncommon for sensitive intellectuals to retreat from the embattled world of political debate into aesthetic sanctuaries where they could create a new world on their own terms. But even in retreat, they attested their involvement in the political culture of their time. Other painters assumed active roles as protagonists in the political struggles, and in a broad sense their artistic works mirror their deepest concerns. It is in part because of the composite (aesthetic, literary, philosophical, and political) nature of elite roles in Ming China that one can discern points of correspondence between styles and concerns in painting and those in politics. In delineating the political culture in which these painters moved, we will refer to some of these points of correspondence and to the consequences that political culture held for the artist in the late Ming.

During the first decade of the Wan-li period, China's governmental apparatus functioned with greater unity and central direction than had existed

for more than a century.[1] Her frontiers were made secure and governmental finances showed a surplus. The man whose forceful autocratic dominance set the tone during this decade was the Chief Grand Secretary Chang Chü-cheng (1525–1582).[2] Intent on dynastic reinvigoration even at the expense of scuttling traditional procedures, Chang revitalized Neo-Confucian principles and institutional precedents in order to achieve more efficient centralized governmental control. Chang acted with the utmost deliberation. Convinced of his mission to halt the imminent decline of the Ming, he sought to reverse the current trends toward decentralization, the pursuit of private gain, and social and philosophical experimentation.

Chang articulated this theory of decline in terms of the polarity between *wen* (ornateness, elaborateness, culture, and philosophical discussion) and *chih* (simplicity, austerity, clarity, directness, and strict discipline under strong Imperial rule).[3] He sought to eliminate, or at least to check, the existing trend toward *wen*, that to him signified decline. For Chang, the basic identity of the Ming derived from the synthesis of the principle of *chih* (an inheritance from the Yüan dynasty) with the principle of *jen* (kindness). The latter principle he conceptualized in politico-economic institutional terms: the realization of "kindness" required strong governmental leadership to curb the acquisitive and exploitative instincts of the wealthy local elite and bureaucratic officials. His policies struck hardest at the urbane and prosperous Chiang-nan region, which since Sung times had furnished the Empire with some of her finest painters and most noted scholars. In 1577 Chang attempted to collect tax arrears and put exempted lands back on the tax registers. Two years later he proscribed sixty-four private academies in that same area. These academies served as foci for semi-formal educational instruction and philosophical discussion. As meeting places for the local elite, they also posed a potential political threat to Chang.

Chang had hoped to set a pattern of decisive leadership for the reign of the Wan-li Emperor by converting the minor bureaucratic position of Chief Grand Secretary into the equivalent of the former

office of Prime Minister.[4] This hope was unfulfilled. His historic role was rather as catalyst for renewed intellectual opposition. By seizing on Chang's "usurpation" of power as *causus bellum*, certain uncomprising idealists (mostly from the Chiang-nan region and a generation younger than Chang) assumed the role of guardians against any future contravention of the constitutional system set forth by the Ming Emperor T'ai-tsu after 1380. These intellectuals, known as the "righteous circles," shared an intense aversion to autocratic power and did not hesitate to take forthright stands on what to them were critical issues, even when it meant sacrificing their official positions.[5]

Even a strong, responsible Emperor might have had difficulty maintaining a stable political environment. But the Wan-li Emperor, grown weary of official responsibility after Chang's death, turned to a private life of self-indulgence and relied increasingly on palace eunuchs for necessary governmental tasks. (The policy of relying on eunuchs for such tasks culminated in the dictatorship of Wei Chung-hsien from 1624 to 1627.) Officials in the ministries persistently criticized the policies of the Grand Secretaries and as this factional controversy continued, the Grand Secretaries themselves were caught in the cross fire between these outspoken officials and their enemies in the court.

Given this situation at the capital, an aspiring official had three alternatives—unquestioning silence, compromise, or forthright criticism. When Tung Ch'i-ch'ang (1555–1636) attained his *chin-shih* degree in 1589 and received appointment to the Han-lin Academy, he was unwilling to pursue any of these alternatives.[6] He was too critical and self-confident to sustain silence. He had no taste for the role of embattled compromiser or uncompromising martyr. After a little more than a year in office, he took leave and returned to his home town, Sung-chiang, where he spent the next three years collecting works of art and engaging in painting, a pastime he had begun more than a decade before. During his leave of absence Tung avoided one of the most vicious controversies of the 1590s—the dispute over the education of the Emperor's eldest son. In 1594, it was finally resolved that the four-teen-year-old youth begin his education.[7] Summoned to serve as tutor to the future Kuang-tsung Emperor, Tung returned to Peking.[8] He held this position less than four years before someone saw it expedient to "promote" him to a higher rank in the provinces. Instead of accepting this new appointment, which amounted to a political purge, Tung chose "sick leave." He was thoroughly aware of the dilemma posed by political office in Peking at this time, for he asserted in 1597: "The talented ones here in question would be doing the nation a great service if they hide from such unfavorable exposures and preserve themselves."[9] Such was Tung's personal solution. In 1605, disillusioned with the factional controversies and the uncertainty of fate that plagued anyone who conscientiously stood up for his own position, Tung retired to Sung-chiang to enjoy the comfort of wealth and to devote his energies to painting.

For Tung, painting provided an alternative to political activity. His aesthetic activity, however, mirrored concerns evident in the political world of his day. Tung had grown to maturity during Chang Chü-cheng's tenure as Grand Secretary (as did those officials who constituted the leadership of the "righteous circles" in the 1590s). Tung's orientation toward art was similar to Chang's toward politics. Like Chang, Tung had an aversion to clutter, elaborateness, overembellishment; he delighted in clearly perceptible structures. For Chang, of course, this meant centralized, hierarchical authority, and clarity and efficiency in governmental administration; for Tung, it meant a landscape with simple, austere structural components. As Tung manipulated forms for his own purposes of dynamic movement and clear structural design, so did Chang manipulate governmental institutions for his purpose of bringing order to what he felt to be a faltering dynasty. They both tended to view the opposite (complexity and decentralization, for Chang; details and decoration, for Tung) as a sign of decline, a falling away from some pristine truth. Each man also set about his task with a deliberate, self-assertive sense of mission, as if he alone could save his age by his own efforts.

Tung's artistic views never became part of the political dialogue of late Ming, but the manner in which he set forth those views has its analogy in the style of political debate of the time. After Tung retired in 1605, he gathered around him a coterie of artists who shared his aesthetic opinions. From this sanctuary, he sought to dictate artistic standards for his contemporaries. Tung vehemently opposed the Che School and Su-chou painters and set forth specific reasons why they could not measure up to the Sung-chiang standards. He categorized China's artistic heritage in such a way that his own school represented the realization of the orthodox tradition. To be sure, individual differences were sustained within his circle of associates, and few practiced his aesthetic principles as a compelling system of ideas. Nevertheless, Tung's circle maintained its identity *vis à vis* other local schools in the late Ming. Tung's own pronouncements were echoed by other literati artists and writers, but were opposed by still others such as Wang To and Tai Ming-yüeh. In his correspondence with Tai and in inscriptions on painting, Wang denounced the styles of Ni Tsan and his followers, and extolled those derived from Northern Sung works.

Contemporary with Tung's activity in Sung-chiang was the Tung-lin Academy founded in 1604 by leaders of the "righteous circles" who had been purged in the 1580s and 1590s. This academy was established as a meeting place where like-minded men could exchange ideas on philosophy and current governmental policies with the intention of bringing about a resurgence of traditional morality through a new synthesis of the philosophies of Chu Hsi and Wang Yang-ming. As with Tung's circle, the Tung-lin was a loosely cohesive group whose leader, Ku Hsien-cheng, sought to impose Tung-lin orthodoxy. To this end, Ku carried on voluminous correspondence with officials throughout the realm, urging them to take specific stands on issues at Peking.

The analogy, of course, should not be pushed too far. Tung's circle more resembled the literary societies *(wen-she)*, for it served as a retreat from involvement in government service. The Tung-lin

Academy, on the other hand, was destroyed by the eunuch dictator Wei Chung-hsien in 1625 because men associated with it challenged Wei's policies. In the late 1620s, however, political-literary groups were established in the Chiang-nan region. To a certain extent, these groups were modeled on the old Tung-lin Academy, though they began as modifications of the literary societies. Certain artists were members of these societies, especially the Ying-she near Su-chou, the Chi-she in Sung-chiang, and the Fu-she which drew members from the entire Chiang-nan region. Shao Mi belonged to the first group, Yang Wen-tsung to the second, and Fang I-chih to the third. Huang Tao-chou's name is often linked with the Fu-she as well as with the Tung-lin Academy.

Huang Tao-chou is a perfect example of the artists engaged in the political life of the late Ming.[10] In his paintings of pines and rocks, he gave voice to his concern with the contrast between human dignity and degradation, between forceful, purposeful energy and impotence. These extremes of human experience must have been evident to other activists during this turbulent age. For Huang these concerns have their antecedent in his public role as an idealistic and critical participant in the drama of late Ming politics.

Huang received his *chin-shih* degree in 1622 (the same year as Wang To). Late in that year, two of his classmates were dismissed from office because of their outspoken opposition to the increasing power of the eunuch Wei Chung-hsien. Huang, who had agreed to stand with his two friends, remained silent on grounds that he had just invited his mother to Peking. Two years later, he was promoted to the post of Han-lin Compiler. In 1625, at the height of the purge of Wei's opponents (and those suspected of opposition), Huang returned to his native home in Chang-p'u, Fukien, reputedly to care for his ailing mother (a widow since 1607). After his mother died in 1626, he remained in voluntary retirement until 1630.

When he returned to office, his cautiousness had been converted into raw courage and forthright

40 defense of those he felt had been unjustly accused. His defense of a Ming general who had been arrested and executed by Wei's supporters in 1630 led to his dismissal in June, 1631. Huang then left Peking for Chekiang and Fukien where he lectured on philosophy. Recalled to office later that year, Huang returned to the capital, but he was demoted only three years later for defending his friend Cheng Man. In 1640, Huang himself was accused of a hostile political move, summoned to Peking, flogged and imprisoned. Reprieve for men of Huang's persuasion came in 1641, after the leader of the faction opposed to the Fu-she died.

By this time the dynasty was plagued by serious challenges—the Ming military force was fighting defensive campaigns against rebels in the northwest and southwest, and against the Manchus in the northeast. Peasant rebels, pushed to the point of starvation by the excessive increase in taxes and serious famines, were devastating vast areas of Szechwan, Hunan, Hupeh, Shansi, and Shensi, and had earlier ravaged parts of Anhui and Kiangsu provinces. Huang remained in the south lecturing on philosophy until the peasant rebels and Manchu invaders seized Peking in 1644. He then went to Nanking to assume the post of President of the Board of Rites. Finding the Nanking court under the control of the Fu-she's enemies, he quickly fled to Chekiang and joined the resistance there. It was for leading an army against the Manchu invaders that the painter-patriot was executed in 1646. ∎

Notes

[1] Most of the background material for this essay is drawn from Charles O. Hucker, *The Censorial System of Ming China*, Stanford, 1966; Charles O. Hucker, "The Tung-lin Movement in Late Ming Period" in *Chinese Thought and Institutions*, edited by John K. Fairbank, Chicago, 1957, pp. 132–162; Robert Bruce Crawford, *The Life and Thought of Chang Chü-cheng, 1525–1582*, Doctoral dissertation, University of Washington, 1961; Hsieh Kuo-chen, *Ming Ch'ing chih chi tang-she yun-tung k'ao*, Shanghai, 1936; Heinrich Busch, "The Tung-lin Academy and Its Political Significance," *Monumenta Serica*, XIV (1949–1955), pp. 1–163. [2] In addition to Crawford, *Life*, see Robert Bruce Crawford, "Chang Chü-cheng's Confucian Legalism," in *Self and Society in Ming Thought*, edited by Wm. Theodore de Bary, pp. 367–412. [3] Crawford, "Chang," pp. 375–376. [4] See above, Patricia Berger, "Real and Ideal…," pp. 29–32. [5] These men included Ku Hsien-ch'eng, Tsou Yüan-piao, Shih Meng-lin, Kao

P'an-lung. Most were dismissed from office in 1593 and 1594. See Hucker, "Tung-lin," p. 142. [6] The biographical information on Tung is taken from Nelson I. Wu, "Tung Ch'i-ch'ang: Apathy in Government and Fervor in Art," in *Confucian Personalities*, edited by Arthur Wright and Denis Twitchett, pp. 260–293. [7] The "righteous circles" were those pleading that the Emperor agree to commence the youth's education immediately. [8] The Kuang-tsung Emperor served for only a month in 1620; he was allegedly poisoned by the wet nurse of the Hsi-tsung Emperor and her allies among the eunuchs. [9] Wu, P. 285. [10] This biographical information is drawn essentially from J. C. Yang and Tomoo Numata, "Huang Tao-chou," in *Eminent Chinese of the Ch'ing Period*, edited by Arthur Hummel, Taipei, 1967, pp. 345–347. Huang's paintings are discussed in the chapter on "Calligrapher-Painters…" in this catalogue.

The Wu School in Late Ming, I: Conservative Masters

Painting of the late Ming is often seen as either pre- or post-Tung Ch'i-ch'ang. Either it was touched by the currents he initiated, or it continued to be tied to previous artistic conventions. Viewing the art of the seventeenth century solely in terms of the pivotal figure of Tung Ch'i-ch'ang is similar to viewing the history of seventeenth-century China only from a post-1644 perspective. As the latter view tends to see the pre-1644 political situation as one of decline which led to the Manchu invasion, so the former tends to see the painting of the late Wu School of Su-chou as the decline which Tung Ch'i-ch'ang arose to reverse. From this viewpoint comes the inclination to dismiss the art of the late Wu School in simplistic ways. Support for this prejudice can be found in the works of many writers, not the least formidable of whom is Tung Ch'i-ch'ang. His brief indictment is an accompaniment to words of praise for his friend Ch'en Chi-ju who, he finds, "never falls into the sweet, vulgar and pernicious ways of the professional Wu painters."[1]

It cannot be argued that the late Wu School painters attained the heights of their predecessors in Su-chou. It is also true they did not reach the levels of Tung Ch'i-ch'ang and his following in either critical outlook or actual artistic production. They nevertheless produced a substantial body of art, usually interesting and occasionally innovative. They also attempted stylistic solutions to the artistic questions of the day. A more pertinent criticism than "professionalism" might relate to these solutions and point out that they failed to sustain or give substantial redirection to the school. This may in part have been due to the inadequacy of their solutions, or to their diversity. They do lack cohesiveness when viewed as a whole. These painters had available and drew upon many sources. In addition to the traditional Sung and Yüan masters, the artistic heritage of Su-chou in the Ming period provided an impressive array of possibilities from which to choose. Styles were further complicated by their participation in such fashions as the depiction of scenic places, the illustration of poetry, and the use of archaistic manners. Their stylistic solutions were not conceived as radical redirections or with an eye toward the larger artistic flow as were

those of Tung Ch'i-ch'ang. As a result, they had no major following. However, their innovations were not entirely without consequence. They can be seen to form some part of the background for the new directions taken in painting during the following dynasty.

The diverse nature of the production of this school may also be related to the inward nature of its directions. They were inward in the sense of being personal visions, and inward in the sense of being primarily directed through the already existing artistic currents of Su-chou. A tentative division may be made between the works of those Su-chou artists in which the personal nature of the vision plays the most important role, and those in which the reworking of old currents predominates. The artists included in this chapter are primarily of the second variety. Their most observable common characteristic is their predilection for pre-existing forms and formulas.

Within this second group of artists, a further division might be made. Chang Fu, Ch'en Huan, and Yüan Shang-tung worked in styles primarily dependent upon the very self-conscious literati, or scholar-amateur, styles of the old Wu School. Li Shih-ta, the anonymous master of the Lan-t'ing Gathering, and Ch'en Kuan, while also within the Wu School tradition, worked in styles which seem to have been affected more by professional considerations.

The accounts in Chinese books of Chang Fu, who was born in 1546 and died after 1631, indicate the diversity of stylistic sources to which one such Su-chou painter might be related. He is said to have imitated, at different times, the manners of a number of Sung and Yüan dynasty masters. Closer to his own time, in the Ming, he is said to have followed the founder of the Wu School, the fifteenth-century master Shen Chou, and his successor Wen Cheng-ming who dominated the school in the sixteenth century. The painter with whom Chang Fu studied directly was Ch'ien Ku, a lesser master of the school active in the second half of the sixteenth century, who is usually regarded today as a follower of Wen

Cheng-ming. In any case, Chang Fu's landscape of 1596 fits securely in the Wen Cheng-ming tradition.

The following of Wen Cheng-ming was the leading force in the art of late Ming Su-chou. Much of what can be said about Chang Fu's 1596 landscape might likewise be said of the group generally. In composition, it exhibits the then current predilection for the tall, thin format and an organization that depends on a pronounced vertical axis. Overlapping and offset forms build upward, leading the eye through upright and inverted V-shaped patterns which constantly converge on the center. Movement is carried on these diagonals which play off the main vertical. Complex compositional questions are avoided.

The thin and cool manner of surface definition found in this landscape derives from a style of Wen Cheng-ming which was popular during this period for its overtones of scholarly refinement and for its poetic associations. The hyper-refined painting which frequently resulted from the very ingrown artistic values of the late Wu School was not often handled so successfully as it is here in Chang Fu's extraordinarily delicate drawing of the trees, figures, and architecture. He uses dilute washes and a minimum of texturing on his flat and angular mountain forms, unrelieved by any pronounced tonal contrast. This produces a flattened and abstracted pictorial space without any sense of actual spatial depth. The result is a light and lyrical, if unassertive and undramatic painting. This type of experimentation with abstracted forms may also be seen as a background for the angular abstractions of such Ch'ing masters as Hung-jen.

Ch'en Huan, whose dated paintings range from 1605 to 1615, was a native of Wu-hsien, the area around Su-chou, and the descendent of an important official family. Like Chang Fu, he worked primarily in old Wu School manners. His biographies state that his reputation was based on his works in the manner of Shen Chou. Both his landscape of 1605 (cat. no. 2) and the handscroll in the H. C. Weng Collection (cat. no. 3) belong in the Shen Chou tradition.

The hanging scroll dated 1605 is inscribed as being in the manner of the late Yüan dynasty painter Wang Meng. Throughout the entire Ming period, paintings were done in the manners of Yüan masters. In the late Ming, that of Wang Meng was especially popular as it suited the complex compositions that were then produced. Frequently it was not a matter of direct derivation. Earlier masters such as Shen Chou had executed works in the manner of Wang Meng, and later Ming works tend to be based on the earlier Ming versions rather than on Wang Meng's works. This is the case with Ch'en Huan's landscape. It relates most directly to Shen Chou's "Lofty Mt. Lu"[2] of 1467 in the manner of Wang Meng.

While Ch'en Huan used a compositional plan which is in many ways close to that of "Lofty Mt. Lu," he avoided the compositional problems that Shen Chou set for himself. While the artists of the late Ming enjoyed doing complex compositions, they were frequently unable to solve the problems that attend them. Ch'en Huan has divided the composition into two parts and offset the central axis slightly to the right. Forms pile upward along both sides, emphasizing the vertical path between. Diagonals form upright and inverted V-movements that converge on the axis. It is a plan not unlike that used by Chang Fu. However, Ch'en Huan's softer forms make the ascent more gentle.

Like Shen Chou, he treats the surface with a massing of small strokes. Yet it is as if they have been filtered through the finely calculated style of Wen Chengming. By limiting the variety and number of strokes, Ch'en creates an almost transparent fabric, in place of the dense fabric and tonal contrast that Shen Chou had used to support his complex compositions. Such reinforcement is unnecessary in this becalmed evocation of monumental landscape of the past.

The handscroll by Ch'en Huan in the H. C. Weng Collection (cat. no. 3) draws its inspiration from another of Shen Chou's styles. In this style, Shen Chou composed with simpler units and emphasized the importance of the individual brushstroke. He

utilized conventional "type-forms" within a context of intentional naiveté. Ch'en Huan has likewise simplified the composition, limiting it to a few large and repeated shapes. He borrows such externals of Shen Chou's style as the sharply cut river banks and the little faceless figure types. He also emphasizes the brushline. However, it is not the strong and rather abrupt brushstroke of Shen Chou, but one that is frequently long, wavering, and dry. Running through the curling clouds and over long diagonal forms, it creates a lulling effect. His use of this linear patterning together with the standard literati warm-and-cool color scheme, blue-green set off by brown-orange, results in a design-like, even decorative painting.

Similarities can be found between this scroll and the album by Shao Mi (cat. no. 20) which will be considered in the following chapter. These include the abstract simplification of trees and the relating of these trees to the land formations in terms of design rather than of natural growth. Also similar are the patterned and sketchily outlined clouds. However, this scroll by Ch'en Huan lacks the complexities and the expressive qualities that form Shao Mi's more personal vision. Rather, it is a more standard evocation of a pleasantly poetic mood.

Yüan Shang-t'ung (1570–1661) was a native of Su-chou and his stylistic ties were to the same literati traditions as those of Chang Fu and Ch'en Huan. His large hanging scroll, "The Road to Shu," (cat. no. 4) might properly be judged less successful and without the appeal of the works of the other two artists. The interest of this work lies less in what it accomplishes than in what it attempts. It illustrates the range of sources from which these artists drew. Yüan Shang-t'ung can be seen here to participate in the revival of interest in Northern Sung landscapes then taking place at various artistic centers. Like Wu Pin and others, he has utilized a large landmass of a Northern Sung type as the foundation upon which to compose his picture. He does not avoid the problem of organizing a large landscape composition, as was common, by hanging everything on a strong central and vertical axis. However, problems arise when he is unable to pro-

vide any other means of stability. The mass is made up in the old composite, piled-up manner. But now it is freed of the constraints of the vertical edges and is without the stability these constraints once gave it. In the absence of strong vertical or horizontal movement, the diagonal has taken over. The smaller movements which attempt to counter it fail and a restless and uneasy composition results.

In his use of the brush Yüan Shang-t'ung has also tried to push further old modes. Using short brushstrokes, laid side by side, in the manner of the antique *ts'un* or texture strokes, he creates a surface quality that may remind us of the color flecks of Impressionism. In some areas the effect is close to pointillism. The visual vibration thus effected is not of any help to the uneasy composition, but it is interesting on its own terms. It might be compared to similar, if more pronounced, directions taken by his Su-chou contemporary, Chang Hung.

"The Road to Shu," in keeping with the general artistic situation of late Ming Su-chou, holds new ideas and diverse potential, but is without the unity of vision needed to pull it into a cohesive whole.

Li Shih-ta was a native of Su-chou who became famous for his paintings of landscapes and figures. His known paintings are dated from 1589 to 1620. A short essay describing the five defects and the five merits of painting is attributed to him. His artistic personality is complex, and includes elements that reflect his professional status. While his roots may be found in the Wu School tradition, the figures in his hanging scrolls, such as "Men in a Bamboo Grove" (cat. no. 5) and "T'ao Yüan-ming Cultivating Chrysanthemums" (cat. no. 6), do not belong to the literati painting idiom. Most often found in literati paintings are small, quickly drawn figures belonging to established types, wandering anonymously through the landscape. Those found in the Ch'en Huan scroll are of this kind. Li Shih-ta's figures, by contrast, are executed carefully in fine line and color, and are large and close to the viewer. He has also introduced an element of narration and a dimension of time through these figures. In both paintings the attention of the figures is specifically directed toward something of a point, conveying a sense of the dramatic moment. Such concern with narration connects Li Shih-ta with such earlier Su-chou professionals as Chou Ch'en, T'ang Yin, and Ch'iu Ying.

Li Shih-ta's inclinations toward the professional stylistic idioms are modified in two ways. First, he interweaves them with elements from literati traditions. Second, they are modified by his own personal power of artistic expression, which adds a dimension to his work that is exceptional among the painters of this group.

Professionalism in the Ming was usually related to the Che School styles with their Southern Sung antecedents. Li Shih-ta instead aligns his work with the Wu School. For example, his pines have been subjected to many changes, but they nonetheless go back to the type created by Wen Cheng-ming. His compositions have Yüan dynasty prototypes. Yüan styles were favored by the literati painters of the Wu School, as opposed to the Southern Sung styles which were favored by the Che painters.

Although Li Shih-ta uses compositions with Yüan prototypes, he alters them in ways that relate to late Ming compositional practices. For example, "Men in a Bamboo Grove" employs a compositional formula that had been used by the early Yüan artist Kao K'o-kung. This consists of a foreground entrance over water, a middle ground obscured in clouds, and large background mountains of heavily rounded forms, with closed vistas to the sides. The changes made by Li Shih-ta, the splitting of the mountains to create the familiar central axis and the crowding of everything up to the picture surface so as to eliminate comfortable space, are in keeping with late Wu School landscape styles. Similarly, "T'ao Yüan-ming Cultivating Chrysanthemums" is based on a common Yüan formula which combines a foreground land mass, a wide middle ground water plane, and distant hills. This has also been subjected to pictorial distortion of a kind common in late Ming paintings. The space between foreground and background has been stretched to such an extreme that the mountains seem to hover

directly over the trees, and the expanse of water to extend straight up rather than back.

In addition to using the externals of the literati style, Li Shih-ta brought to these works a powerful and expressive distortion of forms. The rounded figure type, enclosed in a long contour, is typical of late Su-chou painting, but the extremely squeezed heads and the repetition of the strangely proportioned facial features are his own touches. Like the figures, objects of nature are subject to distortion. The heavily formed and shaded pine trees twist threateningly downward. Both the figures and the trees have flattened curves on top as if subject to pressure from above. Another expressive device he employs effectively is that of contradictory relationships of weight and scale. The lightweight figures of "Men in a Bamboo Grove" seem oppressed by the excessively heavy mountains. The rounded figure of T'ao Yüan-ming looking down to the delicate chrysanthemums contrasts with the tall and corporeal pines rising behind him.

An early work of a different nature, a handscroll painted in 1589 (cat. no. 84), provides some background for the two later paintings, and fills out our understanding of Li's artistic personality. It depicts a group of gentlemen in a courtyard composing poetry as they drink wine from cups floated to them on a stream; the scene is of course meant to recall the Lan-t'ing Gathering (cf. cat. no. 7). The painting is tranquil and refined in style, without the stronger expressive devices and bolder forms of his hanging scroll pictures, and is another instance of his skill in depicting narrative themes. It reveals clearly his early dependence on Su-chou traditions, particularly that of Chou Ch'en and T'ang Yin; both the landscape and the figures, as well as the contrast between the broader manner of the former and the fine, sharp brushwork of the latter, recall the paintings of these two artists. The scroll is divided into two sections by the garden wall, the first half recording the actual gathering of poets, while the second is impersonal, functioning both physically and psychologically to evoke the proper mood and setting for this gathering.

The painting specifically commemorates a party given for the fortieth birthday of a member of the Keng-she Literary Club. Such clubs were popular at the time, as were scrolls of this kind in which poems by the members were assembled for presentation to one of the group. Li Shih-ta may himself have been a member, although his simple and modest signature suggests rather that he may only have been commissioned, as a professional painter, to provide a pictorial record of the event. The painting creates a sense of a specific moment in the active postures of the figures: the servants moving a table and tending a fire to heat wine or water for tea, the scholars in attitudes appropriate to their literary concentration. Juxtaposed with this temporal world, on which the viewer's attention is focused by brighter colors, is the eternal realm represented by the unassuming hills seen beyond the wall.

A handscroll (cat. no. 7) illustrating one of the most famous of Chinese literary gatherings, that of 353 A.D. at the Lan-t'ing or Orchid Pavilion, exemplifies, in the choice of subject, the antiquarianism in vogue among the late Su-chou painters. The artist is unknown; a "Wen Cheng-ming" signature is a later interpolation. This painting can be compared to one of the same subject and similar style painted in 1560 by the late Ming painter Ch'ien Ku, who was mentioned earlier in connection with his student Chang Fu, as a follower of the Wen Cheng-ming School.[3] It might also be noted that Ch'ien Ku was a professional artist, and that as in the works of Li Shih-ta, elements found in the Lan-ting scroll belong primarily to the more professional Su-chou traditions. For example, the large figures are carefully delineated within a specifically narrative context. The anonymous master, like Li Shih-ta and Ch'ien Ku, has provided his professional idiom with a typical Wu school literati setting, in which the brush techniques and the foliage patterns are based on those of Wen Cheng-ming and are accompanied by the favored two-tone, blue-green and brown-orange color scheme.

This scroll shares many traits with the works of Li Shih-ta, but it does not have as strong an emphasis on expressive distortion. The figures are of the same round and compact Su-chou species favored by Li Shih-ta, and are likewise delineated in long curving outlines which subordinate bodily structure to idio-syncracies of drapery drawing in an archaistic manner. However, their heads and faces show less intentional distortion. This artist was also unconcerned with interrelating the figures psychologically in a specific dramatic moment. He has simply narrated the event in an appropriate and poetic context. He also does not exploit strange juxtapositions of size, shape, and weight; the figures more or less comfortably relate to the landscape elements. Rather than individual expressiveness, important to this artist was his theme and a careful choice of the manner in which to depict it.

Ch'en Kuan, a native of Su-chou, was active from about 1610 to 1640. It is said that famous men who came to that city competed with each other to obtain his works on silk. A collection of his literary works is extant. His biographies emphasize his interest in poetry and the excellence of his calligraphy in the "running script."

His large "Landscape with Cranes" of 1638 (cat. no. 8) shares with Li Shih-ta and the artist of the "Lan-t'ing" scroll the use of Wu School amateur-painter elements in combination with more pro-fessional manners. He draws upon the Wen Cheng-ming tradition for his tall pines and thin, neat manner of delineating mountain forms. His more professional inclinations include his use of colors on silk and an abundance of enlivening detail. He does not employ large and carefully drawn figures to create a narrative focus, but instead distributes his points of visual interest all over the picture. These include six cranes in various postures, several people, man-made elements such as houses and gates, different areas of water, two types of clouds, and trees presented in a variety of sizes and scales bordering on the irrational. One has the feeling that the longer he looks, the more he might find. These varied elements, unlike the simple unobtrusive types that contribute to a larger poetic mood in literati works of such artists as Ch'en Huan, take on independent visual values.

Like Yüan Shang-tung, Ch'en Kuan has made an attempt to come to terms with the problem of the large landscape composition. Offset and simply modeled forms overlap insistently and carry the eye up and back through the composition along the movement of the mountains, which builds upward to the summit. This use of a strong directional impetus running through the forms relates to the *lung-mo* or "dragon-vein" movement emphasized by the early Ch'ing Orthodox masters. Ch'en Kuan's com-positional solution still relies on a centrally divided composition, but all movement is not into the center; strong diagonal pulls away from it set up pictorial tensions, both with the vertical constraints of the very tall trees to each side, and with the insistent movement of the mountain itself.

Ku Ning-yüan and Hsiang Sheng-mo
The essentially derivative and "pre-Tung Ch'i-ch'ang" works of Su-chou present a picture of diversity untempered by strong authoritative leadership. These artists worked without the well-defined, common theoretical base Tung Ch'i-ch'ang provided for his circle at Sung-chiang. However, Sung-chiang was not an island, and its styles and theories reached Su-chou. Within the Su-chou artistic tradition, "post-Tung Ch'i-ch'ang" artists are also to be found. Ku Ning-yüan was one such artist. The only known date for his life and work is 1636, from an inscription on a painting. He came from an old Su-chou family of officials, but never held an official position himself. He collected antiquities, painted, and wrote. It is in his capacity as a critic and connois-seur, rather than as a painter, that he is of importance to the history of Chinese painting. His critical essay titled *Hua yin* is considered a characteristic expression of the attitudes of Tung Ch'i-ch'ang's Southern School. Ku Ning-yüan considered the Su-chou painting of the late Ming as the art of a period of decline and Tung Ch'i-ch'ang as the sav-iour from Sung-chiang.

His "Landscape in the Style of Chao Meng-fu" (cat. no. 9) can be seen as an extreme example of the purely literary man's style. The suppression of skill is extreme. The hills are built of slow and unshowy

brushwork. The unassertive trees are painted with foliage in heavy color, without ink drawing, a tech-nique known in Chinese painting as the "boneless" style. It is a thoroughly unexciting painting. The *Hua yin* extolls the virtue of primitivism or awk-wardness, saying that "once lost it can never be recaptured." Better painters had indeed turned awk-wardness into a positive value, but as Ku Ning-yüan exemplifies it in his own painting it can hardly be seen as a positive attribute. He seems to have been unable to carry successfully into his own works the tenets of the artistic revolution he so admired.

Ku Ning-yüan, in aligning himself with the correct lineage according to Tung, maintained a very limited stylistic outlook. This might be seen as a decided contrast to the "pre-Tung" artists of Su-chou who borrowed freely within the loosest of boundaries and recombined their borrowings within a variety of frameworks. This diversity of outlook is found also in a "post-Tung" artist, Hsiang Sheng-mo (1597–1658). He was a native of Chia-hsing in the northern part of Chekiang province. Although in a different province, Chia-hsing is actually not far from Su-chou and it produced artists whose styles were linked with the school at Sung-chiang. Hsiang Sheng-mo may best be related to Su-chou in terms of his style which borrowed elements from the school of Wen Cheng-ming.

As the grandson of the famous collector and con-noisseur Hsiang Yüan-pien (1525–1590), in whose home Tung Ch'i-ch'ang had once served as a tutor, Hsiang Sheng-mo had access to a rich collection of painting. His approach to painting was both experi-mental and very eclectic; he utilized the many sources and variety of styles available to him. Also, like the Su-chou artists, he drew on sources other than those purely in the literati tradition, and the question of professionalism is again raised. His biographies state that after the pillage of his family's property by the Ch'ing army in 1645 he lived in comparative poverty, and although he sold his paintings, he would not sell them to a rich buyer whom he disliked.

Both of his works included here date from this late period. His handscroll of 1648, "Meditative Visit to Mountain Cliffs," (cat. no. 10) and his album of 1649 in the collection of Mr. J. T. Tai (cat. no. 11), together allow us to survey rather thoroughly this varied artistic personality. The opening passage of the 1648 handscroll introduces the most singularly recognizable motif in his painting, the ungainly tree. The trees of this initial group possess neither charm nor grace, but are contorted. In addition to heavy shading, they have not one outline, but many. Even the outlines of the leaves have been reworked. The final outlines are heavy and black. One must grant that in these trees he has successfully achieved Ku Ning-yüan's ideal of awkwardness. However, by contrasting these trees to the beautifully formed pines which appear toward the end of the same scroll, it can be seen that the oppressive nature of these trees is intentional and for expressive purposes. His pines relate to the Wen Cheng-ming species of Su-chou painting. Very tall, with gracefully downswept branches, they frame the small scholar. In these pines Hsiang Sheng-mo has again used very dark outlines, but has chosen to do so unobtrusively.

It is the middle area of this scroll, with its complex land mass, that testifies to the fact that Hsiang Sheng-mo is indeed a "post-Tung Ch'i-ch'ang" artist. This mass is abstractly and systematically constructed. It uses a limited and repeated repertory of forms, similar in shape to those often used by Tung Ch'i-ch'ang. Like Tung's formations, these attempt a compromise between dynamism and stability. Pushing forms with directed angles are enclosed within long and slow contours. Through repetition of this formula the mass is made to recede. Unlike Tung Ch'i-ch'ang's use of dark and light value contrasts, his are highly irregular and do not result in tonal patterning. Rather, as in his trees, his darkest values are reserved for punctuating, unsettling effects. The darkest values to be found in the entire scroll are in the strange recessed cave-like area. The clarity with which the rest of the land is constructed breaks down in this area. It is true that the elements of the bizarre found in this scroll are less pronounced than in others of his long hand-

scrolls, but his ties to the masters of the fantastic landscape are clear enough.

In his album of landscapes of 1649 at least two leaves are in styles close to those of this handscroll and might be discussed in the same terms. Several other leaves show the rather mundane and probably professional side of his artistic character in their design. These leaves, with their distant views and plays on empty space, their willows and birds in flight, and their atmospheric effects, recall the concerns of the artists of the Southern Sung. However, even in these leaves the experimental nature of Hsiang Sheng-mo's art can be seen in his use of color. He gives it an importance, an independent pictorial value, beyond that of the simple literati color schemes and equally removed from the descriptive color traditionally used by the professionals.

Two leaves from this album stand out. In one, he places his trademark, the ungainly tree, in the center and elaborates it to the point of the grotesque. Here is truly the antithesis of the impersonal "boneless" trees of Ku Ning-yüan. This fantastic structure physically dominates the leaf and psychologically dominates the entire album.

If diversity in source as well as diversity in product is the key to these derivative artists, then the last leaf of this album is a fitting conclusion. In this leaf, Hsiang Sheng-mo seems to have reached so far afield as to have included artistic modes of Western inspiration. It seems likely that this landscape, with its naturalistic and coloristic reference to the specific time of day, draws its low horizon and rationally conceived single viewpoint from Occidental sources. This sort of influence may be discussed with more confidence in connection with other artists and artistic centers. However, the truly eclectic nature of the art of Hsiang Sheng-mo, and his free usage and combination of the artistic currents of the day, make such speculation seem quite reasonable. ∎

[1]Tung Ch'i-ch'ang, *Jung-t'ai chi*, chüan IV, 44a. [2]Osvald Siren, *Chinese Painting*, London, 1958, vol. VI, pl. 175. [3]Earl Morse Collection; see *In Pursuit of Antiquity*, Princeton Art Museum, 1969, no. 4.

1. Chang Fu (1546–after 1631). *Landscape with Waterfalls.* Dated 1596. 40-1/4 x 12-1/4″. Ching Yüan Chai Collection.

2. Ch'en Huan (dated works 1605–1615). *Landscape in the Manner of Wang Meng.* Dated 1605. 44-5/8 x 18-1/2″. University Art Museum, Berkeley.

3. Ch'en Huan (dated works 1605–1615). *Landscape:* handscroll
   section. H. 8″. Wango H. C. Weng Collection, New York.

48

4. Yüan Shang-t'ung (1570–1661). *The Road to Shu*. Dated
   1631. 52-7/8 x 23-3/4″. Ching Yüan Chai Collection.

6. Li Shih-ta (active late 16th–early 17th century). *T'ao
   Yüan-ming Appreciating Chrysanthemums*. Dated 1619.
   62-9/16 x 22-11/16″. University of Michigan Museum of
   Art, Ann Arbor.

5. Li Shih-ta (active late 16th–early 17th century). *Landscape with Figures: Men Seated in a Bamboo Grove.* 57-1/4 x 39″. Collection Yuji Eda, Tokyo.

7. Anonymous. *The Lan-t'ing Gathering:* handscroll section.
  H. 13″. Ching Yüan Chai Collection.

52

10. Hsiang Sheng-mo (1597–1658). *Meditative Visit to a Mountain Retreat*. Dated 1648. 12 x 107-1/2″. Cleveland Museum of Art: Purchase from the J. H. Wade Fund.

9. Ku Ning-yüan (active ca. 1636). *Landscape in the Style of
Chao Meng-fu*. 21-1/4 x 12-1/4". Ching Yüan Chai Collection.

84. Li Shih-ta (active late 16th–early 17th century). *A Gathering
of the Keng-she Literary Club.* Accompanied by an
inscription dated 1589. 11-5/8 x 55-1/2″. Collection J. T. Tai,
New York.

55

11. Hsiang Sheng-mo (1597–1658). *Album of Landscapes:* leaf e.
   Dated 1649. 10-1/4 x 13″. Collection J. T. Tai, New York.

The Wu School in Late Ming, II: Innovative Masters

by Lucy Lo-hwa Yang

Innovation in late Ming painting was by no means limited to Tung Ch'i-ch'ang and his circle of friends and followers. Among the late Wu School artists in Su-chou were some who had original ideas in painting and embodied them in their works. While they had no such impact on either contemporary or future painting styles as did Tung, and thus are accorded no such historical position, they produced many paintings of great quality and beauty, and deserve more attention and admiration than they have usually received from either Chinese or Western critics.

For the purposes of this exhibition and catalogue, we have classified three of them as representing the more innovative side of late Wu School painting. The line between them and some of their fellow artists in Su-chou is not very sharp, however, and others, such as Li Shih-ta, are not far below them, if at all, in originality. Still, they are the leading exponents of a direction that this school of painting took in the late Ming, the last new direction before its demise. The artists to be treated here are Sheng Mao-yeh (active 1594–1637), Chang Hung (1577–after 1660), and Shao Mi (active ca. 1620–1660). Each in his own way relinquished many ties to tradition and launched on new stylistic explorations. All worked in a variety of styles; but their most typical works have important features in common which should allow us to define this last stage in the development of the Wu School.

Chinese books tell us very little about Sheng Mao-yeh, beyond the conventional bits and pieces that so often pass in these books for biography.[1] He seems to have been highly regarded in his time, especially in relative evaluations with other Su-chou artists; but this does not imply a very high appraisal, since most of those others were ranked so low. Like Chang Hung, he does not appear to have had any literary talents or training; such is the impression one gets from the short poems that accompany many of his smaller paintings, charming as some of them are. Thus, our interest in the artist is based entirely on his paintings.

The "Waterfall on Mt. Lu," a recent acquisition of the University Art Museum, Berkeley, exemplifies the grand and impressive side of his style (cat. no. 12). The artist's intention is to impress us with the power of the thundering fall as it drops from a great height. The spectacular scene is observed not only by us, but also by small gatherings of gentlemen situated at ideal vantage points in the landscape. The painting is composed of three large land masses: one in the lower left corner, one that scales the right edge, and one rising straight up the middle. This configuration is conceived primarily in terms of two-dimensional space, with the artist carefully partitioning the surface of the silk into three distinct areas, each occupied by a rocky mass. Empty space has been kept to a minimum, limited to band-like passages that separate the forms. This sense of two-dimensionality is reinforced by the consistency of the textures and patterns of the picture surface, where near and far are perceived with equal clarity and treated as visual equivalents. The same flattening of space is notable in the upper left corner, where the boats seem to be sailing in the sky. Sheng's interest in surface pattern and tonal unity relate his painting to other late Wu School landscape manners.

Mt. Lu, an imposing background for the waterfall, exhibits some geological oddities that add to its interest. Although its shape and construction detract from its credibility as a real-world form, they instill in it a heightened expressiveness. A simple, basically cylindrical mass rises from the water, to burgeon above into a great number of small forms, the larger of which are made up of parallel folds encircled by numerous smaller ones lined up neatly in repetitive rows. To all of these shapes texturing has been added in the form of short, blunt strokes, distributed in density and sparseness to leave untextured areas along edges. These untextured strips serve as areas of highlighting, and to set off one form from another. Similarly additive modes of construction are utilized in the other two large masses, but on these the applications of smaller forms seem more haphazard. Individual elements such as trees and human figures tend to fall into types that repeat themselves. The human figures nevertheless play a prominent role in setting the theme of the landscape, which is the old theme of the enjoyment of spectacular scenery.

Sheng Mao-yeh's performance in full-scale, grand compositions is complemented by a fondness for scenes of smaller scope, several good examples of which are in the exhibition. Three leaves now in a private collection from an album originally consisting of eight landscapes[2] (cat. no. 13) illustrate admirably the more modest, mild side of Sheng Mao-yeh's painting.

They are closely related in subject and mood. Each presents a lake or river shore with trees and a hill rising beyond. Sheng is careful to give each leaf its mark of individuality. Toward this end, he manages through the use of outcroppings and other distinctive terrain features to create from each encounter of land and water a composition that is a unique and original conformation. Variety and originality, however, are never ends in themselves, but only represent for the artist a means of giving to nature an unstudied air, a natural and unassuming appearance. This naturalness is also achieved not only in the compositions, which follow no established types, but also in such elements as the groves of trees, portrayed according to the principle of variety within sameness.

Sheng Mao-yeh's approach to landscape in these leaves differs radically from that of the "Waterfall on Mt. Lu" being strikingly visual. This is especially evident in Leaves A and C, where forms, save for the ones in the immediate foreground, are rendered and described without the use of any continuous, firm outline. Against the slightly indistinct ground, a few objects in each picture—trees, buildings, a few rocks, a boat—stand out through being sharply drawn in darker ink, as though only these were quite in focus. In this respect the paintings conform to what we actually see more closely than conventional Chinese landscapes, in which the parts are more evenly weighted and shown with more or less even clarity. Consistent with this end is the attention Sheng devotes to effects of atmosphere, especially to mist, which in its capacity to blur distinctions between filled and unfilled areas, between form and formless, seems to erode and dissolve the solidity and structure of the landscape, instilling it with something of the evocative, and a mood of stillness

58

and purity. The sharp contrasts in tone and in clarity between different parts of the pictures give a strong sense of natural lighting, especially the effect of sunlight breaking unevenly through clouds.

One must also point out in these leaves some features that seem to counteract the overall sense of naturalness and the credibility of the landscape, indicating Sheng's equally strong concern with non-representational considerations of decorative design. One of these is his deliberate setting of crowded against open areas; it can be clearly seen in the shorelines of Leaves A and B, where downward-jutting forms create decorative intrusions into the blank areas of paper but lend little credibility. In addition, Sheng's minor manipulations of the small forms of the terrain, such as in Leaf C where the rocks along the shore are white-topped for an effect of sunlight but are rather rigidly lined up, make the whole landscape seem to be a product of artistic as well as natural ordering. Such opposing devices of naturalism and abstraction no doubt fascinated Sheng, and give to these small landscapes a great deal of intensity and interest.

Two leaves by Sheng Mao-yeh from a group of six now in The Metropolitan Museum of Art (cat. no. 14A–B) reveal the artist's predilection for scenes of quietude, and for themes portraying the leisurely pastimes of the scholar-gentleman.

Leaf A shows two scholars and a servant boating on a river at dawn; Leaf B, a lakeside scene at dusk in which a monk can be seen knocking at the gate of a temple. The couplets written on them by the artist read:

The tall trees, by the light of dawn, regain their
dense detail;
Over distant mountains the sky grows ever clearer.

and:

Birds perch for the night in trees by the pond;
A monk beats by moonlight on the temple gate.

Boating early and returning late are conventional themes in Chinese painting, and Sheng's choice of style seems to suit them ideally. Each landscape is organized into a simple, undistinguished composi-

tion that is rendered in a subdued manner, with soft line drawing and broad, gray washes of more or less even tonality. Leaf A, the boating scene, is easily organized into a low-lying foreground shore on which grows a familiar grove of bare-branched trees and, beyond an intervening stretch of water, a row of conical hills. In Leaf B the various elements are arranged in a succession of planes, all parallel to the picture surface. The planimetric quality achieved through the alternate placement of bands of mist and architectural elements clarifies and systematizes, though also schematizes, the orderly, step-by-step progression into the near distance. Neither leaf exhibits the compositional originality or surface interest of the hanging scroll or the three leaves on paper; it is as though the landscape is thought of only as providing a setting congenial to the actions and reactions of the figures. Hence, nothing in these compositions, including the compositions themselves, is meant to jog strongly the imagination, or to distract the eye from the perception of an overall mood of tranquility.

One of the loveliest examples of Sheng Mao-yeh's landscape painting is the fan-shaped leaf dated 1632 in the Ching Yüan Chai Collection (cat. no. 15). Here, two scholars and a servant, grouped on a terrace, gaze out over a misty valley. The season is spring and the time twilight, as is readily perceived from the presence of blossoming trees and the moon. The gold paper ground gives the evening glow and misty atmosphere an added luminosity. The couplet inscribed by the artist reads:

Scattered shadows slanting, the water clear and
shallow;
A dark fragrance floating, the moon a dusky yellow.

Most of the landscape, save for the foreground, has been given over to mist, which selectively conceals and reveals portions of it, disclosing no single form in its entirety. The parts that we do see, regardless of their relative distance from us, are treated in small, wet dabs of ink, uneven in shape, applied in several layers, to which are added darker accents to indicate patches of vegetation. This treatment of the land surfaces, especially in the complete absence of outline, parallels Sheng's treatment of the back-

ground hills in the three leaves on paper (cat. no. 13). Here, however, the technique has been extended to the foreground as well, and the strokes have been broadened and blurred to make the forms seem all the more dissolved and insubstantial. Nature is conceived as being made up not of solid objects of determinable structure but rather of indistinct forms which are definable almost entirely in their surfaces. In this landscape of intermittently visible, frequently suggested but largely obscured forms, the only substantial objects are the figures and the trees. The former belong to Sheng's small repertory of types, but the latter, drawn as black silhouettes of gnarled, twisted trunks and intricately radiating branches, comprise the most stunning elements in the whole painting. Not only do their dark, clear forms contrast with the murky grays of the mist-filled landscape, becoming in themselves the single most expressive elements in the painting, but in the certainty and order of their individual forms, their fan-shaped design, and centralized position, they function formally as elements of stability, points of reference to which all the other less substantial objects can relate and anchor themselves.

Chang Hung, the next artist of our group, was active about the same time as Sheng Mao-yeh, and was likewise a native and resident of Su-chou. Chang's major works are large hanging scrolls, some of them representing actual places, but unfortunately no painting of this kind could be obtained for the exhibition. Chang also, however, executed some of his finest works in the more modest format of the album, and we are fortunate to have examples from three of them.

The first (cat. no. 16A–H) is a set of eight leaves, originally from an album of twenty, dated 1627 and now in the collection of Mr. Franco Vannotti. The subject is the Chih-yüan, a garden in Su-chou, as is indicated by the artist in a brief inscription on the first leaf. It is reasonable to suppose that Chang Hung executed the work on a commission from (or at least with the intention of presenting the album to) the garden's owner, who, by the size and splendor of his estate, was a gentleman of considerable means. The first leaf is an overview, and the other seven depict smaller, individual gardens incorporated within the extensive complex of buildings, pavilions, lakes, groves, and winding waterways. These scenes are among the most enchanting examples of late Ming painting in their loveliness of design, exquisiteness of detail, and excellence of execution.

The diversity of the leaves arises from the artist's desire to make his paintings accurate and particularized portrayals. Each of the seven subsidiary scenes can be located within the map-like, almost aerial overview of the first leaf. But although Chang Hung seeks in the manner of a portraitist to record accurately the features of the Chih-yüan, he nonetheless manages to infuse his portraits with his personality, through the use of a personal style.

For instance, the houses and their gardens are always seen from an elevated point of view. The distance between the viewer and the landscape is kept more or less constant except, of course, in the first leaf. In each scene, moreover, Chang Hung reveals interest in the convincing rendering of space and the relationship of objects within it.[3] The means he employs to achieve this reveal his contact with devices of Western art, including those of perspective, although his use of it is by no means strictly accurate, at least to Western eyes. This contact is evidenced rather in his careful placement and treatment of all objects, particularly architectural members, so as to give to landscape a consistent and functional ground plane, and his rendering of buildings with clearly understood interior spaces. In addition, he allows the rectilinear forms of his buildings to systematize the spatial recession by placing them in positions diagonal to the frame of the picture, as though they are seen from a corner. In this way, Chang is able to utilize most effectively the parallel lines created by such architectural props as upright posts, walls, steps, and roof tiles, all of which are drawn with meticulous attention to straightness of line, precision of spacing, and angle of alignment. His strictly systematic treatment has the desired effect of giving to the painted landscape a feeling of having both logical relationships and genuine spaciousness. In several of the leaves, a segment of wall or roof is placed diagonally in one lower corner of the painting. This device serves several purposes, of which one is, of course, to define, with the other walls, the area of the garden. However, as the nearest element in the painting to the viewer, it also permits him to understand clearly his physical position outside the garden walls while still allowing him, from this vantage point, to visually explore the interior, to catch a glimpse of somebody else's private domain.

Chang Hung's interest in consistent ground planes and in other devices, some Western-derived, for handling space and depth is accompanied by an interest in color to a degree exceptional for a Chinese artist, and again we can assume some effect from contact with Western art. For Chang, color is an effective device for organizing the parts of the landscape through tonal contrasts. In this role color is able to counteract his strong tendency toward evenness of surface, which in part results from the uniform use of short, dabbing strokes to describe all objects in the landscape except the architecture. The capacity of color to organize and make legible dense areas made up of similar shapes and textures can be especially appreciated in Leaves E, F, and G, where adjacent objects depend almost solely for their differentiation on contrasting areas of color. Chang Hung also exploits the sensuous appeal of color, greatly expanding the traditional Wu School formal system of simple and cool tones by adding light hues of brown and gray, as well as stronger tones of orange and red and a full range of blues and greens. His application of color is also unconventional; instead of conceiving of painting as a creation in ink to which color is added as a minor embellishment, Chang uses color independently of ink, in a way that had scarcely been done in China until this period. The most notable examples are in his plots of flowers, where among chartreuse green stems are clustered a profusion of magenta, white, and pink blossoms; or where, in an orchard of darkly blackened tree-trunks a dazzling cloud of pure white blossoms bursts forth.

Chang Hung's album of landscapes in old manners, dated 1636, in the Ching Yüan Chai Collection, shows him as an artist not only of consistently high quality, but also of some versatility (cat. no. 17A–K). Albums such as this, composed of leaves in the manners of various earlier artists, enjoyed a vogue in the late Ming and early Ch'ing period, in keeping with the "art-historical" orientation of artists as well as critics. Eleven leaves survive from an original set of twelve. Each comprises an interesting landscape in its own right; together, they provide a good idea of the nature of Chang Hung's understanding of the revered styles of famous Sung and Yüan masters, and his creative transformation of them. Chang appears relatively disinterested in capturing any close likeness to the landscape styles of the old masters, even supposing that he knew these styles from actual examples. Instead, whether by intent or necessity, what he does is distill from each old manner some few aspects that had long been associated with that manner. Such indicators of stylistic traditions had come to function as clues, informing the viewer about the ancient source of inspiration.

Of all the leaves, the one in the manner of the tenth-century master Tung Yüan recalls the most ancient source. A few stylistic features evoke reminiscences of paintings ascribed to Tung. For instance, in treating his hills as similarly shaped, rounded forms, even while incorporating them into a more precipitous terrain than the tenth-century master ever visualized, Chang succeeds in giving his landscape much of the same feeling of uninterrupted, rhythmical rolling movement. In addition, the evenly applied texturing can be looked upon as a free allusion to Tung Yüan's "hemp-fiber" texture strokes. Finally, the appearance of small boulders on the summits of the hills, here treated as a freshly observed geological phenomenon, would nevertheless remind Chinese viewers of a stylistic trademark of Tung Yüan, and so provide further reference to the old master's style. Such distant references, however, matter far less than the success of the picture as a believable landscape, made up of solid and understandable forms in a clearly articulated space. As such, the painting reveals the same preoccupations and the same skills as the leaves in Chang's *Chih Garden* album, where "style" in the Chinese sense was scarcely present.

The leaf in the manner of another tenth-century landscapist, Li Ch'eng, is the most unusual and original in the album. References to the landscape style of Li Ch'eng, the supposed source of inspiration, are minimal, if present at all. Chang Hung is concerned rather with using landscape expressively —that is, in manipulating landscape forms so as to charge his painting with interest. Instead of giving to the landscape a clear overall structure or plan, he achieves a kind of thematic unity through the repetition of forms of tall, vertical spires. Four or five of these jagged, upward-thrusting monoliths dominate the landscape. They are varied slightly in shape, and loosely paired on either side of the zig-zagging path on which the two small travelers ascend—an old, conventional motif in a new, unconventional, and original setting. The rocky masses are textured with the short brush strokes typical of Chang Hung's style, which are here applied at a slant so that they complement the jagged outlines of the rocks. The thrusting forms, further energized by these slanting texture strokes, seem to be pointing the way up the steep ascent; by contrast, the similarly shaped vertical spires visible in the distance are placed less artfully, in a more haphazard and random way.

The leaf in the style of Hsia Kuei is the only one in the series after a Southern Sung period artist; even this small homage to Southern Sung (1127–1279) was rare in Chang's time, and virtually unknown afterwards. It is a quite admirable and sound little painting, which manages to capture much of the style and flavor of its model. The composition is relatively simple, consisting of a foreground with trees growing on a slanting-topped boulder, and a homeward-bound farmer crossing a bridge—these lifted fairly directly out of Hsia Kuei paintings—a middle ground with bamboo groves and houses, and in the right background, a dominating mountain ridge, with tall vertical peaks (owing their shapes ultimately to Li T'ang) beyond. The most interesting feature of the painting is the uppermost portion of the mountain at the right, described in terms of intersecting, angular facets formed by wet areas of wash—a direct reference to Hsia Kuei's descriptive technique.

The leaf in the style of Ni Tsan, one of the Four Great Masters of the Yüan dynasty (1279–1368), is even closer to its model. Not only does Chang Hung preserve the components of the Ni Tsan compositional formula—a foreground with tall trees and a pavilion, separated from piled background hills by an expanse of water—but he also depicts these components in a technique similar to that of the Yüan master. Ink is used sparsely—Ni Tsan is said to have "used ink like gold"—the line is slow, deliberate, and crumbly, and there are no washes at all. Chang Hung succeeds like the Yüan master before him in giving his form solidity as well as transparence and lightness, and homogeneity as well as variety. Beyond these points of outward resemblance, he matches remarkably Ni Tsan's mood of purity and removal, the expression of an inner austere spirit which gives the painting more of the literati taste and sensibility that his other works generally have. Without the literati prejudices, we may feel that much of the freshness of those other works has been sacrificed in the gaining of that end.

The third work of Chang Hung in the exhibition is an album of compositions, dated 1649, in the George J. Schlenker Collection (cat. no. 18). Fourteen delightful leaves make up this album, depicting either rustic vignettes of a purely genre nature or illustrations to folktales and semi-popular stories, all portrayed with a distinctly homespun air. In each of the leaves, Chang Hung reveals his talent for figure drawing, capturing through gesture, posture, and facial expression a wide range of emotions and personalities. He is also skilled at composing figures into groups that are both formally satisfying and effective as narrative. The figures themselves have a special charm and appeal; they seem to be light-hearted, affable, and simple types.

Leaf I is titled by the artist "The Village School," and shows a schoolroom with tables, benches, books, and writing implements. The schoolmaster is instructing five pupils, pointing to a passage in a book held by one while the others follow. The rural atmosphere is brought out by a peasant woman who kneels by her basket behind a screen, and by the untidy, tattered appearance of the schoolmaster,

whose clothing is covered with patches. The furniture is placed so as to establish a consistent ground plane, with ample consideration to the alignment and interrelationships of the tables and benches, which are arranged in positions diagonal to the frame of the painting. Colors are handled in a way typical of Chang Hung; the tones that predominate are subtly varied shades of lilac, peach, soft blues, grays, greens and rosy buffs, which for the most part are used to give added interest to the clothing of the figures. To these low-keyed hues are added a few whimsical touches of malachite green, turquoise, and bright pink, the high values of which give a certain resonance and dazzle to the small leaves.

Leaf J is entitled "Ni Tsan Washing the T'ung Trees." It illustrates a well-known episode in the life of Ni, who besides being one of the Four Great Masters of Yüan Dynasty painting, was renowned for his exceedingly fastidious nature and passion for cleanliness. The tree-washing anecdote, occasionally represented in painting (a version by Ts'ui Tzu-chung is in the Palace Museum, Taipei), demonstrates how far Ni Tsan carried his intolerance of dirt. In Chang Hung's portrayal, as in others, Ni is seen supervising the washing, which is carried out by servant boys. The massive, columnar tree trunks with their broad-leafed, densely green crowns focus the viewer's attention upon the figures. The socially superior status of Ni Tsan is emphasized by his dignified and aloof bearing. His love of purity is reflected in his elegant peach-colored gown with its gray border.

One of the most entertaining scenes in the series is Leaf M, "The Spring Festival," a name that refers to an early spring festival of ancient origin, in which farmers go to the temple to pray to the earth god for a plentiful and abundant harvest.[4] The festivities include heavy drinking, and the scene usually portrayed, as here, is a group of them coming home drunk at the end of the day, supported by boys. Chang Hung demonstrates his skill in the grouping of figures, making them into a loose procession that is divided into three clusters, in each of which an appropriate event is taking place. In one group, two figures are shown transporting a drunken companion on a cart. They are followed by a happy threesome, one of whom, unable to support himself any longer, clings to his friend who is shown with his hand upraised, gesticulating in wild abandon. The third group, only mildly drunk, is led by a young boy who, cherry-branch banner in hand, has assumed the leadership and points the way.

Shao Mi, the last of the three we have chosen to treat in this innovative group, was also a native and resident of Su-chou. In contrast to Sheng Mao-yeh and Chang Hung, about whom very little is known, Shao, perhaps on account of his status as a litterateur and his association with men of literary ability, seems to have received a relatively large amount of attention and recognition.[5] We are told that he excelled in poetry and calligraphy as well as painting, that he was of an unusually reserved and retiring nature, and that he was inclined toward an extreme meticulousness and cleanliness. Although for reasons of poor health he never attempted the arduous road of advancement through the examination system, by reason of his personality and artistic accomplishments he holds a secure position in the elite ranks of the late Ming literati. Along with Tung Ch'i-ch'ang, Li Liu-fang, Pien Wen-yü, Wang Shih-min, and Yang Wen-ts'ung, Shao Mi is numbered among the so-called "Nine Friends in Painting" *(Hua-chung chiu yu)*. Stylistic traces of Shao Mi's association with this group and especially with its leader and foremost exponent, Tung Ch'i-ch'ang, can be found in his painting.

One of Shao Mi's most exciting and brilliant works is the album of landscapes dated 1638, now in the Seattle Art Museum, of which five leaves are in the exhibition (cat. no. 19). The leaves, so varied in subject and style, are united by a single theme, which Shao Mi reveals in a brief inscription on the last leaf. According to this, the paintings are intended as pictorial records of a divine fairy realm frequently visited by him in his dreams.[6] As dream visions, they partake of both other-world fantasy and real-world credibility, and are unique and special places.

Scenes of majestic height and jutting peaks figure importantly in Shao Mi's dreams, as leaves C and G

illustrate. The artist's overt purpose in these two paintings is to infuse the landscapes with elements of drama and awe: summits made up of thrusting cliffs and rocky promontories, isolated worlds in themselves, rise above heavy mists and swirling clouds. Their structure is quite complex; each is constructed of many variously shaped smaller forms which lean sideward so as to give the whole mountain a sense of jarringly rhythmical, dynamically thrusting movement and rising force. This kind of animation is seen at its best in Leaf C, where the successive thrusts of large boulders and small rocks together direct the viewer's eye in a surging movement up and around the curving ridge of the summit.

In Leaf G, although something of this dynamism is still present, it is played down in favor of an emphasis on the awesome and dominating presence of a symmetrically disposed, frontally viewed, squared-off monolith. The rectilinear formation of this monument is reiterated in the more active forms of the lower cliff face, which is surmounted by a long railing marking a path leading to the temple on a plateau at the left. The composition is filled almost entirely with expanses of sheer rock, forming rising walls that are treated as hard, clean, multifaceted surfaces. Shao Mi's use of ink here is brilliant in its textural and tonal virtuosity, which, apart from its inherent interest, contributes to the persuasiveness of the picture, rendering light and shadow, rockiness and solidity. His way of applying the ink is fairly consistent. Wet strokes of wash are first applied to the forms with a studied unevenness, to model them rudimentarily and define the fluctuations of their surfaces. Dry, dark ink *(chiao-mo)* is brushed over this for accents and to render texture. Some parts of the forms are left untextured, in reserve, either broad areas of surface or, more characteristic and interesting, narrow bands along the edges and tops of rocks. These narrow, untextured strips function as formal devices for setting off forms clearly from neighboring ones or from their surroundings. This schematic treatment of rock forms is associated most closely with artists of the Hua-t'ing area, notably Tung Ch'i-ch'ang and Chao Tso. As in Chao Tso's work, these bare areas serve as highlights, indi-

cating the direction of the light source with a consistency unknown in earlier Chinese painting.

To complement the lofty summits of Leaves C and G and the deep ravine of Leaf A, Shao Mi in Leaf F narrows the scope of his scenery to a single secluded dwelling, an idyllic summer residence of a scholar-gentleman, which we see from nearby. Although the painting's overt theme, the visit of one scholar to another, is conventional, the setting provided for it is ingenious and enchanting. Host and visitor are seen through a screen of tall, twisted pine trees planted in a random row that cuts a disorderly path diagonally across the leaf from lower left to upper right. Behind this patterned barrier of unkempt spear-shapes lies the summer retreat, delightfully planned so as to zig-zag somewhat haphazardly through the blossoming lily pond. This device of separating the focal area of the composition from the viewer by a screen of trees is another link with the Sung-chiang painters; it is used, for instance in Sung Hsü's album of 1605 (cat. no. 26).

Much of the appeal of the picture is due to the conscious quality of naiveté apparent in such features as the crooked pines and meandering pavilion, as well as in minor elements such as the stubby, big-leafed trees and the bubbling pools made by small rivulets that feed into the pond. Congeniality of mood is due also to Shao Mi's choice of color. Here his warm and cool tones, usually used decoratively, are not only made to correspond more to the natural colors of the landscape and plants, but are also supplemented with brighter pinks and reds, giving to the landscape a certain effect of colorism which, though reminiscent of Chang Hung, cannot be said to reflect the same kind of precision or originality.

Like Sheng Mao-yeh and Chang Hung, Shao Mi worked in a flexible range of styles, one more of which is illustrated in his "Waterfall on Mt. Lu" *(K'uang-lu pao)*, an undated album leaf in the University of Michigan Museum of Art (cat. no. 20). The discrepancy between Shao Mi's leaf and Sheng Mao-yeh's hanging scroll depiction of the same subject is quite striking. Shao makes no such attempt at grandeur as Sheng did; his vision is less ambitious, his scope narrower. Mountain and water are parts of a mild, contemplative scene filled with spray-dampened trees, cascading streams, and moisture-soaked clouds. There is no such display of versatility of brush and ink as in the Seattle album; instead, Sheng restrains their potentialities, employing exclusively a heavily loaded brush for outlines, washes, and texture strokes. This self-imposed confinement to wet ink, though it suits the mood and theme of his mist-filled landscape, has the effect of reducing the tactile quality of the surfaces, and requires an increased use of outline to enclose and separate individual forms. The source of the landscape manner used here is the work of the earlier Su-chou master T'ang Yin (1470–1523), as we can see from resemblances to a leaf by Shao Mi in an album in the Palace Museum, Taipei, which is designated by the artist as being in that style.[7]

The third example of Shao Mi's painting in the exhibition is a landscape handscroll entitled "The Hsiang-li Dwelling" (Hsiang-li kuan) in the collection of Mr. Wango H. C. Weng (cat. no. 21). In the accompanying inscription Shao dedicates the work to Mr. Chin-p'ing, who was the owner of the mountain retreat. The "Hsiang-li Dwelling" presents us with yet another side, a more conservative one, of Shao's landscape painting. In contrast to the more innovative works previously discussed, Shao here draws upon older styles and conventions. Even the composition seems a bit old-fashioned in its simple two-part division into a foreground land mass at the right and two much more distant ones at the left with right and left being separated by a diagonal expanse of mist. One is reminded, for instance, of Chou Ch'en's "Dreaming of Immortality" handscroll in the Freer Gallery of Art.[8] Moreover, the style harks back to an early stage in the Wu School, the paintings of Wen Cheng-ming (1470–1559) and his circle, particularly in the delicacy and sensitivity of execution. The closest affinity, however, is with his contemporaries; he treats the opening passage, with a house above leafy trees (as Chang Hung might have done it) as an area of continuous rich texture in which forms are not set off by outlines, while the passage at left is strongly reminiscent of Sheng Mao-yeh.[9]

Unity in the "Hsiang-li Dwelling" is obtained largely through repetition of forms. For instance, the decoratively scalloped outlines of the trees in the first section are echoed in the edges of the clouds, in the crowns of the pines, and in the distant mountain summits of the second section. The dotted patterns that render the vegetation on the background mountain tops are reiterated in the leaves of the foreground trees, giving a surface unity and harmony to widely separated portions of the composition.

That the works of Sheng Mao-yeh, Chang Hung, and Shao Mi rise above the generally degenerate state of painting of the Su-chou School in their time is because they were more original and altogether better artists than the others (only Li Shih-ta might be excepted from this statement). Apart from inherent quality, however, their paintings can be seen to represent a new direction taken by the Wu School in this last phase of its history—for it was a new direction never followed, or scarcely, by later artists. It can be characterized as a more visual approach to landscape painting, in which certain conventions that had seldom been challenged previously in landscape painting came to be all but disregarded. Among these were: clear bounding lines or distinct edges for forms; a treatment of the parts of the landscape—trees, rocks, segments of mountains, etc.—as more or less separate entities, generally not run together into larger visual units; brushstrokes of a defined character that did not become blurred or muddled even when closely interwoven in rendering a textured area; color that was clearly subordinated to a basic structure painted in ink; compositions that followed a limited repertory of types, and certain canons. Departures from all these can be found in the works of our three artists. To Western eyes, not conditioned to these Chinese conventions, the originality of the paintings may not be striking, but to the artists' contemporaries it must have been. Their compositions are often quite unconventional; in the case of Chang Hung, particularly, they are often based on the real appearance of actual places, a near-revolutionary idea for the Chinese, and the other two convey the impression of representing actual places, whether or not they do so. The dissolution of solid mass into areas of indistinct outline

rendered in flecks of ink or color, and the use of mists as a naturalistic justification for this device, goes further in their works than it ever had before. Chang Hung uses color in a daring way, often as local color pertaining to the thing depicted, which sets him apart from other unconventional colorists in late Ming such as Hsiang Sheng-mo.

The new and original, however, comprise only one side of their landscape styles. They continued to draw heavily on the Wu School tradition, whether it was (as in the case of Sheng Mao-yeh's "Mt. Lu") that phase of the school directly preceding them in time, or (as in some works of Chang Hung and Shao Mi) on the master who stands at the high point of the tradition, Wen Cheng-ming. Shao's handscroll representing the "Hsiang-li Dwelling," and, to a lesser degree, Chang's pictures of the Chih Garden, have a refinement of style and a delicacy of mood that evoke reminiscences of the age of Wen Cheng-ming and his circle. This willingness to paint in more old-fashioned as well as more forward-looking styles indicates an absence of genuine commitment to innovation and fundamental change. Instead of destroying old ties and initiating a clean departure, which is just what Tung Ch'i-ch'ang and others of the Hua-t'ing group succeeded in doing, these masters sought to resuscitate a declining tradition through significant but unspectacular innovations, and by using their artistic genius to raise it again to a high level of quality. They succeeded, but only for their own time; theirs was not the current that determined the future. ∎

Notes

[1]There is some discrepancy in the additional names given for Sheng Mao-yeh in literary sources. His hao is sometimes given as Yen-an (in Wu-sheng-shih shih, Hua-shih ts'ung-shu ed., chüan VI, p. 70; or Yen-an in T'u-hui pao-chien, Hua-shih ts'ung-shu ed., chüan I, p. 6), and sometimes as Nien-an (in Hua-shih hui-yao quoted in P'ei-wen-chai shu-hua p'u, chüan LVIII, p. 11a; T'u-hui pao-chien, I-t'ang ed. of K'ang-hsi period[?], chüan VI, p. 20b). In Ming-hua lu, Hua-shih ts'ung-shu ed., chüan VIII, p. 3, Nien-an is given as his tzu. [2]Five leaves from the original album of eight are now owned by the Center of Asian Art and Culture, Avery Brundage Collection, San Francisco. Unfortunately, they could not be included in this exhibition. [3]Chang Hung's concern with the portrayal of space and depth appears to have been recognized among his contemporaries as a distinguishing feature of his painting style. Chiang

Shao-shu in *Wu-sheng-shih shih*, *Hua-shih ts'ung-shu* ed., chüan VI, p. 76, writes: "When he painted landscapes, his brush was stern and outstanding in its power, and his compositions had great depth." [4]See Morohashi Tetsuji, ed., *Dai Kan-Wa jiten*, vol., 5, p. 5459. [5]A biography of Shao Mi has been prepared by Ellen Laing, who kindly allowed me to read and use her manuscript. [6]Siren interprets Shao's inscription as referring to a specific place: "These studies…are, if we may believe the words of the painter, meant to illustrate the road to Ling Ching, the divine scene (or, spiritual dwelling place) 'where the Immortals hide' and to which he often came in his dreams." It is probable, however, that it is a more generalized realm of Taoist immortals that he intends. (*Chinese Painting: Leading Masters and Principles*, vol. V, p. 33). [7]Palace Museum Collection, Taipei, MA52, Leaf F. [8]James Cahill, *Chinese Painting*, pp. 138–139. [9]Compare, for instance, one of the leaves in the eight-leaf album not in the exhibition (cf. note 2): Siren, *Chinese Painting*, vol. VI, pl. 279A.

64

12. Sheng Mao-yeh (active 1594–1637). *Waterfall on Mt. Lu.*
81-1/2 x 39-1/4″. University Art Museum, Berkeley.

13. Sheng Mao-yeh (active 1594–1637). *Album of Landscapes:*
leaf a. 11-1/4 x 18-5/8″. Private Collection, New York.

15. Sheng Mao-yeh (active 1594–1637). *Moonlit Landscape.*
   Dated 1632. 9-1/8 x 20-1/2″. Ching Yüan Chai Collection.

14. Sheng Mao-yeh (active 1594–1637). *Album of Landscapes:*
leaf b. 11 x 11-7/8''. The Metropolitan Museum of Art,
New York, The Sackler Fund, 1969.

68

17. Chang Hung (1577–after 1660). *Album of Landscapes in Old Manners:* leaf a. Dated 1636. 12-5/8 x 7-7/8″. Ching Yüan Chai Collection.

16. Chang Hung (1577–after 1660). *The Chih Garden:* leaf g.
    Dated 1627. 32 x 34-1/2″. Vannotti Collection, Lugano.

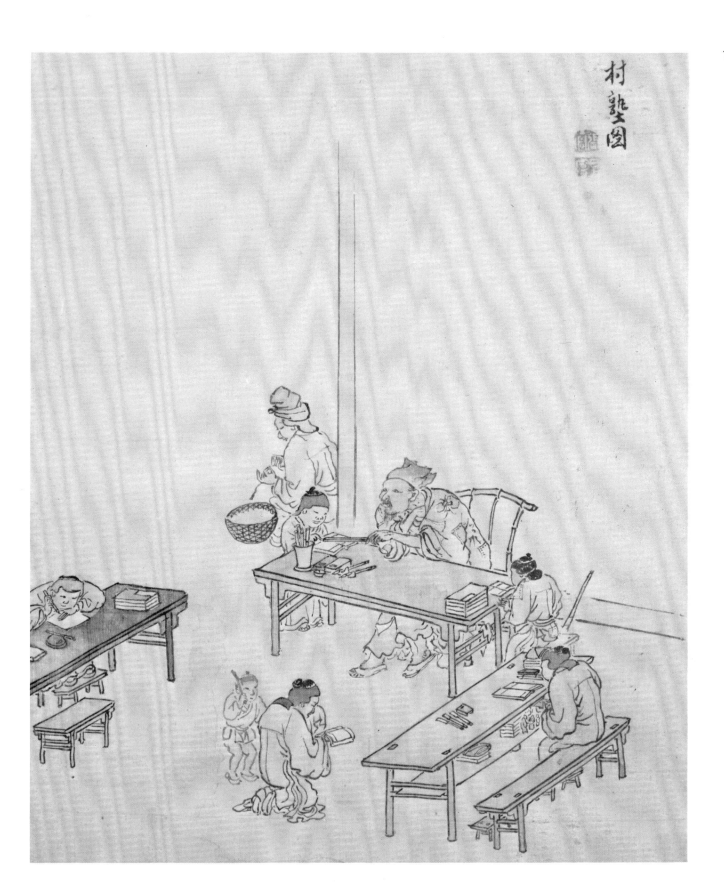

18. Chang Hung (1577–after 1660). *Album of Figure Compositions:* leaf i. Dated 1649. 11-1/4 x 8″. George J. Schlenker Collection, Piedmont, California.

72

20. Shao Mi (active 1620–1640). *The Waterfall on Mt. Lu.*
14-1/8 x 13-7/8″. University of Michigan Museum of Art,
Ann Arbor.

73

21. Shao Mi (active 1620–1640). *The Hsiang-li Dwelling:*
handscroll section H. 10-9/16″. Wango H. C. Weng
Collection, New York.

The Sung-chiang (Yün-chien) Painters, I: Sung Hsü and His Followers

by Yoko Woodson

From the second half of the sixteenth century, the region of Sung-chiang, near Su-chou, came into prominence as a new art center. Sung-chiang was a *hsien*, or township, of which the old name was Yün-chien; the chief city within it was Hua-t'ing. (The three names are used more or less interchangeably in discussions of painting, although they are also used, rather arbitrarily, to designate separate schools, as will be noted below.) Su-chou still retained its position as the home city of Wu School painting; but what had begun as an offshoot of that school now became a rival. The artistic goals of the Sung-chiang masters had become distinct from those of the Wu School. In part, their break represented a reaction by the scholar-amateur painters against the conservatism of those Su-chou artists who were reproducing the ideas and styles of their predecessors without adding much of their own.

The shift of the artistic center from Su-chou to the new city was described by a contemporary Su-chou artist, Ku Ning-yüan: "Towards the end of the Wan-li reign, painting again began to decay (in Su-chou), but fortunately Tung Chi'i-ch'ang arose in Yün-chien, and his talents and eminence in Tao and art again spread glory over the peaks and gave fresh impetus to the spirit. He was indeed a man who opened up new paths."[1]

The fame of Sung-chiang as an important center of painting was mainly due to the dominant figure of Tung Ch'i-ch'ang. Surrounded by privileged gentlemen with intellectual status, wealth, and leisure, he headed the new movement that was to determine the direction of Chinese painting long after his time. Active at the same time in Sung-chiang, however, was a somewhat separate group of artists who represented a different current, although they moved in the same social circles and sought artistic goals generally similar to those of Tung and his associates. These were Sung Hsü and his friends and followers. Taking as their basis, at least in the earlier phase of their development, the tradition of Shen Chou, they produced paintings that were quite different in style from those of Tung and the others. It was in their later phase that their works came closer stylistically to those of Tung.

Sung Hsü (whose *hao* was Shih-men) was born in 1525 in Chia-hsing, and died in 1605. His art was inspired chiefly by Shen Chou. He was active as an artist during his early years in the region of northern Chekiang province. Some time later he probably moved to Sung-chiang, and became a friend of Ku Cheng-i and Mo Shih-lung, who were to be, respectively, a mentor and a close friend of Tung Ch'i-ch'ang.

The undated album of twelve landscapes in the Ching Yüan Chai Collection depicts actual scenes,[2] reflecting the interest of the people of the time in famous and familiar places (cat. no. 22). On each leaf the painter inscribed the name of the place he was depicting, but the scenes are represented in a manner that is far from naturalistic. Nature is recreated in the mind of the artist by manipulating odd shapes, as in Leaf G in which extremely tall and thin mountain peaks are repeated, or by placing a huge land mass in the center of the composition or pushing it to the corner for the best artistic design. Yet Sung succeeds in depicting the striking features of each scene. The broad and fluid lineament, tending to a distinctive undulating movement which does not have the capacity of defining three-dimensional form, the curling texture strokes, the repetition of similar shapes, and the deliberate evenness in ink tone and colors, all reveal the source of the style of Sung Hsü to be in the Shen Chou tradition. At the same time, the soft surface quality of the sparsely used ink ties his art with the later Wu School styles in Su-chou.

Like many other Chinese artists from ancient times to the present, Sung Hsü loved to feature waterfalls in his landscape. The hanging scroll owned by Mr. J. T. Tai, dated 1587 (cat. no. 23) shows his favorite subject matter at its best. The tall mountains and the winding stream are standard compositional elements in his hanging scrolls. To emphasize the verticality of the waterfall, the artist simplified the picture in many respects; the foreground is minimally established with a few rocks and trees, and the middle ground is omitted entirely, leaving the mountains along the stream as tall, unbroken masses with uneven surfaces only at the top. The forms of the

rocks and mountains are simplified and smoothed out. The recession into space created by the stream and the overlapping mountains is suddenly halted by the vertical screen of the waterfall, which drops down between the cliffs. In this painting, again, one can observe Sung Hsü's characteristic brushwork at its best in the very broad outlines, sometimes fluctuating in thickness, which tend to flatten the forms. In spite of this, however, the mountains and rocks are given some convincing solidity by a combination of graded, grayish washes, curling texture strokes, and a scattering of dots.

The very tall and narrow composition which was common in the late sixteenth century, especially among the Su-chou painters, is seen in extreme form in another hanging scroll by Sung Hsü, a landscape with waterfall done two years later, in 1589, now in the Ching Yüan Chai Collection (cat. no. 24). This waterfall scene, which still retains some of the naturalistic quality of the earlier work, is extremely stretched or attenuated, as if the artist had pulled the upper and lower sections of the composition apart, to a point where they seem only tenuously related. In spite of the repetitious folds of the cliffs, and the small-scale buildings fusing in the distance, recession into depth is almost entirely denied. The mountain extends up beyond the picture area so that the sky, of which small areas were visible in the earlier hanging scroll, is totally eliminated and the waterfall flows suddenly down from the very extremity of the picture. Contributing further to this flattening tendency is the absence of any extensive washes and the restrained use of texture strokes and dots. Both the rocks and the mountains have lost their solidity, and the total effect achieved is one of surface patterns dominated by the several verticals of the waterfall. In spite of the loss of realistic quality from the scene, it still conveys by means of abstract devices the grandeur and coolness of the waterfall in winter.

The hanging scroll on silk in the Hochstadter collection dated 1604 (cat. no. 25) is basically similar in composition to the landscape of 1587. A river winds from the foreground to the upper left, with cliffs rising along its sides. But here Sung Hsü works

76

in a detailed manner; the painting is much more filled with small elements, creating a very different total effect. Something of the Northern Sung mode, in which a multiplicity of forms is organized into a monumental structure, must have been Sung Hsü's aim. The rocks, mountains, plateaus, and trees alternate or repeat their similar forms, and are arranged in a clear and tight sequence of mountain ridges so that each contributes to the creation of a sweeping S-curve, recessing into deep space from the right foreground upward to the left, then turning again to the right. This construction is closely akin to the "dragon vein" method of organizing mountain masses, which was to later become a principal compositional device in the theory and practice of painting, especially among the Orthodox masters of the Ch'ing dynasty. This dominating S-curve recession into space had been anticipated by Huang Kung-wang, one of the "four great masters" of the Yüan period, and one might see a close derivation of this compositional device in Sung Hsü's painting from Huang Kung-wang's famous *Tien-ch'ih Shih-pi*, a work that has survived to our time only in copies.[3] In other respects, however, the painting still adheres to the earlier style of Sung Hsü: the forms clearly defined by smooth and unbroken lines, the curling texture strokes, and the scattered dots.

As revealed in the composition of the Hochstadter scroll, Sung Hsü in his later years seems to have become interested in Huang Kung-wang and other Yüan dynasty masters. This change in interest and style marked a turning point that was important not only for his own artistic development but also for other artists of the school. The leaves of the album in the H. C. Weng Collection, dated 1605, the year of his death (cat. no. 26), show his new interests more clearly and depart further from his early manner. He is obviously experimenting with the new artistic possibilities suggested by the Yüan masters. The twelve leaves are painted in ink and tints of blue, green, and orange-brown. Some are drawn in derivatives of his own earlier style (Leaves E and L), or of the Shen Chou style (Leaf D). His typical lineament and texturing is seen in these leaves, but in others he attempts things that are very new for him.

He takes an analytic approach to landscape by dividing the natural forms into more distinct structural units. This is most apparent in the leaves painted in the Huang Kung-wang manner (Leaves A and C). Each motif has a clear and simple shape, and its relationship to others is distinct. The angular plateaus and tall, rough mountains engage in dynamic interplay, seeming to push and pull at one another. The rocks and mountains are given an earthy appearance by a combination of fine, dry brush strokes and horizontal dots.

In other leaves (B and I) he experiments with new, imaginative compositions. In Leaf I, tall pine trees are shown in close-up view, with their trunks and branches stretching to the top of the picture. Through the screen of trees we see a wall and beyond it a house with a further grove of pines fading into mist. In Leaf B, the picture area is divided horizontally in the middle by the flow of a river. On the opposite bank are undulating, low mountains, and in the foreground tall tree groups function, as in Leaf I, as a screen through which a man in a boat is visible. This device of setting a house or other point of interest into middle distance, separating it from the viewer by trees and so creating a sense of seclusion or remoteness, was much used by this group of painters in the later phase of the school.

This album shows not only Sung Hsü's new inventiveness in composition, but also a tranquility and poetic sensitivity which are quite rare in his paintings. Most of the leaves reveal a great change in his brushwork and in his concept of form. The brushwork has become dry; the smooth and wetly-drawn lines and washes are replaced by dry-brush strokes that give earthy textures to the rocks and mountains. The horizontal dots are abundantly used to model forms or to soften their contours. Shapes are reduced to the simplest, such as cubic or rounded rocks and mountains. The trees are also simplified, losing all detail. A strong contrast in light and dark, replacing the deliberate monotony of ink tone in his earlier works, adds dramatic effect to the pictures.

Perhaps the album reflects the artistic situation in Sung-chiang at the beginning of the seventeenth

century. As Tung Ch'i-ch'ang's theory of art became influential, the styles of Yüan masters, especially Huang Kung-wang, won increasing respect among the artists of Sung-chiang, including Sung Hsü, who had until then represented a different stylistic current.

Sung Hsü had a number of direct pupils. One was Sung Mou-chin, a native of Sung-chiang. He was active from the end of the sixteenth into the beginning of the seventeenth century. In the pair of landscapes in the Bissinger collection (cat. no. 27A and B), he works in a curiously abstract style. In each leaf, a land mass occupies the center of the picture. This compositional plan, and the scheme of dividing the land mass into two vertical parts, recalls some of the leaves in Sung Hsü's album of river scenes (cat no. 22). But such strange features as the contorted rocks, the deliberate imbalance between the land mass and the open space, and the distortion in scale between the hills and the trees take away any natural quality from his pictures and make them seem abstract and man-made.

Sung Mou-chin's bold designs, with rocks and mountains taking strange shapes, may be inspired by the art of garden design, which was popular at that time. The history of gardens in China begins before the T'ang dynasty. For the Chinese, gardens gave not only pleasure but also peace of mind. They saw all of nature in the small, secluded space of a garden. By the late Ming dynasty, the art of garden design had been perfected technically and aesthetically, and gardens became even more important in the lives of scholars, painters, and intellectuals, who often gathered in them to discuss poetry and art. The villa of a host was often located in a quiet suburban area, away from the noisy world. Such villas always had gardens with ponds, flowers, strange rocks, and sometimes a stream. Such gardens themselves could be the subjects of paintings. For example, Sun K'o-hung (1532–1610), another important Sung-chiang painter who was a contemporary of Sung Hsü, portrayed actual gardens faithfully, giving us a good idea of the state of garden design as well as the elegant life of gentlemen at that time.[4]

Like Sun K'o-hung, Sung Mou-chin was inspired by the art of the garden, but in quite a different way. Where Sun K'o-hung's concern was with naturalistic depiction of gardens and the ideal life of scholar-painters, Sung Mou-chin appears to have been interested in the principles of garden design. Here, on a piece of paper, he tried to recreate nature by submitting it to the principles of garden design. The brushwork is dry and looks as if it had been done with a worn-out brush. The broken lines are very short, looking sometimes like series of dots, and the texture strokes drawn in different shapes, sizes, and directions seem to betray a lack of control. But the variety of gray tones gives some solidity to the forms, and creates a strong effect of light and dark. These paintings are done with an air of naiveté, but at the same time exhibit, in their interesting abstract designs, a freshness and playfulness that we have not seen before.

If we characterize Sung Mou-chin as an untrammeled and carefree painter, the next artist we consider, Chao Tso, was his opposite in many respects, and with him a new direction in the treatment of nature was to come to this group of artists. The difference between the two is well described in the local history entitled *Sung-chiang Chih;* "Whereas Sung Mou-chin painted in a loose and sprinkling fashion, Chao Tso never worked carelessly."[5]

Chao Tso was born in Sung-chiang and was active from shortly after 1600 to around 1630.[6] Like Sung Mou-chin, he studied under Sung Hsü. He belonged to the same generation as Tung Ch'i-ch'ang, and seems to have had a close relationship with him socially and artistically; the *Wu-sheng-shih shih* and other books refer to their close friendship and cooperation. The handscroll to be discussed below bears a seal of Tung, who thus must have seen it; perhaps it was even painted for him. We may judge the extent of Tung's influence on the painting of Chao Tso if we compare this handscroll with Tung's scroll painted ten years earlier (cat. no. 33).

Chao Tso's handscroll entitled "Lofty Recluses Among Streams and Mountains" in the Ching Yüan Chai Collection, dated 1609–1610 (cat. no. 28),

shows that the artist was already capable, by this early date, of creating a continuous landscape design with structural unity while retaining in it a naturalistic quality. Introduced by a slanting tree which points into a wide stretch of water, the landscape becomes progressively more complex with clusters of rocks, mountains, water, houses, and luxuriant trees. It finally ends with the climax of a jagged rock formation and a strongly patterned waterfall. Although complicated and crowded with many elements, some of which are themselves complex and strange in form, the landscape is tightly organized and has structural unity. Chao Tso here takes an analytic approach to nature and reconstructs his landscape intellectually. In this approach lies some of his affinity with Tung Ch'i-ch'ang. The brief text on painting ascribed to Chao Tso under the title *Wen-tu lun-hua,* or [*Chao*] *Wen-tu's Discussion of Painting,* reflects his concern with structure and logical relationship between elements in landscape. He says that in a large landscape a principal desideratum is momentum or *shih;* stones and trees will have this *shih,* no matter how complicated they may be, if they are drawn with structural logic or *li.* He also mentions that form and momentum depend on how the elements are placed, and how hidden or shown. In doing this, he continues, the artist should first work with a dry brush, and then scrutinize every part to make sure that no changes are needed before he spreads on the ink washes.[7]

Although constructed on the principles of *li* or structural logic, this scroll retains much of naturalism and organic quality. The rocks and the mountains are solid and earthy; the strong effect of light and dark on them suggests that phenomena of sunlight and shadow have been scientifically observed. This has led to suggestions of Western influence, which may be well founded. More Chinese is the practice of leaving between the mountains undefined areas which are to be read as mist or openings into deep distance. Shallower pockets of space become sunlit valleys where the secluded dwellings of scholars are seen.

The brushwork varies through a fairly narrow range from wet to dry; for the darkest accents he

uses *chiao-mo,* "roasted ink." There is very little of properly linear drawing. The combination of small dots and short texture strokes in gradations of ink tone creates the surface textures. Forms are softened by repeating small dots along the contours. Vestiges of Chao's early training with Sung Hsü are manifested in small details, such as the pointed distant mountains, the narrow-trunked pine trees, the houses seen between hills or trees, and the distinctive way in which some tree roots flow into their bases of earth, with dark triangular shapes marking the juncture. All these and other features are to be seen in Sung Hsü's album of 1605.

Chao Tso's analytic attitude toward nature operates even more strongly in the undated hanging scroll in the collection of Mr. and Mrs. Allen Christensen (cat. no. 29). The picture is again crowded with many landscape elements, but here they are more or less evenly distributed on the picture plane, without much contrast between masses and open space. The design emphasizes minor details such as the pointed peaks made up of many cubic blocks with slanting-cut ends. Each form is carefully and clearly defined, but the profusion of small elements without much differentiation in form and size, or much dynamic interaction between them, seems somewhat to weaken this composite landscape. Some elements, such as the houses and the trees in middle ground, are quite naturalistic, but the organic quality and rhythmic movement that were exhibited in the Ching Yüan Chai handscroll are lost here, and a degree of artificiality sets in. The brushwork is even dryer; the shading on the objects is done with very fine dots, looking like wash, which gives a chilly, wintry appearance to the landscape.

The analytic approach revealed in these paintings is in some ways similar to that of Tung Ch'i-ch'ang. The difference between them is that the landscape of Chao Tso is much more crowded with smaller elements, whereas Tung's is divided into much larger units; Chao Tso's formal inclination is toward pointed, triangular forms, Tung's toward rounded and conical shapes; Chao Tso's brushwork is dryer, shorter, and more refined in touch than that of Tung.

Chao Tso did not always use this analytic approach to landscape. In some of his works nature is not treated in terms of distinct units at all. In these other pictures, he takes a more pictorial approach to nature and painting, grasping an impression of nature in a particular time or season, without much concern for tight organization of landscape elements; they are loosely unified with mist or water giving some atmospheric continuity to the paintings. Thus Chao Tso maintained dual stylistic tendencies, the analytic on one hand and the "impressionistic" on the other. He succeeded to the new landscape style of Sung Hsü, the dry brush manner that Sung explored in his later years, and pushed the concept and techniques of this manner further through close association with Tung Ch'i-ch'ang. But Chao did not commit himself only to this style; his temperament was perhaps more that of a poet than of a theorist and he retained also an "impressionistic" approach. Sometimes he combined the two styles, without (like Tung) pushing either to the extreme. This gives his paintings the perfect harmony between sensitivity and structural unity that we can see in the Ching Yüan Chai handscroll.

One of the last painters of this school, who was much influenced by Chao Tso, was Shen Shih-ch'ung. He was born in Hua-t'ing and was active from around 1610 to 1640. He studied under Sung Mou-chin, and later Chao Tso.

Perhaps his finest surviving work is the series of album leaves in the Hochstadter collection, dated 1619 (cat. no. 30). In these, Shen Shih-ch'ung has used a number of old styles, mainly those of the Yüan masters; he does not identify these with inscriptions but they are apparent in the paintings. The two leaves in the Huang Kung-wang manner are simple in plan, with fewer landscape elements. However, the compositional device of dividing the picture into upper and lower sections by entirely eliminating the middle ground dramatizes the scenes. With this aim, the artist has emphasized the waterfall and the overwhelming background mountains in one leaf, and in the other has set a vivid image of a luxuriant tree group against fading mountains. The angular rocks and the effect of

strong light and dark show the influence of Chao Tso. Some of the forms are clearly defined—even the splashing water around the foreground rocks is drawn in line, as a decorative pattern—but in other areas the forms tend to be diffuse.

The same diffusion of landscape elements is seen in the other leaves. The one painted in the Li Ch'eng manner preserves the earthy quality and solidity of rocks and mountains, but the distinction between masses becomes subtle and they tend to fuse with each other. The tendency is most obvious in the leaf imitating Wang Meng. There the rocks, mountains, trees, and houses have lost their clear forms and structure, and are all fused into a continuum of nervous surface textures made up of dots and lines. In the leaf in the manner of Chao Ling-jang this diffusion of forms is further developed into an atmospheric rendering, in which everything—the bamboo grove, houses, and mountains—dims in the mist and rain. Here in Shen Shih-ch'ung's painting, the atmospheric quality of some of Chao Tso's work has gained an added dimension of tranquility and romantic lyricism.

Shen's brushwork is dry like that of Chao Tso, but his softer and lighter touch makes his painting more delicate, and contributes in part to his atmospheric and diffusive style. The difference can be seen clearly if we compare Chao's handscroll with one by Shen Shih-ch'ung, a river landscape dated 1622 in the Stanford University Museum of Art (cat. no. 31). This peaceful water scene is depicted in ink and light colors. Opening with an expanse of water, the landscape reaches a climax with large land masses in the central portion and ends with an extensive stretch of water again. The cubic and angular rocks, the pointed distant mountains, the earthiness of the forms, and the dry brushwork tie the artist with his teacher, Chao Tso, but the lighter and softer touches of the brush, and the milder use of light and dark make the landscape his own work. Again, a certain diffuseness both in individual forms and in the composition as a whole, an atmospheric quality achieved by use of mist and the larger proportion of open space, give a poetic sensitivity to this otherwise imposing landscape.

Perhaps because of this quality in his works, Shen Shih-ch'ung is credited by Chinese writers with having founded a new school, the Yün-chien School. It is true that the stylistic tendencies exemplified in his paintings were to be carried further by early Ch'ing artists working in this region, such as Lu Yüan, into a declining stage marked by excesses in dissolution of form and incoherence of composition. It would seem more valid, however, to regard the group of artists considered in this chapter as a single, true school of painters, and one of the most homogeneous in the late Ming period, when individual departures and diversity were the norm.

Thus viewed as a whole, the school can be seen to have a clear, definable direction, which in the early period is set by Sung Hsü as he moves from his Shen Chou-derived early manner into a later one affected by a new attachment to the Yüan masters. Tung Ch'i-ch'ang's rise to dominance in Hua-t'ing painting circles, and the wide acceptance of his theories, evaluations, and stylistic assertions, surely was instrumental in deflecting Sung Hsü's own course of development and that of his followers. In particular, it affected Chao Tso, especially in some of his more carefully organized compositions. In the end, however, it was not the orderly formal construction to be seen in works of Huang Kung-wang and other Yüan masters, but their fondness for dry-brush drawing and quiet scenery, that Chao and later painters of the school found most attractive. Perhaps in reaction to the harshness of much of Tung's work, they moved into milder modes of painting, sacrificing strength to sensitivity.

The direct following of the school in later periods was not impressive—it may, for practical purposes, be considered virtually to end with Shen Shih-ch'ung—but such artists as Pien Wen-yü (cat. no. 40) and Wang Shih-min (cat. no. 39), although not properly to be classified within this group, were significantly influenced by its styles, which thus form an important part of the background of the early Ch'ing painting of the "Orthodox" current. ∎

Notes

[1] Quoted and translated by Osvald Siren, *Chinese Painting*, Vol. V, p. 3. [2] See the Catalogue section, p. 163, for identifications of some of the places depicted. [3] Hsieh Chih-liu, *T'ang Wu-tai Sung Yüan ming-chi*, pl. 27, is the best among surviving versions; see also the versions in the Palace Museum, Taipei (YV61) and the Freer Gallery of Art (16.966). [4] One of the best examples is the handscroll titled "A Long Grove and Stone Table," dated 1572, former Nü Wa Chai Collection, now in the Center of Asian Art and Culture, San Francisco. This excellent painting unfortunately could not be obtained for the present exhibition. [5] Siren, *Chinese Painting*, Vol. V, p. 20. [6] For a list of recorded works dated between 1603 and 1619, see Hsü Pang-ta, *Li-tai liu-chuan shu-hua tso-p'in pien-nien piao*, pp. 105–106. A landscape dated 1629 is reproduced in *Kokka*, no. 372. [7] *Hua-hsüeh hsin-yin*, chüan III, pp. 36A–37A. The source of the passage is not given, but it may be an inscription on a painting.

80

81

25. Sung Hsü (1525–1605). *Thousand Peaks and Myriad Gulleys.*
Dated 1604. 60 x 27-1/8″. Collection Walter Hochstadter,
Hong Kong.

28. Chao Tso (active 1600–1630). *Lofty Recluses Among Mountains and Streams:* handscroll section. Dated 1609–1610. H. 12-1/2″. Ching Yüan Chai Collection.

29. Chao Tso (active 1600–1630). *Winter Landscape.* 69-1/4 x 37″. Collection Mr. and Mrs. Allen D. Christensen, Atherton, California.

30. Shen Shih-ch'ung (active 1610–1640). *Album of Landscapes:*
leaf k. Dated 1619. 13 x 8-3/4″. Collection Walter Hochstadter, Hong Kong.

86

30. Shen Shih-ch'ung (active 1610–1640). *Album of Landscapes:*
leaf c. Dated 1619. 13 x 8-3/4″. Collection Walter Hochstadter, Hong Kong.

31. Shen Shih-ch'ung (active 1610–1640). *Landscape:* handscroll
section. Dated 1622. H. 9-1/4″. Stanford University
Museum of Art; Gift of the Committee for Art at Stanford.

27. Sung Mou-chin (active late 16th-early 17th century). *Pair of Landscapes:* leaf b. 12-1/4 x 15-1/2″. Collection Mrs. Paul A. Bissinger, San Francisco.

Tung Ch'i-ch'ang (1555–1636) and his friends among the scholar-amateur painters of Hua-t'ing were recognized by their contemporaries as making up the strongest regenerative force in late Ming painting. They were praised not only for their own achievements but also for rediscovering the stylistic strengths of masters of the past, especially of the Yüan dynasty (1280–1368), and for having incorporated their understanding of this past greatness into their own new artistic expressions. Fan Yün-lin, after a denunciation of the Su-chou painters for commercialism, which we have quoted elsewhere, writes: "This idea [i.e., the creative use of the past] is understood only by the gentlemen of Yün-chien [the Hua-t'ing area]. It is such famous gentlemen as Chao Tso, Tung Ch'i-ch'ang, and Ku Yüan-ching who can both trace their lineage back to the ancients and create styles of their own."[1] Hsieh Chao-chih, writing around the same time (ca. 1600), makes this perceptive statement: "Hou Mou-kung and Mo Shih-lung followed the style of Huang Kung-wang, but without transforming the form and substance of the style. The styles of Ku Cheng-i and Tung Ch'i-ch'ang have their source in the manner of Huang Kung-wang.... Therefore, in recent times the 'robe and bowl' [i.e., the carrying on of the tradition] falls on Hua-t'ing."[2]

Mo Shih-lung's surviving paintings bear out Hsieh's judgment of him as an artist who had little that was new to contribute. Mo was a native of Hua-t'ing, distinguished early in life as a talented youth who passed the prefectural examination at the age of fourteen and excelled in poetry, calligraphy, and painting. For the rest of his life, however, he struggled to pass the state examination without success. Stricken with disappointments and misfortunes to his impoverished household, he could have only an intermittent interest in painting and in collecting within his limited means.

His landscape dated 1580, now in the collection of Mr. Ernest Erickson, is a conservative performance in the Huang Kung-wang manner (cat. no. 32). This manner had already been used frequently by artists of the Wu (Su-chou) School, in whose hands it was generally characterized by sparse and delicate appli-

cations of ink. The Erickson painting resembles landscapes in this manner by Shen Chou (1427–1509) in the additive nature of the composition: rising, rounded hills depicted with relaxed lines and even wash; trees drawn in thick, even, and blunt strokes. It was Shen Chou who had, about a century earlier, discovered in the Huang Kung-wang manner certain devices of formal construction, which Mo employs here without adding much of his own. The painting also has stylistic affinities with some works by such Sung-chiang School artists as Sung Hsü and Chao Tso; like their typical pictures, it is peaceful, pleasing, relatively unexciting.

The painter who went beyond Shen Chou in discovering new possibilities in the Huang Kung-wang landscape mode for the abstract manipulation of form, and who made of them a viable new direction for painting, was Tung Ch'i-ch'ang. He was born into a poor family in Shanghai, and later moved to Hua-t'ing. His early interest in painting developed through his access to the collections of a local gentleman-collector-painter, Ku Cheng-i, and of the great collector Hsiang Yüan-pien (1525–1590), a rich merchant who employed Tung as a tutor for his son. After passing the state examination in 1589, Tung Ch'i-ch'ang began his official career in which he was to rise to such high posts as President of the Board of Rites and tutor to the heir apparent. His government service was interrupted, however, by long intervals of retirement in Hua-t'ing. Away from the chaotic situation of the court in Peking, he took a stand of non-involvement and non-action in politics, and devoted himself to the world of art in painting and collecting.

An early work dated 1599, a river landscape handscroll done in ink on paper in the H. C. Weng Collection, begins our series of dated paintings (cat. no. 33). Tung Ch'i-ch'ang painted it while taking a leisurely boating trip on the T'ai-hu (the Great Lake) with his close friend Ch'en Chi-ju (1558–1639). Ch'en was a native of Hua-t'ing, and Tung did the painting as a present for him.

As though in reaction to the sheer beauty of color and surface texture in other paintings of the time,

this river landscape moves very far in the direction of restraint and austerity. A serious tone, a conscious renunciation of the attractive and appealing, is given it by rough, seemingly artless application of brush and ink. It begins with distant hills seen through a screen of twisting pine trees; continues in a stable movement with passages of assorted trees, rocky cliffs, and groups of houses; and diminishes at last into rolling distant hills encircled with fog.

The terrain forms and tree types are mostly derived from the Huang Kung-wang manner and in these basic materials the picture does not go so far beyond Shen Chou. The brushwork, however, is closer to that of the Yüan master in its dry, crumbly textures. Sudden shifts in scale and direction of vision occur among the trees and houses. The painting also illustrates Tung Ch'i-ch'ang's search for a new style by foreshadowing stylistic features of his later period: (1) the making of an abstract formal vocabulary, seen here in an early stage, still comparatively naturalistic; (2) the systematic way of depicting rocks with repeated contours, treating them as smaller forms enclosed by larger ones, and of shading with small brushstrokes to create the effects of concavity and convexity, leaving at the same time some undefined blank areas; (3) rather standardized tree types, including foliated trees and shaggy feather-like trees, all done with an air of naiveté and apparent clumsiness.

Another, more exciting, handscroll by Tung Ch'i-ch'ang from the H. C. Weng Collection is also in the exhibition, again a river landscape done in ink on paper (cat. no. 34). It is titled "Calling on the Hermit at Ching-hsi" and was painted in 1611 for a friend. It is such a forceful and vigorous piece of work that by comparison the 1599 landscape appears mild and calm. The artist appears here to be attacking the hard paper with outbursts of creative energy in his search for new artistic forms. Perhaps the emotions behind such an attack included anger and the frustration and anguish brought about by feelings of ineffectuality in politics. Tung Ch'i-ch'ang had been in his second retirement since 1605, for six years. Hints of political disenchantment are present in his inscription on the scroll.

In this painting, Tung Ch'i-ch'ang goes beyond Shen Chou and all other Ming artists in infusing his forms of rocks and trees with a sense of thrust, or momentum *(shih)*, and interrelating them into coherent, dynamic compositional movements. This was the method Tung discovered in the style of Huang Kung-wang, and partly stated in his writing: "In paintings, all mountains must have a sense of [substantial] form, which is a matter of concavity and convexity. One should begin by outlining the mountain in such a way that its form and momentum are already grasped. Then within the outlined form, one applies straight texture strokes. This is the method of Tzu-chiu (Huang Kung-wang)."[3]

Shifting of vision, a device likewise derived from Huang Kung-wang which is accomplished with subtle and clever transitional passages, is used for spatial contrasts and dissonances among trees and houses, with a sense of unresolved tension. However, under the impression of disarranged space, a feature that resembles the *Autumn Colors on the Ch'iao and Hua Mountains* dated 1296 by the early Yüan master Chao Meng-fu (1254–1322), there are in fact coherent dynamic movements. The landscape begins with rows of trees tapering in height, like musical chords in diminuendo from foreground to midground, a motif belonging also to the Huang Kung-wang manner. Suddenly, their movement is counteracted by the wave-like motion of a plateau jutting diagonally into the picture. At the same time, distant rolling hills seem to be sliding away. The dynamic inward movement of the plateau is continued by another plateau penetrating into the rock mass at the back. It is also counterbalanced by two leaning funnel-like plateaus which complete the inward movement. Echoing it, an S-movement begins with the tall trees near the end of the scroll. Tall trees decreasing gradually in height are pointing diagonally inward to the stream, where the boulders are also creating movement. Winding gracefully in a zig-zag motion, the stream leads to houses in the distance. The horizon and ground plane are also shifting and tilting.

As though denying the external world in order to express the intensity of the artist's inner world, these dynamic movements are brought out more forcefully by stripping away the more naturalistic and attractive aspects of the Huang Kung-wang manner. Rocks are depicted with rough, short brushstrokes, leaving occasional blank areas, so that they have a coarse, artificial, wood-like texture. Trees are also painted in rough brushwork with apparent carelessness, and are portrayed with what seems to be intentional awkwardness, enhanced by the obvious inconsistencies in the angle of vision among trees and houses.

An explanation of the function of dynamic compositional movements as a unifying device in painting can be found in Tung Ch'i-ch'ang's writing: "The form of the mountain should first be outlined, and then texture strokes applied. People nowadays pile up small bits to make up a large mountain. This is one of the worst mistakes. When an ancient master worked on a large scroll, he made only three or four large 'proportionings' and 'unitings' (*fen* and *ho*), and in that manner accomplished the whole composition. Although within the composition there are many small parts, the principal aim is to grasp the momentum (or force, *shih*) of the forms."[4]

In another passage in his writing, Tung gives his opinions on the principle of composition and of formal construction which he must have derived from the Huang Kung-wang manner: "In painting landscapes, it is necessary to understand the principle of 'proportioning' and 'uniting.' The 'proportioning' brushstrokes mark the general framework of the composition. There is the 'proportioning' of the whole painting and 'proportioning' within each individual section. If one understands these aspects, one has already grasped the larger half of the way of painting."[5]

Such mastery in composition is achieved in a monumental landscape done in ink on paper, a hanging scroll by Tung Ch'i-ch'ang dated 1617 in the C. C. Wang collection (cat. no. 35). Based very loosely on the compositional plan for river scenes originated by the Yüan master Ni Tsan (1301–1374), the landscape rises with a monumentality and grandeur that recall Northern Sung landscape. The intensity and bursting vigor of the 1611 painting have given way to a style more controlled and understated within a milieu of maturity, sophistication, and elegance.

Movements are held in quiet balance. A screen of slightly bizarre trees inaugurates a gentle upward movement which is continued by sweeping shores held stable by flat-topped mountains. This upward sweeping movement is repeated more vigorously by swirling, turning, and surging mountains at the top of the painting. The adjacent promontories seem to be gently swept into this swinging motion, so that their ground plane is slightly tilted.

Although the play of ink values is rich and subtle, the overall effect is of an abstract tonal and textural patterning, with an almost schematic alternation of light and dark throughout the landscape. These ink patternings lead to new formal implications of substantiality and insubstantiality. By their very blankness, empty areas on the land surfaces tend to question and deny the substantiality of the forms they have defined. The uppermost mountain, for instance, seems punctured by a blank hole in its lower part.

The artist's intentions as explained in his writings, again match our observations:

> Then one must understand the principle of "insubstantiality" and "substantiality." By "insubstantiality" and "substantiality," one means the varying degree of using the brush in a detailed or summary manner in each part of the painting. A detailed area must be followed by a summary passage. The "insubstantiality" and "substantiality" must complement each other. If a painting is too sparse, the landscape will lack depth and distance. If it is too dense, it will lose spirit resonance. Only when a painter subtly weighs the "insubstantiality" against the "substantiality" and incorporates both aspects to his conception will his painting naturally become extraordinary.[6]

Rich ink play and stippling brushstrokes also render some landscape elements with indeterminable and enigmatic textures; for example, the top mountain: crusty like charcoal, fluid like a surging wave or a dark foreboding cloud; furry and velvety like the wings of a butterfly. Rising from a quieter to a more intense mood, from a slower to a faster tempo, from a more definable to a less definable state, the landscape seems to express an attempt at flight from the earthbound, an attempt in which, by metamorphosing into a semi-fluid state, it finally succeeds.

In spite of its systematic approach, the 1617 painting achieves freshness and strength in vision. Moreover, it restores to painting a monumental form, as well as depth and coherence in composition.

The fourth work by Tung Ch'i-ch'ang in our exhibition is an album of eight leaves of landscapes done in ink on paper, now in the Princeton Art Museum (cat. no. 36). It was painted in 1630, when Tung Ch'i-ch'ang was seventy-five years old and in his third period of retirement. The paintings are done in a mild and relaxed manner with a certain sense of playfulness and mellowness. Gone are the intense seriousness and fighting spirit of his earlier works. Now, his artistic vocabulary and grammar firmly established, he has realized what he set out to accomplish in his painting; for example, dynamic movements and unity in composition, abstract play with form and ink tonality.

Most of the landscapes in the album are based essentially on the Ni Tsan river landscape composition, which is however treated with amazing flexibility and variation. In Leaf A, a quiet river landscape is depicted in softly applied, dilute ink. Trees in the lower right corner are drawn in a casual, playful manner with leaves in a variety of brushstrokes—feather-like dry strokes, or light touches of moist ink. Counteracting the tapering contour of the trees is a small spit of land that pushes diagonally rightward and upward on a tilted ground plane. Soft grassy hills, depicted with a spontaneous overlaying of soft texture strokes, gently rise to the upper right corner.

Especially interesting is the river landscape in Leaf D which was, according to the artist's inscription, painted in imitation of the brush manner of Chüjan, a painter of the Five Dynasties (906–960). Allusions to Five Dynasties landscapes in motifs such as the monumental cliffs, distant temple, angular outlined rocks, and mountaintop boulders are

incorporated into Tung's own manner. An energetic surge is generated by the highlighted areas of the cliff, which rises and spreads out like a vase, then diminishes in height as it recedes, converging to the off-center focus of the temple at the left edge of the picture.

A river landscape of extraordinary visual excitement is seen in Leaf E, which is inscribed by Tung Ch'i-ch'ang as representing the mountain retreat of a lofty scholar. Contributing to the excitement are the foreground trees, uneven in height and depicted in a rich variety of ink and brushstrokes. It is increased by a profusion of shimmering horizontal dots on the rocks of the upper shore, which gives an impression of something more of energy than substance, such as a sandstorm. However, beneath this vision-like surface excitement is structural form created by a network of dry, earthy but resilient brushstrokes. The secluded scholar's retreat is seen through the rocks, as though through a carved window, and enclosed by a towering cliff at the back. Against this state of constant flux and busy activity, the retreat offers peace and quiet repose, and focuses our attention on the left edge of the picture, as does the temple in Leaf D.

A more complex landscape depicted in level-distance view in Leaf H concludes the album. An overall zig-zag movement implying multiple horizons rises from the more stable horizontal base of the foreground trees to a more active diagonal movement of hills at the top of the picture. Solid forms of rocks, trees, and houses enclosing flat planes of water and earth thus divide the picture surface into abstract areas.

Tung Ch'i-ch'ang, as we can observe in these paintings, was single-minded in finding new means of artistic expression. He grasped intellectually the innovations in the brilliant style of Huang Kung-wang in terms of ideas and principles which were systematically articulated in his writings and in his paintings. He brought to the fore the revolutionary abstract elements in the Huang Kung-wang manner, and developed them into new abstract possibilities with new formal vocabularies and textures. Although

he was consistent in this development of a few ideas and items of formal vocabulary, he always succeeded in creating new visions with endless variations and freshness. He thus created a style that is analytical and austere, but also individualistic, vigorous, and dynamic. He restored to painting the qualities of strength, vitality, order, and coherence. Most of all, he succeeded in bringing painting a step further in the direction of formal abstraction.

A work that is very different from Tung Ch'i-ch'ang's in its warmth and spontaneity is by another late Ming master of this group, Li Liu-fang (active 1537–1619), a native of Anhui Province but a resident of Chia-ting in Kiangsu Province, not far from Hua-t'ing. He passed the provincial examination in 1606 but did not succeed in obtaining a higher degree. He then retired to a life of leisure, devoting himself to poetry, calligraphy, and painting. He was later numbered among the "Nine Friends in Painting," with other friends and followers of Tung. As a lover of beautiful landscapes, he made frequent excursions to the West Lake to enjoy the marvelous winter scenes. Excursions of this kind taken in 1604, 1610, and 1614 were recorded in inscriptions on his paintings. He was particularly enchanted by the luster and luminosity of snow.[7]

In the exhibition is a beautiful handscroll in the George J. Schlenker Collection, a winter landscape done in ink on gold-surfaced paper in an individualistic manner. It is entitled "Snow-gazing Along River Banks" (cat. no. 37). According to Li Liu-fang's inscription written at the end of the scroll, it was painted in 1616 when he was traveling by boat and stopped at T'ang-hsi in Chekiang Province. The quiet landscape emerges from brushstrokes that resemble the "grass" or cursive script in their free and fluid movements. These swift, spontaneous brushstrokes seem to have been improvised with ink flowing freely and the untrammelled spirit of the artist dancing in light-hearted abandon. Bare trees are depicted with strokes that resemble the wings of birds in flight. The softness of melting snow is conveyed by moist, undulating lines. With the sky and river darkened by ink wash, the shimmering and glittering effects of light and shade on snow are evoked by the luminous gold paper shining through rapid movements of fluctuating and overlapping strokes. Thus, besides the sheer beauty of brush and ink, the conception of a snowscape is vividly conceived and expressed.

Perhaps no one could reveal the intentions of this snowscape better than Li Liu-fang himself, who wrote: "When the ancients did a painting of a snowscape, they used dilute ink to depict trees and rocks. For the entire area of the sky and water, they used white powder. This method was considered extraordinary. My idea is that this method and the [opposite] method of using ink washes to fill these areas both serve the purpose of obtaining a true likeness. As the brush is put down, there should suddenly appear on the paper the effects of fluttering and blinking, and of light and shade. This is real snow."[8]

A beautiful landscape in ink and color on paper in hanging scroll form, distinguished by its sensitivity of execution, belonging to The Metropolitan Museum of Art, is by Ku I-te (cat. no. 38). Ku was a native of Hua-t'ing and a nephew of the gentleman-collector-painter Ku Cheng-i, who was mentioned earlier as a patron of Tung Ch'i-ch'ang. According to the artist's inscription, it was painted in 1628 in the manner of another Yüan period master, Wang Meng (ca. 1309–1385). It also bears an inscription by Tung Ch'i-ch'ang, who says that it is based on a Wang Meng painting titled "Enjoying the Moon from a Bridge Over the Brook," and that it surpasses the original.

The poetic sensitivity and refined elegance recall similar qualities in works of the earlier Ming painter Wen Cheng-ming (1470–1559) and his circle of Wu School artists. An idyllic mood is awakened by exquisite colors and delicate brushstrokes that are bewitching in their poetic softness. Subtle variations in tone and intensity within the high-key range are achieved by a sensitive interplay of two hues of blue and red-brown which are shaded by ink and highlighted by the white paper. Dark blue and silvery grey are accentuated by fresh light blue or salmon. With the area of the houses and the lower part of the tall mountain lighter than their surroundings,

the landscape appears bathed in moonlight. This dream-like quality is enhanced by the marvellous textures of the foreground pine trees, with mosaic-like bark and soft bunches of needles, and of grassy rocks that are depicted with fine, wavering brushstrokes. The dense, furry, rich texture of the brush manner of Wang Meng is thus recaptured, but without the powerful and passionate nature of the original. Its existence is made convincing by trees depicted carefully, in a manner based on detailed observations of nature, and houses drawn with fine craftsmanship. Surrounding the houses, nearly bare trees with a few leaves fluttering and falling arouse a nostalgic, autumnal mood. Thus, we have an idealized world such as might be dreamed by poets or hermits, created by an artist who deserves all the praises bestowed on him by Tung Ch'i-ch'ang.

Another of the "Nine Friends" associated with Tung Ch'i-ch'ang was Wang Shih-min (1592–1680), a native of T'ai-ts'ang in Kiangsu Province, who was born into a prominent official family and inherited his father's official title. Being very fond of poetry, calligraphy, and painting, he spent much of his time in these pursuits. Moreover, he was a younger friend of both Tung Ch'i-ch'ang and Ch'en chi-ju, and was Tung's pupil as a painter. He is best known today as the oldest of the so-called "Four Wangs," the leaders of the Orthodox School of landscape in the early Ch'ing period. His landscapes of that period tend to be dry and rather monotonous, so that such a painting as we include here, a long handscroll in the H. C. Weng Collection which he did in 1636, must raise him in our estimation (cat. no. 39). Unlike most of his later works, it is poetic in conception and sensitive in execution.

In his inscription at the end of the scroll, Wang records that it was inspired by a long handscroll by Huang Kung-wang which he had once seen. Wang finds other possibilities in the Huang Kung-wang manner than did Tung Ch'i-ch'ang, and paints a very different kind of picture. It captures the deep and dense appearance of forests and foothills that Huang's landscapes have; it takes from them also, and presents in altered form the tall overhanging cliffs, crowded hills and valleys with dense forests

and boulders, winding paths, pockets of space enclosing houses, distant jutting shores, and waterfalls and streams.

The element of repetition within the style of Huang Kung-wang is here brought into full play; the repeated shapes, tinted with placid bluish-green and brownish-red colors and disposed to spread interest evenly throughout the painting, impart a flavor of pleasant monotony which is quite different from the dullness and heavy-handedness of Wang's later, "Orthodox" paintings. The composition is enlivened by subtle surface patterning of tonal values and textures; the forms tend to be flattened into distinct shapes by the evenness of color and by the long, continuous outlines with angular turns. Sparse areas of rocks and paths that are crystalline and lucid in tonality are contrasted with darker and denser areas in a harmonious surface patterning punctuated with green jewel-like spots of moss. Within this delightful abstract interplay, the landscape retains a sense of naturalism in its haziness and in the luxuriant growths of misty trees. Especially fine in touch are the fading mountain peaks, which in their vaporous effect really speak of clouds and mists. As a sublime summation of poetic sensitivity, the landscape concludes with a passage of distant islands with trees, evoking feelings of drizzling rain and shivering water.

Like Mo Shih-lung's work and Tung Ch'i-ch'ang's of 1599, this early work by Wang Shih-min betrays stylistic affinities to paintings by other artists of the Sung-chiang School. Dry and earthy textures resemble those of Chao Tso and Shen Shih-ch'ung but are less rich and diffused. Delicate, pure outlines of forms have a sensitivity reminiscent of Sung Hsü; for example, the wavering lines that suggest the soft textures of small boulders.

A work that appears to be heavily influenced by contemporary styles is a landscape hanging scroll in ink on paper painted by Pien Wen-yü in 1648 (cat. no. 40), now in the collection of Mr. Pihan C. K. Chang. Pien was a native of Su-chou and, like Wang Shih-min, was a young friend and pupil of Tung Ch'i-ch'ang. The landscape is composed in a con-

94

servative manner again reminiscent of paintings by Chao Tso and Shen Shih-ch'ung. It opens in the foreground with rocks and a group of trees stretching in different directions. They are echoed in movement by a group of smaller trees pushing up from a split hill in the middle ground. The landscape is then enclosed by tall mountains with a waterfall and cliffs which by their verticality unify the composition.

Conventions learned from Tung Ch'i-ch'ang are evident, but without the implications they have in Tung's work. Rocks that are similar in shape, repeated and then enclosed in one large containing form, tend to suggest geological formations rather than to engage in abstract formal play. Scale disparities among trees in the middle ground do not, as in Tung's works, create spatial tension, nor does their relationship to the foreground trees and to the formations of the mountains create dynamic compositional movements. As a whole, the landscape elements are slightly static and the composition relatively episodic. Thus we have a painting which, although "homogenized" and tamer in style, has a mild, gentle beauty. Some affinities with the Wang Shih-min landscape suggest that such works as these form an important bridge between Tung Ch'i-ch'ang's achievements and the less adventurous ones of the early Ch'ing Orthodox School.

The intensity of Tung's style, the seriousness and daring of his manipulations of form, were in fact to escape most of the painters who followed him, perhaps all of them until Wang Yüan-ch'i (1642–1715). Another of the milder, more dilute derivations may be seen in a long river landscape by a little-known artist named Ku T'ien-chih, painted in 1649 and now in the Cleveland Museum of Art (cat. no. 41). Ku T'ien-chih was a native of Hua-t'ing, a nephew and pupil of the painter Ku Yin-kuang, who was himself a nephew of Ku Cheng-i. In his inscription on the picture, also written in 1649, Ku Yin-kuang praises it as resembling two famous works of Huang Kung-wang which he had seen at the home of Mr. Hsiang, presumably the collector Hsiang Yüan-pien. However, this landscape is in fact much more influenced by Tung Ch'i-ch'ang's transformation of

the Huang Kung-wang manner than by the work of Huang himself. It appears to have been composed with ready-made formal items of vocabulary and phrases from Tung's manner, but again, without the same structural logic in its construction. Tung Ch'i-ch'ang's device of leaving blank areas on rocks appears here as areas of blue or red-brown untouched by ink, but lacks the formal implications of insubstantiality. The vital force and energy of the Tung Ch'i-ch'ang manner seem tamed and subdued; forms are not so dynamically charged, nor does the ground plane rise or fall although the horizon shifts. With soft rocks depicted by dry and earthy application of ink, resembling brushwork in paintings by Chao Tso, over colors of blue and brownish-red, a quiet and soothing landscape progresses in a stable horizontal movement, without any spatial tension.

This painting is significant in that it foreshadows also the style of the early Ch'ing Anhui School, as seen in handscrolls by Hung-jen (1610–1664) and others, for instance in its use of multiple horizons defined by projecting shores. It also foreshadows the style of Wang Yüan-ch'i, grandson of Wang Shih-min, in the device of depicting solid land masses which are disposed so as to enclose empty expanses of water or flat areas of land.

With the group of amateur scholar-artists in Hua-t'ing whom we have considered, painting was indeed a humanistic pursuit in which paintings were collected, studied, discussed, and written about, as well as painted. Since they never took the paintings of past masters as objects for slavish imitation but rather as sources of inspiration, they discovered new ideas in their works and transformed them into elements of their own manners of expression. Determined very much by their temperaments, interests, and motivations, their styles were quite distinct from each other; this is illustrated by the different ways in which the Huang Kung-wang manner was reworked by Tung Ch'i-ch'ang and Wang Shih-min. Some of the artists, such as Mo Shih-lung and Ku I-te, were also influenced by paintings of their immediate past; Li Liu-fang, untypically for these painters, was inspired by the beauty of nature. There was also significant stylistic interaction among the

artists within this group, as well as with other artists of the Sung-chiang area, as the paintings of Pien Wen-yü and Ku T'ien-chih reveal. Thus, creating within tradition, each of the artists in this group, in his own way, played some part in the development of painting, which was constantly renewing, remaking, and transfiguring itself. However, only such an individualistic and strong personality as Tung Ch'i-ch'ang could rise above his contemporaries and his immediate past to revolutionize painting, becoming a source of inspiration for painters of his own time and for future generations. ∎

Notes

[1]Fan Yün-lin, *Shu-liao-kuan chi*, ca. 1600, quoted in Yü Chien-hua editor, *Chung-kuo hua-lun lei-pien*, Peking, 1957, Vol. I, p. 126. [2]Hsieh Chao-chih, *Wu-tsa-tsu*, ca. 1600 (Shanghai edition of 1959), pp. 195–196. [3]Tung Ch'i-ch'ang, *Hua-ch'an-shih sui-pi*, compiled in 1720 by Yang Wu-pu, *I-shu ts'ung-pien*, Taipei, 1966, Part I, Vol. 28, p. 39. [4]Tung Ch'i-ch'ang, *Hua-chih*, in *Jung-t'ai pieh-chi*, compiled by his grandson Tung T'ing. Preface by Ch'en Chi-ju dated 1630 (Taipei edition of 1968), chüan VI, pp. 9a–b. [5]Tung Ch'i-ch'ang, *Hua-ch'an-shih sui-pi*, p. 36. [6]*Ibid.* [7]Li Liu-fang, *Hsi-hu wo-yu t'i-pa*, in *Mei-shu ts'ung-shu*, Part I, Vol. 10, pp. 141–142. [8]Li Liu-fang, inscription on a painting, quoted in *Chung-kuo hua-lun lei-pien*, Vol. II, pp. 751–752.

33. Tung Ch'i-ch'ang (1555–1636). *Landscape Painted for Ch'en Chi-ju:* handscroll section. Dated 1599. H. 12-3/4″. Wango H. C. Weng Collection, New York.

96

荊谿招隱圖
辛亥人日董其昌
寫于寶鼎齋

32. Mo Shih-lung (ca. 1550–ca. 1585). *Landscape after Huang Kung-wang.* Dated 1581. 46-7/8 x 16-1/8″. Collection Ernest Erickson, New York.

35. Tung Ch'i-ch'ang (1555–1636). *Landscape.* Dated 1617. 65-3/8 x 20-5/8″. C. C. Wang Collection, New York.

34. Tung Ch'i-ch'ang (1555–1636). *Calling on the Hermit at Ching-hsi:* handscroll section. Dated 1611. H. 11-1/8″. Wango H. C. Weng Collection, New York.

98

37. Li Liu-fang (active 1537–1619). *Snow Gazing Along River
Banks:* handscroll section. Dated 1616. H. 11-1/8″. George
J. Schlenker Collection, Piedmont, California.

王舟朗溪橋翫月圖
顧原之光祿臨本有
青出于藍之致

戊子清明寫扵
東岩草堂
卞文嵩

38. Ku I-te (active ca. 1620–1633). *Enjoying the Moon From a
    Bridge Over the Brook* (Landscape in the Manner of Wang
    Meng). Dated 1628. 60-3/4 x 19-1/4″. The Metropolitan
    Museum of Art, New York, Gift of John C. Ferguson, 1913.

40. Pien Wen-yü (active ca. 1620–1670). *Landscape.* Dated 1648.
    38 x 10-3/4″. Collection Pihan C. K. Chang, Hong Kong.

41. Ku T'ien-chih (active mid-17th century). *River Landscape:*
    handscroll section. Dated 1649. H. 10-1/8″. Cleveland
    Museum of Art: Purchase, John L. Severance Fund.

39. Wang Shih-min (1592–1680). *Landscape After Huang
Kung-wang:* handscroll section. Dated 1636. H. 12-1/2″.
Wango H. C. Weng Collection, New York.

Professional Painters in Fukien and Nanking

by Elizabeth Fulder

The critical problem about late Ming painting is how we may take hold of it, what accommodations we must make to grasp it both narrowly on the level of the individual paintings and broadly according to the late Ming's own widely diverging canons. To do both is difficult. The choice among modern art historians has always been one-sided: a sacrifice of selectivity in the interest of totality—clearly one of art history's most disturbing and challenging characteristics.

One of the peculiarities of traditional Chinese painting, though not without precedent in the West, is that it offers something of an alternative to this dilemma, indeed, makes an exceptionally strong profession of that alternative: the geographic approach. It is a chronologically secure system that works sideways, as it were, for its historical ties as much as backward and forward. It contains the paintings efficiently and, if one can keep the threads looped with the immediate past and future, will remain taut enough to give a picture of the standards by which late Ming painting, in this instance, was sustained during its period of rapid change and crisis.

The dominance of this geographical aspect will therefore set the limits for this group of painters to be selectively discussed. The parameters are these: the painters must work in Nanking or its environs between the years 1600 and 1640. This will include Wu Pin, Kao Yang, Wang Chien-chang, and Cheng Chung—in effect, two pair of painters separated by approximately one generation—a geographical conjunction in the lives of four painters who are moving in not always similar directions.

Some subtleties will tend to elude such a narrow, yet broad, crab-working category: the ambience of a truly creative imagination, acknowledgments to non-Nanking teachers, or adaptations of painters from other circles. Moreover, the whole geographical system itself, and the professional-amateur painter categories which were tied to it, were becoming blurred by the new cross-currents of the early seventeenth century. The geographical conjunction nevertheless gives a view, necessarily an incomplete one. Nanking was, in a sense, an artistic backwater compared to Sung-chiang, and similar flaws in this group of painters make them kin. Of course, geographical conjunction alone cannot be asked to explain how Wu Pin came to paint masterpieces which still belong in museums while some of the other painters have so far been given over to the art historians alone.

Critical thought on these Nanking painters has produced some general notions. In their own time, because their work was in a style which was losing favor even in the more conservative Chinese critical circles, they were treated with little thoughtful regard, or with embarrassed disregard. Wu Pin was commonly singled out for the oddness of his figure painting and the mysterious quality of his landscapes; Kao Yang for his splendid rock painting; Cheng Chung for his fine range of manners, both in painting and deportment. These notions are not without point, but are also not adequate to the cases.

Modern writers have given most attention to Wu Pin,[1] occasioning a sharp rise in his reputation. No one inspects the other three too closely. But these also deserve to be analyzed and considered for their own sakes—not so much to give the kiss of life to them as to try to understand whether they are or are not makers of good works of art.

Wu Pin, the most formidable of these four artists, was born in P'u-t'ien, Fukien Province. His paintings are dated between 1583 and 1626. It is reported that during the early Wan-li period (1573–1620) Wu Pin assumed the position of *chung-shu she-jen* in Nanking, an official sinecure for painters. His biographies affirm that he was a professional painter—presumably sharing with the other three painters in this group all the preoccupations which professional painters acknowledged and failed to acknowledge. The artistic climate in Wu Pin's native province, Fukien, was not a revolutionary one. Its generally conservative nature is illustrated by the circumstance that, already in the early Ming, Fukien painters were closely preoccupied with the revival of Sung styles.[2] This conservative geographical background underscores the contrast between Wu Pin's stylistic options and the local amateur developments in Su-chou and Sung-chiang.

The two Wu Pin landscapes in the exhibition show different but related aspects of his landscape style. The first is a handscroll, dated 1607 (cat. no. 42). The work depends for its strength on reflexive, controlled variation of smoothly contoured, carefully textured mountain shapes. Integral to Wu Pin's purpose in this composition is an event of strange and dramatic prominence.

The handscroll opens with three bulky mountains in the middle ground framing a large U-shaped vista; this vista echoes the contours of the mountains in inversion. Smaller hills and trees clearly distinguish the foreground plane. The effect of this opening is one which, as it were, lulls us into a false confidence, for we need to reorganize our perceptions to face what follows. A narrow spire in the foreground abruptly introduces a middle section of sharp contrast, where the fore- and middle-ground planes merge in a comparatively irrational mixture. This sharp gesture is abrupt, but convincing, for it is informed by a dramatic compression and narrowing of the initial elements of the handscroll. (The startling vertical elements are given point by the placement here of the artist's signature—an unusual detail which intensifies the abstract character of the structure.) Reinforcing this area of uncertainty is the manner in which Wu Pin emphasizes the vertical contour and the grotto-like shape with the compensating certainties of the trees.

There is a sense in which the opening is an adumbration of the close. The mountains continue undistorted but with some evidence of the central crises that the handscroll has undergone. The bulky shapes return, but bring with them manifold variations on the more vertical shapes from the central section.

One of the great temptations of the late Ming is toward the dramatic gesture, the explicit attempt at emotion—or commotion—without the attendance of drama itself (the second landscape by Kao Yang, [cat. no. 45] is a fair example). Strong effects are often produced, but the effects are improbable because of their lack of accommodation to the formal needs of drama. Wu Pin's handscroll has many kinds of excellence to offer—its close-grained brushwork, its spatial layout, the individuality of its character—but the unique value it has to offer us is that its tension arises from a structure that is closely argued. Not an architecture of instants, there is as much drama in the structure as in the details. And this makes a difference.

Wu Pin's second landscape (cat. no. 43), a large hanging scroll, does not depend on a slow exposition, dramatic development, and varied recapitulation, but upon muscular shapes that overlap and flow boldly into and around each other. Here, one formidable superstructure encompasses the entire composition. The two groups of trees in the foreground set the scale and spatial reference for the rising vertical three-part mountain above—the double foundation providing space and support for the narrower five-part articulations of the middle, which in turn support the triple peak at the top. The sinuously articulated superstructure is divided horizontally by drifting mists. Architecture, solidly but precariously situated on inaccessible plateaus, defines small areas of three-dimensional space on an otherwise two-dimensional plane. The solidity of forms is constantly denied or made ambiguous by the insistent juxtapositions of flat edges and articulated recessions.

The element of drama is once again the energizing thesis of the work, as in the handscroll. Wu Pin's formulation this time, however, derives from the tension between weight and balance. The superstructure is made to sustain its pose with support only in the lower right-hand corner; the left-hand foreground, heavily freighted with architecture and stone, cantilevers dramatically over the water. It is an essay in torsion. The total effect is the more startling because of the architectural solidity of the superstructure. It is a formal poise, but a formal poise that releases a great deal of excitement because of the tension of its precarious balance. This landscape shows Wu Pin in his best and most char-

acteristic role: a solid weight-lifter, rich and dense, with a muscular style that receives an added grace, a boon, through its being entrusted with the fertile force of drama.

Kao Yang, a more marginal figure even in his own world of Nanking, was born in Ning-p'o, Chekiang Province, and was active at the end of the Wan-li period (1573–1620). The occasion for his move to Nanking was reportedly a legal dispute initiated by a government official who had commissioned a portrait from Kao Yang with which he was dissatisfied. In Nanking "he changed to painting landscapes and became even more famous."[3] He is also mentioned as a painter of rocks, which enterprise he is said to have carried out with considerable geological accuracy.

Kao Yang's landscape on paper from the Ching Yüan Chai Collection (cat. no. 44) is dated 1608. The ample scene includes lofty peaks, waterfalls, a lush foreground, and a pensive figure. These elements establish a rather loose network of relationships within the narrow format. Relatively self-contained, massed patterns are placed left and right alternately along the entire height of the composition. Mists are used to separate the meandering elements, while a waterfall bestows a contrasting vertical gesture on the mountains, architecture, and figure. This frame—reminiscent of the academic formulations of the late Wu School—allows the surface energy of line the modicum of ambiguity in spatial definition and the play with natural shapes that Kao Yang wants for his subject. The scenery is pleasant and accomplished. The lacy and open quality of the texture shows skill in surface design, especially in the misted mountains. Not peaceful, not agitated, it is a work of scholarly caution.

In the following year, 1609, Kao Yang produced a landscape on silk (cat. no. 45) which shows him working on a new problem. The format and basic arrangement of the foreground are similar, but there is an attempt at re-forming, reworking the background. This attempt he pursues through a greater employment of fantasy and through a more conscious deployment of shapes. The traditional

mountain view is distorted by a shuffling of the conventional contours to leave a lacuna in the center of the composition. The loose, diamond-shaped superstructure allows Kao Yang to exploit the contrast between the stable imagery of the foreground and the distorted images at the top. It is important to keep track of the interplay between various kinds of line and the kinetic relationships which, interwoven, make up the large superstructure.

As against his panorama of 1608, this landscape is more complex, more comprehensive and ambitious. It is also more dramatic, though the modern viewer may find neither realistic nor aesthetically satisfying the tension between the two types of imagery, the one natural and stable, the other distorted and impulsive. These two planes of meaning are easier to develop independently. The landscape, in the end, teases the understanding; some questions stimulated by the drama remain unanswered.

The third Kao Yang painting (cat. no. 46) reveals another aspect of his work. The subject, two fantastic rocks, is not unusual in the late Ming, with its delight in the bizarre and the traditional. The notion of presenting uncommonly formed stone as a pseudo-mountain is an ancient one in China, and has a specialized literature dating from the twelfth century.[4] Paintings of large perforated garden rocks as an imposing part of landscape and figure compositions occur at least two centuries earlier.[5] During the late Ming period paintings using stones as their sole subject matter became inordinately popular. Kao Yang's reputation, oddly, appears to have been won largely as a painter of rocks. Many of his works in this genre passed over into woodblock prints and were preserved in the *Shih-chu chai shu-hua p'u*, a late Ming didactic manual on the painting of rocks, bamboo, orchids, and other natural objects.

Inherent in Kao Yang's painting of two rocks is the idea of a contrast that is at the same time a complement. The strong prominent stone on the left is generated by a complicated intertwining upon itself, producing much dexterity of surface within depth. The three-dimensional space defined is not completely closed; the gaps in the structure are many and varied. In contrast, Kao Yang defines the smaller rock on the right by a light surface reticulation over a closed, two-dimensional shape. This shape is not only a slick contrast, but a decisive complement as well, for the second rock echoes the shape of the first, balances the critical equipoise of the taller stone, and, together with the two miniature stones, establishes a supporting ground plane.

One is left in some doubt whether this curious genre of rock painting fully engaged Kao Yang's energies. It is not that his painting of two rocks lacks form, but that it lacks form of the traditional type that sustains, for example, the landscape of 1609. It is possible that the tradition of rock painting, with its concentration on brushwork and technique, had precipitated certain accepted intertwined shapes and gestures on the proposition that these would make up for the carefully structured conception that is lacking. It does not. Still, as a rock painting it is a success; but that is a success of a limited kind.

The third painter in this group is Wang Chien-chang, a man of prolific and varied talent, active in the Ch'ung-chen era (1628–1644). Although many of his paintings are known, most of them preserved in Japan, we know little of his life. Born in Fukien, he was reportedly a friend of Chang Jui-t'u, whose compositions at times resemble his. The three landscapes exhibited here give some idea of the range of his style.

His conservative side is seen in the undated landscape from the Ching Yüan Chai Collection (cat. no. 47). The composition is traditional in the sense that it incorporates many late Wu School elements characteristic of numerous other late Ming painters —a high viewpoint, several reiterations of the ground plane in the distance, tall mountains, lush trees, and a bridge in the foreground. Although the scope is wide and deep, and the carefully depicted forms are varied, the stability and unity of the composition depends on a careful and simple placement of the parts along a zig-zag line reaching from the lower left to the upper right of the painting. Relationships along this line are scrupulously maintained, gaps are carefully bridged, and tones deep-

ened at strategic points. Areas of definition are limited to spaces between angles of the ridge.

The competence of the artist is attested by the coherence of the design and the fully accomplished details. It is a pleasant painting, but not profound, not exciting.

The landscape painting dated 1628 (cat. no. 48) shows Wang Chien-chang attempting something less traditional and more exciting. Focusing on the middle ground of a more traditional landscape (one indeed like the previous painting), he amplifies it to a dramatic prominence. This takes the form of a distended yeast-like configuration which dominates the entire composition from the center, reaching into the foreground for support. To provide contrast with the abstracted character of this crucial area and to capture its vivid prominence, he surrounds it with more spatially conceived sections of descriptive detail which are all related by meandering shapes similar to those of the previous painting.

This is odd behavior for a painting, and from the standpoint of coherence it is not well made. It has elements of tension, placed to remind us of the tradition in a new way. But not much is there to bind the central configuration to its setting, so that the dramatic gesture becomes blunted, improbable, too self-consciously specialized in relation to its natural surroundings. It is not well done, but then, one is surprised to see it done at all.

The handscroll in the Seattle Museum, "The Isles of the Immortals on a Spring Morning" (cat. no. 49), dated 1638, a decade later, shows two salient characteristics not evident in Wang Chien-chang's previous paintings. The brushwork is more close-grained, more finely drawn, and the structure is more compressed. The key to the composition is a progressive angularization of shapes. This is its generating, its operating principle, and a significant aspect of the painting is how its structural elements cooperate to define its abstract idea.

The view at the opening is of a secure, well-regulated scene of rounded shapes, architecture, and fig-

ures. The first section, composed of three large mountains, is unified by a supporting curve set up by the first large mountain and culminating in an explicitly angular leaning rock in the foreground. Although this subtending curve appears to be supporting the second mountain, its more important function is to lead the viewer through greater and greater angularity to the dramatic abyss which terminates the curve. Progressive angularization and abstraction of forms, the leaning pointing shapes preceding the misted abyss, and now finally the dropping-off of the foreground are all marshaled by Wang Chien-chang to support the proper dramatic apprehension of the radically rectilinear and abstracted mountains on the left.

It is unfortunate that a textual emendation is not possible at the end of the handscroll, omitting the pavilions of the immortals—the clue for which is in the title of the painting. For the closely developed drama of the landscape proper does not end when Wang Chien-chang has nothing further to add, but with a totally unprepared afterthought. Yet even though the end is not compositionally valid, Wang's dramatic conception touches all the other elements with an excellence that at every moment makes us aware of the whole development of the action and of the relevance of all the parts to one another. For many of us, this is enough.

Cheng Chung was born in Anhui, an important painting center in the early Ch'ing period. He later moved to Nanking where he was active in the Ch'ung-chen era (1628–1644). His biographers mention that he copied Sung and Yüan styles, and painted figures and Buddhist images as well as landscapes. He was apparently a Taoist of meticulous tastes, following rituals of burning incense and drinking tea. It is said that he fasted and bathed before he lifted the brush.

Evidence of this fastidiousness for detail can be seen in the handscroll included here, dated 1632 (cat. no. 50). The painting is divided curiously into two halves, each showing a completely different formal structure and corresponding handling of scale—a close foreground view contrasted with a wider panorama. This loose conjunction of ideas might tentatively be offered as the key to Cheng Chung's notion of the total painting. But from a narrow application of the standard of unity, the integrity of the whole is seriously compromised in its disparate halves. The fact that Cheng Chung mentions in the colophon, dated six years later than the painting, that he spent several years working on the painting, may go a good distance to explain this problem.

The first half of the composition is divided into three parts. The first part is introduced by a calm, triangular section of water, bounded at the top by a half-concealed cliff slanting downward toward the left—a movement which prefigures that of the first large land mass and lends momentum to the forms. In the next section similar terrain is carefully organized into a large curved shape. The structure of the mountains is compressed, tense, and tightly wound, and based on curved repetitions of similar lines and shapes. The trees often provide a contrasting pattern in tone and texture to the spare cool line of the furrowed hills. In the third section of this half vertical, more dramatically abstracted hills are placed in another arc between water and a sharply cut-off mountain backdrop. This dramatic turn terminates the first half of the handscroll; and because of its intensification and prominence near the center of the composition becomes the dramatic focus of the total composition. This first half, arranged by a series of curved superstructures, at times loses its reference to reality in its contorted and abstracted patterns, but at the same time Cheng Chung pursues vivid detail in the genial figures and animals tucked into narrow crevices, caves, and dense groves of trees.[6]

The second half shares little with the first, other than the careful elaboration of detail. The close patterns and designs escalated and concentrated in the explicitly close foreground view give way to a calmer broader panorama contained within the edges of the painting. The scenic detail is no less carefully drawn, but it is used less insistently as abstracted pattern, and is more casually organized around four large areas of open space, cultivated land and architecture. Foliage and color echo this relaxation of the formal relationships by following the natural contours of the mountains.

Cheng Chung is skillful at converting a structural weakness into an acceptable style. For, in the end, it is his gift for detail and his technical accomplishment, not his structural imagination, which produce a work of great charm. This is what we attend to in the painting.

To begin a summary of these four painters it is useful to mention that in the colophon to the last work discussed, Cheng Chung modestly dedicates his work to Hsü Hung-chi, his patron and a well-known collector in Nanking. The reference is of interest not only because it establishes the relationship between the two men, but also because Hsü Hung-chi is the same person at whose home Wu Pin, Kao Yang, and Cheng Chung reportedly spent some time together on another occasion.[7] It is also important because none of the four painters had literary inclinations. None has left extensive colophons like Wang To, diaries like Ch'en Hung-shou, or critical treatises like Tung Ch'i-ch'ang—which makes the paintings themselves the more important. This conjunction in the lives of three of our four artists establishes some evidence of a common facing of the predicaments of the late Ming, as well as overtly suggesting the possibility of contrasting, if not comparing, their artistic achievements.

All four painters waver with some distress between three commitments: the tradition of the Wu School; the tradition of the Northern Sung; and a new, more fantastic mode just emerging in the early seventeenth century. In their milder, more conservative works each painter often depends for a repertory of forms and structures on the formulae developed by the followers of Wen Cheng-ming. Thus Kao Yang's 1608 landscape and Wang Chien-chang's landscape from the Ching Yüan Chai Collection are both efficient works, but many late Ming painters could have painted them and no doubt did. The more simple and solid superstructures of the Northern Sung, on the other hand, are more often called upon to organize and support more original, personal emotive fantasies. Wu Pin discloses a potential for dramatic possibilities in this tradition, never previously explored, which Kao Yang, Wang Chien-chang, and Cheng Chung did not fully acknowledge. He saw in the Northern Sung a force to stand against the formless expressionism of the average talent. This is not to say that emotional intensity, if not drama, is lacking in late Ming painting, but the required structure to subtend the emotion often is. Alongside Wu Pin, only Wang Chien-chang in his handscroll reveals an architectural gift for drama as a force penetrating deeply into the structure. A painting like his "Fantastic Landscape" is interesting but a structural failure, while Kao Yang's "Fantastic Landscape," though more dramatic, disappoints because he offers no comprehensive interrelated network of relationships to order the details.

It is easy to understate the values that sustain the paintings of these late Ming professionals. There are no reasons in the paintings to lead us to neglect them for a preeminent concern with either fantasy or the revival of a past tradition. Moreover, they all display a class of qualities not fashionable today—precision, elegance, consistency, propriety, measure.

Nevertheless, from the point of view of aesthetics to take no risks is the greatest risk of all. A comparison of Wu Pin, Kao Yang, Wang Chien-chang, and Cheng Chung reveals that Wu Pin took far greater risks; risks that probably would have been suicidal for Cheng Chung or Kao Yang. It is not only mere size, but the confidence with which Wu Pin entrusts all of his resources to the strength and accuracy of the structural relationships that stamps his paintings with his own individual signature. The muscles of structural restraint that he developed, if not great, are certainly large in their qualities.

It was of course a rear-guard action. It was too late in Chinese history to be a champion of permanence and stability and still expect to have followers. But Wu Pin was obstinate; and so Wu Pin was an end. It was not an uncommendable obstinacy. ∎

Notes
[1]Especially James Cahill. See *Fantastics and Eccentrics in Chinese Painting*, New York, 1968, pp. 28–36; and also "Wu Pin and his Landscape Paintings," a paper presented at the International

Symposium on Chinese Painting at the Palace Museum, Taipei, June, 1970 (in press). [2]Pien Wen-chin and Li Tsai, among others, were both from Fukien. [3]From *Ning-po fu-chih*...quoted in *Li-tai hua-shih hui-chüan.* [4]See for example Tu Wan's *Yün-lin shih-p'u* (translated by Edward Schafer, *Tu Wan's Stone Catalogue of Cloudy Forest,* Berkeley, University of California Press, 1961.) [5]Chao Yen's "Eight Riders on a Spring Outing," for example, a tenth-century painting. [6]The general layout of the composition itself shows some affiliations with the famous Wang-ch'uan Villa composition of Wang Wei. [7]Quoted in an edition of T'an Chüan's *Tsao-lin i-tsu,* once owned by Mr. Cheng Chi. Not included, however, in the editions seen first-hand.

42. Wu Pin (ca. 1568–1626). *Scenery on Mount T'ien-t'ai:*
handscroll section. Dated 1607. H. 11-3/4″. Honolulu
Academy of Arts.

43. Wu Pin (ca. 1568–1626). *Landscape.* 84-5/16 x 34-1/4″.
Ching Yüan Chai Collection.

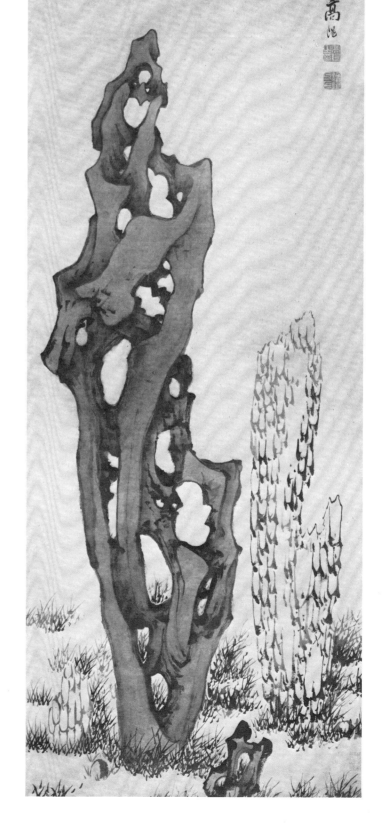

44. Kao Yang (active early 17th century). *Landscape with Waterfall.* Dated 1608. 79-1/4 x 17-3/4″. Ching Yüan Chai Collection.

45. Kao Yang (active early 17th century). *Rocky Landscape.* Dated 1609. 69-1/2 x 26-5/8″. Ching Yüan Chai Collection.

46. Kao Yang (active early 17th century). *Strange Rocks.* 52 x 22-1/4″. Collection Walter Hochstadter, Hong Kong.

47. Wang Chien-chang (active 1628–1644). *Searching for a Poem in the Mountain Shade.* 60-7/8 x 19-3/8″. Ching Yüan Chai Collection.

48. Wang Chien-chang (active 1628–1644). *Returning Home from Gathering Fungus.* 33-1/2 x 20″. Dated 1628. Private Collection, Chicago.

49. Wang Chien-chang (active 1628–1644). *The Isles of the Immortals on a Spring Morning:* handscroll section. Dated 1638. H. 7-11/16″. Seattle Art Museum.

50. Cheng Chung (active ca. 1610–1644). *Landscape:* handscroll
    section. Dated 1632. H. 11″. Collection Cheng Chi, Tokyo.

Calligrapher-Painter-Bureaucrats in the Late Ming

by Judith Whitbeck

Among the stylistic practices that were carried to further extremes in late Ming painting than ever before was the use of calligraphic styles. The art of calligraphy stressed the individual brushline—tense or relaxed, swift or slow, thick or thin, straight or curved—and the abstract configurations of the characters written with it as vehicles for personal expression, capable of provoking an emotional and aesthetic response. The same values could easily be transferred to painting. Typically, the artists who did so were the true amateurs, men whose primary commitment was elsewhere than to painting. Such amateurs could apply in their paintings the disciplined use of the brush that the practice of calligraphy had given them, and so had less need to learn the special techniques of painting that other styles would have required of them. Artists of this category in late Ming were often involved in political life; most of them served as officials, many in the second capital at Nanking. It is on these admittedly loose criteria—political involvement and the practice of calligraphic styles—that the painters treated in this chapter have been grouped together; they made up no local circle or true stylistic school of painting.

The aesthetic of calligraphy as personal expression, and the association of it with literati painting were not new in the late Ming; the former goes back at least to the Six Dynasties period, and the latter had been articulated by the poet, painter, and statesman Su Shih, or Su Tung-p'o (1056–1107). Su's principles were realized during the late Yüan period, in what one scholar has labeled an "aesthetic revolution."[1] Painting as a result became "more expressive than descriptive," lines and forms were used "to carry meaning somewhat independently" of what they represented.[2] The degree of emphasis put on calligraphic skill as the particular expertise of the literati painter, even at the expense of lyrical expression or realistic depiction of natural phenomena, however, is a distinguishing characteristic of this branch of late Ming painting.

This new emphasis can be credited in large measure to the crusading zeal of Tung Ch'i-ch'ang who assumed the role of spokesman for the amateur ideal in painting from the 1590s through the 1630s.

Tung, who was himself a major calligrapher, combined calligraphic skill with an equally strong emphasis upon the painterly concerns of form and structure. The group of painters who concern us here largely ignored the more difficult stylistic features of Tung's work, the clear sense of structural, interlocking relationships of forms and the incessant agitation of the brush. Although some may have adopted a few of Tung's stylistic devices, and were perhaps sensitive to the need for clarification and simplification, they never thought of Tung's innovations as a compelling system of ideas. For the most part they turned to painting as a pleasant diversion from their bureaucratic world. When they wanted to express momentum and energy in their landscapes, they tended to do so through the use of swift-moving lines, rather than through the dynamics of interlocking forms. With the exception of Mi Wan-chung, whose painting in this exhibition is less calligraphic than most of his others, these amateur artists hold more interest for us as calligrapher-painters than as painters per se.

Hsü Wei (1521–1593) preceded the rest of this group of amateur painter-politicians by at least two generations.[3] It is not only chronologically that he stood apart from the others, most of whom received wealth and social prestige through family inheritance or attainment of high political office. All but Yang Wen-ts'ung (1597–1646) received the highest degree obtainable through the civil service examinations. Hsü Wei only fleetingly knew gentry-style comfort. He sought, but never attained, bureaucratic office. Nevertheless, like these younger men, he aspired to serve his age and to live the "good life" of an articulate, independent man. Independence, with all its overtones of financial disinterest, self-expression, and cultivation of literary and aesthetic pursuits for one's own pleasure, lay at the core of the amateur's ethic.[4]

Hsü Wei was, to be sure, an amateur painter by temperament. He claimed to be, and was in fact, a versatile intellectual. He only turned to painting seriously in his later years—his dated paintings fall within the 1570s and 1580s. He disdained commercialism in art, and yet his precarious financial posi-

tion occasionally forced him to paint on demand for remuneration. It was perhaps to fend off any charge of professionalism that he developed his own "suffused-ink" style, within which virtuoso performances of an "amateur" character were possible. As he stated in one of this poems: "It is impossible for me to be a professional painter. Let the moss dots be poured and the banana leaves smeared."[5] Such deprecation of skill and precision was common among artists who claimed amateur status. But Hsü was not one of those, common enough in late Ming, for whom such assertions masked an actual ineptitude.

Hsü Wei was born to a moderately wealthy official family in Shang-yin (present day Shao-hsing, Chekiang). He traveled extensively from Canton to Peking, but spent most of his life in the region of Hang-chou, near his native home. Orphaned in his early teens, he thereafter experienced a series of misfortunes. He repeatedly failed the civil service examinations—his last attempt was in 1564. A lawsuit left him bankrupt in his early twenties and forced him to turn to professional writing of essays and dramas. Perhaps the crushing blow to his own ambitions and personal integrity was the imprisonment on extortion charges of his patron Hu Tsunghsien in the 1550s and his own subsequent hesitation to come to his patron's defense.[6] These misfortunes must have left psychic scars on this brilliant, sarcastic, and proud young man. By the time Hsü Wei turned to painting, he suffered from severe mental derangement.

By the 1570s Hsü Wei was well known for his dramas, which one Ch'ing critic compared to "a dragon in fury riding with the storm, twisting and turning in mid-air."[7] The same creative agitation found expression in his calligraphy (which he himself considered his greatest artistic achievement) and his paintings of flowers and bamboo. In the handscroll belonging to Mr. J. T. Tai (cat no. 51), Hsü Wei shuns the rashly energetic brushwork that characterizes some of his other paintings.[8] Though more reserved, his wet brushwork in the Tai scroll still reveals a striking tension between impetuosity and restraint.

In the section representing hibiscus, he creates a simple composition using asymmetry and dynamic contrast. There is little detail, and no sense of precision. The flowers move away from, and yet are balanced by, the vertical lines of calligraphy. The flattened forms of the hibiscus flowers and leaves are placed on a slender stem which arches upward and backward from the vertically placed, flattened leaves on the right. The contrast between fragile stem and weighty flowers is even more apparent in the chrysanthemum branch that extends beneath the hibiscus. Contrast is achieved not through mere difference in size of the parts, but rather through variation in quantity and tone of the ink, especially in the treatment of the leaves and flower petals of the hibiscus.

In another section of the scroll, Hsü Wei perhaps pays a playful tribute to those who gave him food in exchange for his paintings. The heavier compositional elements—the melon, crab, eggplant, pea pods, and bamboo shoots—frame a pair of informally arranged small fish. This entire section is in turn framed by the calligraphy on the right and the bamboo shoots and pea pods on the left. The eggplant, melon, and crab—like the hibiscus leaves—are executed with an unevenly inked brush, which produces a smoothly shaded stroke. For the pea pods and bamboo shoots, as for the chrysanthemum leaves, he first painted the main form in wet brushwork with dilute ink; then he dropped dark, rich ink into the wet area. This "suffused-ink" technique, for both smooth-single tone and layered tone, requires considerable skill. If too much ink is used or if the darker ink is dropped into the more lightly shaded wet area too soon, the image will dissolve beyond its boundaries of definition.

Through his "suffused-ink" technique, Hsü Wei transforms the flower painting style of the literati artist Ch'en Shun (1483–1544) whom he took as his model. Hsü Wei's own concern with personality in his dramas, his reflection on his personal fate, and his self-proclaimed status as an amateur artist conscious of the ethic of self-expression in painting, all suggest that his "suffused-ink" technique offered a means for expressing the precarious nature of defi-

nition and identity. His technique also offered him the means to realize the quality of "generous spontaneity" for which he praised the paintings of Shen Chou (1427–1509). The spontaneity and immediacy of Hsü Wei's paintings, on the other hand, go far beyond that of Shen Chou, being more reminiscent of the fruit and figure paintings of such Southern Sung Ch'an Buddhist painters as Liang K'ai and Mu-ch'i.

None of the other painters in this group consciously developed his own innovative technique, at least to the same degree as did Hsü Wei. For the most part, they borrowed heavily from the more serious artists among their contemporaries. For artistic inspiration they also turned to literati painters in the recent past, particularly Shen Chou and Wen Cheng-ming, as well as professional and literati painters in the distant past (Northern Sung and Yüan). As noted above, most of these amateur painter-politicians were involved, directly or indirectly, in the political struggles during the last two decades of the Ming. As a group they reveal varying levels of commitment to painting as a pastime activity and as an expressive vehicle. They represent two generations: those born in the 1570s, Mi Wan-chung and Chang Jui-t'u; and those born from the mid-1590s through the first decade of the seventeenth century, Yang Wen-ts'ung, Wang To, Tai Ming-yüeh, and Fang I-chih.

Mi Wan-chung was born around 1570 and died in 1628. The gazetteer of his native locale, Wan-p'ing in the environs of Peking, relate that he gained fame for his painting and calligraphy while still a young man.[9] Mi was considered one of the four best calligraphers of the late Ming.[10] A saying current at that time further testified to Mi's accomplishment: "Tung (Ch'i-ch'ang) in the south, Mi (Wan-chung) in the north."[11] These two wealthy high officials not only represented different regions, they also inclined toward different stylistic traditions in painting and different life styles. Unlike Tung, who lived in retirement during most of his adult years and gathered around him a coterie of literati artists, Mi turned to painting as an occasional, but serious diversion from his official responsibilities.

After receiving his *chin-shih* degree in 1595, Mi served as magistrate in various districts (1595–1607), and then as Secretary to various top ministries in Peking (1607–1610). He was subsequently promoted to posts of Commentator at Court, Overseer to Chekiang, and Judicial Inspector to Kiangsi (1610–1625). It might have been during this last period that Mi first became acquainted with the Nanking professional artist Wu Pin.

A chronicler who served in Nanking in the late Ming wrote that Mi Wan-chung "questioned and learned from Wu Pin from morning to night, so that their styles of painting became similar."[12] In 1615, Wu Pin painted a handscroll of Mi's garden, the Shao-yüan, located at the family estate.[13] Two years later, Mi himself painted a handscroll of Shao-yüan closely modeled on Wu Pin's original.[14] Both painters shared a keen interest in Northern Sung landscape style, naturalistically convincing detail, monumentality, and massiveness. Wu Pin worked toward the creation of dramatic fantasy and surprise in his landscapes by consciously distorting and interlocking forms and by denying spatial depth and clarity within a monumental, organically structural composition. Mi, however, moved from his concerns in the late 1610s in historically eclectic fashion. When he painted a truly monumental landscape in 1625, he emphasized greater spatial clarity, legibility and convincing systematic recession.

The huge hanging scroll dated 1625 and titled by the artist "The Paradise at Yang-so" (cat. no. 55) is Mi's most successful composition.[15] This landscape creates an effect of heroic majesty, stability, and solitude. The composition utilizes the traditional sequential vertical arrangement of early Chinese landscapes. Movement proceeds upward in steady measured cadence. The gaze of the viewer is drawn into the middle ground along a plateau projecting diagonally inward from the foreground tall trees. The vertical zig-zag movement up the mountainside is momentarily halted by the middle-ground plateau on which is set a group of empty houses. Movement is also arrested at this point by the scholar with a cane walking across the bridge. A sweeping S-curve starting in the middle ground focuses attention on the main mountain mass. The arc of the S-curve, formed by grouping together trees and boulders, gives a sense of three-dimensionality and solidity to the base of the mountain mass. This three-dimensionality is accentuated by the curve of the river around the base of the mountain. The shallow meandering river not only lends a certain stillness and languid quality to the overall design, but also suggests that it is a summer scene. The impression of solidity and stability remains undisturbed despite the outward thrust of the rocky masses from the main mountain peak. The slight forward tilt of the mountain face is meant to suggest communion between man and nature.

The painting itself is meant to be more evocative of solitude and withdrawal than descriptive of any one place. Unlike the monumental landscapes of the professionals Wu Pin, Kao Yang, and Wang Chien-chang and those of the amateur Chang Jui-t'u, this is a landscape into which one could walk, a place fitting for contemplation and repose. The evocative spirit of "Yang-so" perhaps embodied an intensely personal longing for Mi, a longing that is reflected also in the rather conventional poem inscribed on the painting. The last two lines of the poem (several characters of which are illegible through damage) can be freely rendered: "On the bridge separating water mallows and dwellings, who is the one burdened with grief? Is it not better to content oneself in repose than beat one's breast?"

Mi had reason to beat his breast in grief in the fateful year of 1625. In that year, the notorious eunuch Wei Chung-hsien had begun an extensive purge of officials believed associated with the Tung-lin Academy.[16] In Nanking, temples were being erected in Wei's honor by officials anxious to propitiate the eunuch's allies. When Mi passed through Nanking on his way from Kiangsi to the north in 1625, the Grand Commandant (himself a eunuch and the leader of the anti-Tung-lin faction in Nanking) reputedly asked Mi to contribute an essay praising Wei's virtue. The piece of calligraphy was then to be placed in one of these temples. Mi's biographer and a fervent defender of Wei's victims, the Ming loyalist Sun Ch'i-feng, recounted that Mi disdainfully

remarked to the messenger sent to obtain the essay: "How could I, an official for thirty years, with old age approaching, degrade myself (in this way)?"[17] For this rebuff, Mi's name was immediately struck from the civil service rolls. Only in 1628, with a new Emperor on the throne and Wei and his more outspoken partisans purged, was Mi's name restored to the rolls. The position then awarded him was that of Vice Minister of the Court of the Imperial Stud. The appointment meant official recognition for Mi's fame as a painter-calligrapher as much as for his former bureaucratic service, for in Ming times this agency was one in which several painters held sinecure positions.

Like Mi Wan-chung, Chang Jui-t'u (1576–1641) was both a *chin-shih* degree holder and a high bureaucratic official who made his name as a calligrapher.[18] Like Mi also, he sought to revive the monumental landscape style of Northern Sung, and associated with at least one professional artist resident in Nanking who had the same aim, his fellow townsman Wang Chien-chang; much of Chang's painting seems a more amateurish rendering of Wang's style. At this point, the similarity between Mi and Chang ends. Chang was a man from the south, born and raised in the port city of Ch'uan-chou in Fukien. A thriving commercial center until the prohibition of foreign trade in 1550, Ch'uan-chou continued to survive through illicit or severely restricted trade.[19] The cosmopolitan aura of the city had yielded to an oppressive insecurity by the late Ming. But the city was perhaps known for reasons other than its nefarious connection with black market trade during Chang's lifetime. Five years before Chang obtained his *chin-shih* degree, his fellow townsman Li Chih (1527–1602) died a martyr for his intellectual and moral convictions.

If Chang shared Li Chih's "final view of life as a 'sea of suffering'" (as his paintings suggest), he did not turn his back on the bureaucratic world.[20] Chang passed the palace examination with high honors (placing third among the first class) in 1607 and in that same year entered the Han-lin Academy. In 1627, Wei Chung-hsien summoned him to the Grand Secretariat. His tenure as Grand Secretary was brief,

for he fell victim to the purge of Wei's supporters under Emperor Ch'ung-chen in 1628. He was condemned to exile but bought himself free and returned to his native Ch'uan-chou. Almost all of his landscapes are dated after this, within his period of "exile."

Beyond an interest in monumentality, the paintings of Mi Wan-chung and Chang Jui-t'u have little in common. The grand scale, rational treatment of "Yang-so" is lacking in Chang's landscapes. Whether because of temperament or local tradition, Chang inclined more toward the excessive verticality and fantasy of Wu Pin and Wang Chien-chang. The label "fantastic," however, does not properly apply to Chang's pictures. His rigid structural simplicity checks rather than accentuates the contorted landscape forms which are set, not interwoven, into the composition.

Both of Chang's landscapes in this exhibition use the simple two-part composition in which the foreground elements are set along a diagonal, and the mountain, composed along an upward-winding "dragon-vein" movement, is centered in the upper portion of the picture. Both feature severely attenuated cypress trees, pine trees defined simply by a single stroke for the trunk and horizontal strokes for the foliage, and houses drawn in precise outline. The hanging scroll in the former Hobart Collection dated 1633 (cat. no. 53) seems stylistically earlier than the undated landscape in the Princeton University Art Museum (cat. no. 54). The Hobart landscape is a good example of the ethereal quality characteristic of Chang's paintings. One is more impressed with motion of line than movement in space. Static verticality is stressed, spatial recession denied. The foreground section is arranged along two diagonal bands, the narrow shore that leads toward the cliff facade and the river bed that extends into a misty forest. The "dragon-vein" mountain peak that dominates the background is set in very shallow space, and seems to press toward the frontal plane. The texturing is executed in dark, sinewy strokes repeated in parallel progression with slight variation in ink tone. Large areas of the cliff and mountain are left unshaded or lightly shaded.

Such texturing and shading technique imparts a withered quality to these forms. Their very flatness makes them appear insubstantial.

Chang is far more successful in evincing a mood of somber and ethereal monumentality in the Princeton hanging scroll. Only the scattered clusters of houses anchor the composition. The shape and arrangement of the other forms work together to accentuate verticality. The thrusting and contorted mountain forms in the foreground are shifted close to the frontal plane, and are separated from the far distance by the river. The mountain forms, although essentially flat, are densely textured. Long, single strokes of dark ink are applied to smooth washes of gray. Only tiny patches of the mountain surface are left untouched. Small ink dots are used not only to enrich the texture of the mountain forms but also to depict foliage in the valley and along the shoreline in the distance. The mists are rendered more convincing by contrast with the densely textured surfaces and graded ink washes. Chang is not so much concerned with forms as with the expressive effect that can be achieved through forms. Still less is he concerned with the dynamic structural relationship between forms.

Such lack of sensitivity or interest in complex ways of organizing a composition is even more apparent in the landscapes of Wang To (1592–1652).[21] In the "Mountain Landscape" dated 1651 belonging to Mr. Cheng Chi (cat. no. 55), the forms are all arranged to occupy an oval shape. Wu Pin uses a similar bound framework plan in his hanging scroll in this exhibition. But where in Wu Pin's scroll the forms move within that framework, in Wang To's they are static. Like Chang Jui-t'u's landscapes, this is a two-part composition: a large rounded hillock in the lower half is separated by mist from the rounded mountain peak in the upper half. This upper half is occupied by a series of mountaintops arranged in the same "dragon-vein" design to be seen in Chang's landscapes as well as in those of other painters working in Northern Sung derived styles. The rounded mountaintops are contrasted with small, triangular-shaped boulders nestled into the mountain ridge.

Wang To is more interested in calligraphic expression through brushwork than in defining solid forms or their interrelationships. A special feature of his brushwork, which relates it closely to his calligraphy, is his fondness for strokes that taper to points at both ends and are usually curved. This type of brushstroke, similar to the so-called "orchid-leaf" strokes, is apparent in the treatment of the mountaintops. The mountains are merely suggested with long and broad strokes of varied ink tone: the small boulders with dark, rich shorter strokes; the hillock in the foreground with long, thin, undulating strokes. The entire composition appears sketchy and exceedingly flat. The brushstrokes at the base of the mountains end so abruptly that the white area below cannot be read as mist. Nor can the mountain surface be clearly read as earth. Although the statement by Chang Keng that Wang's hills were painted without "wrinkles" applies to this landscape, the assertion that his mountains were "massive and lofty" does not.[22]

Chang Keng's praise of Wang's painting represents a tribute to a distinguished official noted for his poetry, painting, and pronouncements on aesthetics. The man brought fame to his painting rather than the painting adding much to the fame of the man. According to Chang Keng, Wang was "a man of noble character who inspired veneration by his height and his long beard...a man of broad learning who was fond of the ancients."[23] A native of Meng-chin, Honan, Wang received his *chin-shih* degree in 1622 and then entered the Han-lin Academy.[24] Like Tung Ch'i-ch'ang, he scrupulously avoided the partisan political controversies of the 1620s and 1630s. Like Yang Wen-ts'ung (1597–1646), he later served in the Ming loyalist regime of the Prince of Fu in Nanking (1644–1646), where he held the post of President of the Board of Rites.

Although he was not himself a partisan political spokesman, much of the "party spirit" characteristic of late Ming politics pervades Wang's critical pronouncements on painting. Chang Keng's praise might in fact be directed more toward the values of strength, vigor, and monumentality that Wang championed than toward their realization in his

painting. These values Wang attributed to the landscape style of Ching Hao (ca. 920), his student Kuan T'ung, and other early Sung masters such as Fan K'uan and Li Ch'eng. By the first decade of the seventeenth century, admiration for early Sung monumental landscape was widespread among professional artists resident in Nanking. One suspects that Mi Wan-chung's preeminence as a literatus and his ability as a painter lent much support to the vogue. It might have been some time between 1625 and 1628, during Mi's retirement, that Wang visited the Mi garden, the Shao-yüan. That he visited the garden is known from poems he wrote extolling it and pleading for understanding of the eremitic life.[25]

Unlike Mi, however, Wang To combined praise of early Sung masters with harsh denunciations of the insipid painting of the many followers of Ni Tsan (1301–1374). In an inscription on a painting attributed to Kuan T'ung in the Palace Museum Collection, Wang To contrasts the two styles:

> This is a genuine work of Kuan T'ung....It is finely detailed but richly mature in style, with a feeling of great expansiveness that goes beyond brush and ink. The works of a great master are substantial in this way. Artists of the lineage of Ni Tsan, on the other hand, compete over who can be thinnest and most mannered. When they have produced two trees, one stone, and a sandy bank, they acclaim it as "a landscape, a landscape!" Ching (Hao), Kuan (T'ung), Li (Ch'eng) and Fan (K'uan) were the ones who opened the gate.[26]

These were not words for public assertion alone. Wang expressed the same sentiments in a letter to his friend and fellow amateur painter Tai Ming-yüeh, a *chin-shih* of 1634 and President of one of the six boards in the Nanking regime (1644–1646): "In regard to paintings that are bland and without strong feeling such as the works of Ni Tsan, although such compositions are suffused with calm, they cannot avoid being dry and weak, like a sick man gasping for breath. Although they are called atmospheric and elegant, they are extremely insipid and limp. Great masters do not paint this way."[27] Wang To avoided the insipidity he so vehemently denounced, but lacked the technical ability to realize his aesthetic principles and achieve "substantial" works like those of the early masters.

Tai Ming-yüeh did attempt, on at least one occasion, to paint in the manner of Ching Hao. The painting, a mountain landscape dated 1647, bears an inscription by Wang To. Tai's earliest known painting, however, is of a different genre. This painting dated 1618, "Bamboo Bending Over a Rock" in the Ching Yüan Chai Collection (cat. no. 56) is a stylized and languid composition in ink on satin. The attenuated bamboo stem curves elegantly down over a small rock drawn in outline with dry ink. The painting of the bamboo leaves in rich, wet ink is based on Yüan prototypes.

Bamboo had been a favorite subject of literati artists since the eleventh century, both for its symbolic value and because the painting of bamboo posed the fewest representational problems for the amateur. Bamboo symbolically expressed sturdiness and steadfastness, cardinal virtues of Confucian statesmen. The bamboo, prunus, and pine were known collectively by the Chinese as the "Three Friends of Winter" and served to symbolize constancy in adversity.

The pine, a symbol of longevity as well as manly strength, courage, and endurance, was the favorite subject of the Ming loyalist Huang Tao-chou (1585–1646).[28] Legend relates that on the morning of his execution in 1646 he painted a long handscroll of pine trees. The undated handscroll representing "Three Scenes of Pines and Rocks" in the Osaka Municipal Museum, which could not be included in this exhibition, is the finest surviving example of Huang's strikingly expressionistic style. Huang clearly was not seeking to depict pines and rocks in nature. His intent is neither mere aesthetic play with brush and ink nor the portrayal of the structures of these natural objects. On the other hand, the scroll is something less than symbolic narrative or allegory, for Huang depicts different, non-sequential scenes.

In each scene, Huang uses the pine, symbolic of man's strength and will, and the rock, symbolic of

man's earthly existence, to exteriorize qualities or attributes. In one scene, he presents the pines and rock in sharp contrast: both the stately and stolid pine and the smaller one stand serene and unperturbed beside the fiercely deformed rock mass drawn with sharp, jagged brush strokes. In the next scene, the two forms are engaged: the pine stretches its branches around the boulder that juts upward from the rocky plateau, which itself merely defines a ground plane. The sense of struggle in the second scene gives way to a precarious equilibrium in yet another. Six pines stand upright, but insecure, on top of a skeletal rocky cliff. In contrast with the first scene, this last one negates life: the rocky cliff appears brittle and drained of all energy, the pines stunted. Although one cannot read this scroll as the artist's explicit historical or biographical statement, it clearly does express his concern with the contrast between human dignity and degradation, between forceful, purposeful energy and impotence. Such concerns have their antecedent in Huang's own involvement in the culture of his time, and in particular his public role as an idealistic and critical participant in the drama of late Ming politics.

Yang Wen-ts'ung (1597–1646), like Huang Tao-chou, died a martyr to the Ming cause.[29] Appointed to supervise the military affairs along the Yangtze in 1644, he fled to Fukien after the Manchu armies captured Nanking. When his army was defeated by the advancing Manchu forces, he refused to renounce his allegiance to the Ming. His partisan allegiance during the final decades of the Ming is much less easy to discern. His close friends included Hsia Yun-i (1596–1645), the Ming loyalist and political activist who organized a branch of the Fu-she called the Chi-she.[30] His family ties pulled toward the opposing faction, the supporters of Wei Chung-hsien, for his brother-in-law and fellow townsman Ma Shih-ying was a lifelong, intimate friend and classmate of Wei's henchman Juan Ta-ch'eng.[31]

Why Yang relied on the influence of his brother-in-law to obtain the appointment as Supervisor of Ming forces along the Yangtze in 1644 will perhaps never be known. Friends considered the move an outright betrayal, for as virtual dictator at the Nan-

king Court, Ma Shih-ying condoned the wholesale arrest of Fu-she members. Yang's action was immortalized decades later in the drama "Peach Blossom Fan," in which Yang is portrayed as the artist who painted the fan by converting bloodstains (of his friends) into peach blossoms.[32] Although it condemns Yang as a turncoat, the play testifies to Yang's former alliance with these Fu-she men and to the chief concern of his life, painting.

Painting was an appropriate concern for one inclined to minimalize political action. Yang was never conspicuous as a political partisan; and one suspects that his friendships with Fu-she members were based on common intellectual and aesthetic interests more than on shared political stands (though the two were never clearly separate in the late Ming). A native of Kuei-yang, Kuei-chou, Yang was raised in the Chiang-nan region where his father, a *chin-shih* of 1601, served as an official. After taking his *chü-jen* degree in 1618, Yang was appointed Director of Studies at Hua-t'ing, the district in which Tung Ch'i-ch'ang and his circle resided. Except for a brief tenure at the very end of the Ch'ung-chen period (1628–1644) as a magistrate in Chiang-ning, Nanking (a post which he reputedly received through his brother-in-law and from which he was dismissed in 1644 on charges of corruption), Yang spent his adult years among the literary and artistic circles in Hua-t'ing. Some time after his appointment at Hua-t'ing, Yang began to study painting with Tung Ch'i-ch'ang and became known as one of the "Nine Friends in Painting," the doyen of which was Tung himself.[33] By 1630, Yang had already become well known as a painter-calligrapher in the Yangtze valley area. The connoisseur Chou Liang-kung even claimed "Yang's genius exceeded that of his teacher (Tung Ch'i-ch'ang)."[34] The amateur painter and Fu-she activist Fang I-chih offered more measured praise: "Of my generation, Yang was one of the three most wonderful at using ink ... with his own talented style, he mastered and went beyond the traditional method, not repeating the styles of Yün-chien and P'i-ling."[35]

The hanging scroll in the Nelson-Atkins Gallery dated to the autumn of 1643 (cat. no. 57) is typical of Yang's small landscapes. In his inscription, Yang relates that during a visit to a friend's home he looked at a painting by Shen Chou. Inspired by the unexcelled spontaneity of Shen Chou's composition, achieved with minimal use of brush and ink, Yang sought to express these qualities in his own painting. One is not so much impressed with motifs borrowed from Shen Chou's version of Ni Tsan style as with the overall unruffled tranquility of the scene. The composition represents a poetic and graceful harmony between brushwork and scenic representation. Nothing is overly embellished; the contours of the distant hills are delineated with long, unbroken, firm, yet gentle brushstrokes. The rocks on the near shore are drawn with heavier ink. Even the sparse trees are poignant without being harsh. There is nothing of the austerity and vigor, nor of the dynamic momentum of forms, that characterizes many of Tung Ch'i-ch'ang's paintings. Wang To, always more astute as a critic than as a painter, aptly commented on Yang's work: "His brush carried vaporous moisture like (the music of) a bamboo pipe, distant and remote."[36]

The remoteness, refinement, and sophistication apparent in Yang's paintings were given different expression by the youngest member of this group, Fang I-chih.[37] Like Yang, Fang came from a wealthy official family and his father also held the *chin-shih* degree. A native of T'ung-ch'eng in Anhui Province, Fang received the *chin-shih* degree in 1640. He was then appointed to the Han-lin Academy and assigned to tutor the third son of the Prince of T'ang (who ruled in Fukien from 1645 to 1646). In February of that same year, his father, Fang K'ung-chao, was censured, imprisoned, and then exiled to southeastern Chekiang.[38] But he was recalled in 1642 and made supervisor of military settlements in Chihli-Shantung. When Peking fell to the invading Manchus, Fang I-chih went south to join the Prince of Fu's regime in Nanking, but found the court dominated by Ma Shih-ying and Juan Ta-ch'eng. When Juan initiated the arrests of Fu-she members, Fang, who was implicated in the movement, fled to the southeast disguised as a drug peddler. In 1647, when little hope remained for the Ming cause, he received the tonsure and adopted the monastic

name Hung-chih, and the monastic style name Wu-k'o, by which he was commonly known. His friend Chou Liang-kung, who took his *chin-shih* in the same year as Fang, chronicles Fang's personality:

> As a youth he was a child prodigy...and obtained his *chin-shih* while still a young man. He ranged from poetic essays, drama songs, calligraphy, painting, literary games, and divination to the arts of playing wind instruments, beating the drum, and acting. He was extremely refined and sophisticated. Before he was thirty he was completely carefree....When he became a tonsured monk he cultivated the life of solitude, wearing coarse clothing and eating coarse food. No one lived in greater poverty. He cut himself off from others and occasionally would indulge his interest with some poems or paintings. He wrote many sutras which he chanted, but they were obscure to all but himself.[39]

The change that Chou recorded—from carefree, indulgent aesthete to somber, obscure eremitic—was not uncommon among Ming loyalists, though perhaps Fang's case was more extreme than most.

"Mountains by a River" in the Ching Yüan Chai Collection dated to the summer of 1642 (cat. no. 58) imparts a feeling of delicate coolness and refinement. It is executed in still another late Ming derivative of the Huang Kung-wang manner.[40] The whole composition is disposed within a triangular area from which the lozenge-shaped foreground projects outward. The outline drawing anticipates that of another Anhui painter, Hung-jen (1610–1664), who like Fang became a Buddhist monk. Cleanness, clarity, and the denial of solid substance, except what is implied in the linear construction, describe the paintings of both men. Hung-jen, however, uses linear, geometric forms to create a bleak and powerful composition. Fang's composition is stark but mild. Such feeling is suggested only in part by the nature of the outline drawing. The tall, oblong mountain forms gently swerve without thrusting; they are compactly set into smaller rectangular forms. Sparsely drawn trees are interspersed on the mountain top. It is the contrast between geometric forms that arrests the viewer's eye: cones, rectangular polyhedrons, and trapezohedrons. And these forms, as noted, are arranged within geometrically conceived areas. Unlike most other painters in this

group, Fang is not concerned with calligraphic virtuosity. His brush, dipped into light ink, is applied to the paper with a firm, steady, relaxed hand in a most understated way. By bringing together the foreground and middle ground in very shallow space and by making the trees half the height of the mountain, Fang has converted a monumental theme (the mountain landscape) into an intimate scene.

All of these amateurs can be related to certain local areas or to past traditions. Hsü Wei, a native of northeastern Chekiang, used as his model the paintings of Ch'en Shun, who lived in nearby Wu-hsien, Su-chou. Yang Wen-ts'ung was among Tung Ch'i-ch'ang's circle of amateur painters in Sung-chiang, Hua-t'ing, and perhaps as a consequence of this association, was more insistent than others in this group on making his brushwork accentuate the quality and direction of the form he was depicting. Huang Tao-chou, a native of Fukien, spent many years in Chekiang. In a loose way, Huang's brushwork suggested the harsh and jagged quality found in the Che School painters of the late sixteenth and early seventeenth century. Fang I-chih, a native of Anhui, shared with his fellow provincials Ch'eng Chia-sui and Hung-jen the immaculate and geometric quality that suggests a local Anhui style. Chang Jui-t'u gave less rigorous expression to the style of painting of his friend and fellow townsman, the professional painter Wang Chien-chang. The men from the north, Mi Wan-chung, Wang To, Tai Ming-yüeh, shared with professional painters in Nanking (some of whom were natives of Fukien) an interest in the monumental landscapes of the Northern Sung. The very number and variety of school styles reflects an important aspect of late Ming painting. Also significant, in this ecological sense, is the association of amateurs with professionals or with other literati who engaged in painting in a sustained and serious way. With the exception of Hsü Wei, the styles of these amateurs were derivative, not innovative.

Neither local style nor past tradition provides a satisfying explanation of these stylistic differences. No one local area served as the orbit of their bureaucratic and artistic activity. But more important, a shared assumption affirms their work as individual amateurs (although many professionals also shared this assumption) and denies any stylistic grouping in terms of locale. This shared assumption, the basic tenet of the literati ideal in painting, was simply that painting involved individual expression rather than faithful representation of nature and natural forms. Obviously, one cannot draw from these paintings any detailed evidence about the specific activities or the precise philosophic school of the painter. Nor can one in the end, and contrary to the Chinese assertion, determine the moral character of a man from his handling of brush and ink. Indeed, one even suspects that the Chinese themselves rather read what they knew of the person into his paintings. Chang Keng's praise of Wang To serves as a case in point.

When amateurs argued that painters should "write the idea" *(hsieh-i),* this meant, first of all, that they should communicate something of their personality, temperament, orientation to the world, or their beliefs, aspirations, and ideals. In an age when literature reflected an increasing awareness of personal idiosyncrasy and psychology, one would expect that painters were more than ever conscious of these extra-aesthetic, expressive concerns. The passage from ideal to achievement—in painting as in the other arts—requires expertise, which is seldom acquired without disciplined and persistent activity. Yet, even when a verbally expressed ideal is not transformed into achievement, or when only the paintings themselves exist to speak for that painter's intent, one is told something through the composition and subjects chosen, the structural relationships and calligraphic style employed. What then can one find in the paintings of these amateurs that offers us some personal testimony, beyond the aesthetic act itself? The works in this exhibit by Hsü Wei, Mi Wan-chung, Chang Jui-t'u, Yang Wen-ts'ung, Wang To, and Fang I-chih tell us something (and for each, something different) which has personal significance.

Hsü Wei, the frustrated aspirant for political office, was the only one of the painters in this group who worked for pay, insofar as he accepted food and wine in exchange for his paintings. Perhaps to avoid

the stigma of the professional (catering to others' tastes) and to affirm his allegiance with the literati, he chose motifs associated with the amateur artists as vehicles for the expression of his personal concern with the tenuous nature of individual existence and identity. Hsü sought neither to defy nor to defile identity. He rather represented, through his "suffused-ink" technique, the integrity of individual identity at the point where it threatened to go beyond the boundaries of definition. He asserted identity against, but in dim awareness of, its possible dissolution into the imperceptible and the dissolved.

Mi Wan-chung's "Paradise at Yang-so," certainly the sustained activity of one who truly loved to paint, communicates solitude, serenity, stability, and clearly perceptible measured movement. These qualities are not abstracted from reality, but are communicated through the palpable reality of "Yang-so." To extract a more definite personal meaning, one must read the painting in conjunction with Mi's life in the context of late Ming society. Whether through coincidence or conscious intent, Mi painted "Yang-so" in the same year that he was dismissed for refusing to lend his hand in praise of the eunuch Wei Chung-hsien. If painted before his dismissal, one cannot interpret the work as expressing a heroic withdrawal into solitude.

But, whether painted before or after his dismissal, "Yang-so" testifies to Mi's orientation in that crisis. He must have appreciated the stillness and majesty of nature not as a spur to bold, innovative action (as does Mao Tse-tung), but as an ordered and congenial setting for solitary contemplation and repose. This was a man who lived not for the moment, but with a sense of the orderly changes of time. "Yang-so," like Mi's garden Shao-yüan, was a "magic garden" retreat apart from the political world. One suspects that such a man would hardly be inclined toward group action. The independence, the standing alone, and the sure sense of purpose, both of which are expressed in "Yang-so," seem consistent with what we know of Mi's action in 1625, for this proud scholar-official could not be flattered into paying homage to one he must have despised. And yet, Mi went no further than refusal. To be sure, the

qualities of serene solitude and restrained, deliberate action, evoked through "Yang-so," which is both in time (summer) and out of time (eternal), expressed Mi's highest ideals and orientation to the world. To live these ideals and to maintain one's independence took Mi out of political controversy and into the eremitic life.

There is nothing grand or majestic in the intellectual landscapes of Chang Jui-t'u, Yang Wen-ts'ung, or Fang I-chih. The sense of loving involvement with natural scenery, so apparent in "Yang-so," is lacking in these paintings. Does this presage an alienation from nature? Has the idea superseded an immediate feeling for landscape? One is inclined to answer yes in both cases.

In the Princeton hanging scroll, Chang manipulates the landscape elements to achieve a definite expressive effect—pessimistic, somber, brooding, and ethereal. We have seen how the placement of the contorted and attenuated forms and their texturing work toward this end. Seen as a view of life, the painting is consistent with the disillusionment that follows lost splendour and glory. Chang does not affirm another, more lyrical world where the glorious past can be relived. Almost harshly, he negates the existing world—denying it substance and solidity, poetry and light. Here, too, one finds consistency between the man, disgraced for his connection with eunuch Wei, and his work during his "exile."

The paintings of Yang Wen-ts'ung and Fang I-chih suggest that they shared Chang's reluctance to affirm the world of palpable reality. Rather than manipulate forms so as to deny worldly existence, they delineated the contours of forms so as to present clearly ordered and immediately apprehensible scenes. Their concern was more with principles of order than with an ordered composition through which they could enrich the viewer's emotional feeling for nature. Nevertheless, their paintings communicate certain qualities—refinement, tranquility, deliberate restraint, and remoteness—which are consistent with their own genteel, cultured elite backgrounds, their intellectual commitments, and their reluctance to involve themselves in the political activities of their troubled times. Yang stayed out of extra-government politics, preferring instead the personal, literary, and artistic relationships of his local area. Fang shied away from taking a conspicuous position in any political crisis and even debated the value of participation in government service. His most forthright public action constituted a direct response to an immediate and personal crisis—his filial protest against the incarceration and threatened execution of his father.

Chang Jui-t'u, Yang Wen-ts'ung, and Fang I-chih shared with Wang To a disregard for, or insensitivity to, substantiality. In the Princeton painting, Chang Jui-t'u denied substance by his rendering and texturing of forms. Both Yang and Fang used line to depict abstract structures, and thus reduced or eliminated the more tactile treatment of surfaces. In Wang To's "Mountain Landscape" (as in Chang's 1633 hanging scroll and Huang Tao-chou's "Pines and Rocks") activity replaced substance; by insisting on the integrity of individual strokes and by executing each stroke with decisive strength and boldness, Wang disembodied the forms of his composition, turning mass into movement. We are here presented with the calligrapher-painter as a man of action, exalting activity and power. And, what is more, we are reminded that the literati ideal in painting was not merely to express oneself, but to communicate as a literate intellectual through a kind of "writing"; and for this, calligraphic styles were best suited. ■

Notes

[1]Sherman Lee, "The Art of the Yüan Dynasty," in Sherman Lee and Wai-kam Ho, *Chinese Art Under the Mongols: The Yüan Dynasty (1279–1368)*, Cleveland Museum of Art, 1968, pp. 51–52. [2]James Cahill, *Fantastics and Eccentrics in Chinese Painting*, New York: Asia Society, 1967, p. 10. On Tung Ch'i-ch'ang, see *ibid.*, pp. 16 and 19; and Wen Fong, "Tung Ch'i-ch'ang and the Orthodox Theory of Painting," *National Palace Museum Quarterly*, II:3 (1968), 1–26. [3]Hsü Wei's style name was Wen-chang and his long series of fancy names (*hao*) included Wen-ch'ing, Ch'ing-teng, and Shui-t'ien-yüeh. [4]On the sociological and cultural meaning of this ethos, see Joseph Levenson's brilliant essay, "The Amateur Ideal in Ming and Early Ch'ing Society: Evidence from Painting," in *Modern China and Its Confucian Past: The Problem of Intellectual Continuity*, New York, 1964, pp. 19–55. [5]Cited in Yu-ho Tseng, "A Study on Hsü Wei," *Ars Orientalis*, V (1963), 253. The biographical information here is drawn from Tseng's article. [6]Hu was Chief Censor and later Commander-Governor of the seven southeast coastal provinces in the 1550s with the responsibility for suppressing the Japanese pirates along the coast. He was denounced by the Grand Secretary Yen Sung. [7]Cited in Tseng, 251 (see note 5). [8]For instance, the handscroll in the Nanking Museum and sections of the handscroll now in the Freer Gallery of Art. Both are reproduced in Tseng (see note 5). [9]Mi's style was Chung-hao and his fancy name was Yu-shih. This extract from the Wan-p'ing gazetteer can be found in Hung Yeh, *Shao-yüan t'u-lu k'ao*, Harvard Yenching Indices Series, Supplement 5 (1933), 3. Hung has gathered extensive biographical material on Mi from various sources. For a brief biographical account of Mi's life, see Arthur Hummel, editor, *Eminent Chinese of the Ch'ing Period*, Washington, D.C., U.S. Government Printing Office, 1943, pp. 572–573. [10]The others were Tung Ch'i-ch'ang (1555–1636), Chang Jui-t'u (1576–1641), and Hsin T'ung (1551–1612). Tung and Chang were from the south, Hsin from the north. [11]Lan Ying and others, *T'u-hui pao-chien hsü-tsuan*, chüan I, p. 8. [12]Chiang Shao-shu, *Wu-sheng-shih shih*, chüan VI, p. 67. [13]Sections of this handscroll have been reproduced in H. C. Weng, *Gardens in Chinese Art*, New York, China House Gallery, 1968, pp. 14–15. [14]Mi's version has been reproduced in Hung, *Shao-yüan* (see note 9). [15]Yang-so is located near the eastern border of Kwangsi Province. The early T'ang poet and essayist Han Yü had written on the exquisite scenery of this area. Mi might have traveled there during his tenure at Kiangsi. [16]On the Tung-lin, see above, pp. 00–00. [17]Cited in Hung, *Shao-yüan*, p. 4. This extract is from Sun Ch'i-feng's (1585–1675) collection of biographies on distinguished personalities in Chih-li, written in 1658. [18]Chang's style was Ch'ang-kung and his *hao* included the names of Erh-shui and Po-hao-an. This biographical information on Chang is chiefly drawn from Osvald Siren, *Chinese Painting, Leading Masters and Principles*, London, 1956–1958, vol. V, pp. 47–49. [19]De Bary, William Theodore, "Individualism and Humanism in Late Ming Thought," in *Self and Society in Ming Thought*, New York, 1970, pp. 188–189. [20]*Ibid.*, p. 213. [21]Wang's style was Chüeh-ssu; he also had at least a score of fancy names. [22]Chang Keng, *Kuo-chao hua-cheng lu*, Part I, p. 21. [23]*Ibid.* [24]This biographical information on Wang is drawn from Siren, *Chinese Painting*, V, pp. 56–57. [25]Three such poems can be found in Hung, *Shao-yüan*, pp. 23, 24, and 41. The first can be rendered: "Removed from residential areas is this quiet place. The twisting snake [movement of the water canal] resembles [the scene in] a Chekiang village. / Pools of water wash the roots of the exotic orange trees from Hua county [in Kiangsi]. / The soil is rich, a soft breeze whispers through the pavilion. The inclining sun casts its rays through the dense woods, the mountains are bathed in twilight. / One should not despise those lofty eremitics. / Ever since ancient times they have loved their gardens." [26]I am indebted to James Cahill for bringing this inscription to my attention and for providing the translation. [27]Chang, *Kuo-ch'ao*, p. 22. A slightly different version of this letter can be found in Siren, *Chinese Painting*, V, p. 57. Tai was a native of Ts'ang-chou, Hopei. [28]For biographical information on Huang, see Hummel, *Eminent Chinese*, pp. 345–346 (see note 9). [29]Yang's style names were Lung-yu (friend of dragons) and Shan-tzu (son of the mountains). This biographical information is drawn mainly from Hummel, *Eminent Chinese*, pp. 895–896, and supplemented with accounts from Chou Liang-kung, *T'u-hua-lu*, chüan III, pp. 37–38. [30]Hsieh Kuo-chen asserts that the Chi-she (The Inception Society) was formed in the mid-1630s with the explicit intention of avoiding the political conflicts in which the Fu-she had become involved. The Chi-she was an outgrowth of a local Sung-chiang literary society and maintained its original identity as a personal and literary grouping. Hsieh Kuo-chen, *Ming Ch'ing chih chi tang-she yün-tung k'ao*, Shanghai, 1935, pp. 187–190. [31]For Ma's biography, see Hummel, *Eminent Chinese*, p. 558; for Juan's, *ibid.*, pp. 398–399 (see note 9). Together, these two men dominated the Nanking court (1644–1646). [32]The play was written by K'ung Shang-jen in 1699. The hero of the play was Hou Fang-yu, a close friend of Fang I-chih. For accounts of Hou and K'ung, the poet and artist, see Hummel, pp. 291–292, 434–435 respectively (see note 9). [33]The epithet was coined by Wu Wei-yeh (1607–1672). The nine friends also included Li Jih-hua, Li Liu-fang, Shao Mi, Pien Wen-yü, Ch'eng Chia-sui, Wang Chien, Chang Hsüeh-tseng, and Wang Shih-min. [34]Chou, *Tu-hua-lu*, chüan III, p. 37. [35]*Ibid.*, p. 38. Yün-chien refers to the Sung-chiang style. P'i-ling was the ancient name of Chin-ling, a district in present day Nanking. [36]Chou, *Tu-hua-lu*, chüan III, p. 38. [37]Fang (1611–1671) was styled Mi-chih. This biographical information is drawn from *ECCP*, pp. 232–233; and Willard James Peterson, "Fang I-chih's Response to Western Knowledge," Doctoral dissertation, Harvard University, 1970, pp. 1–33. [38]Fang's father was Governor of Hu-kuang at the time of his arrest by Yang Ssu-ch'ang, the leader of the faction opposed to the Fu-she. The arrest was a political one and was soon reversed, but only after Fang I-chih himself wrote a memorial written in blood pleading for his father's release, and almost daily prostrated himself and wailed outside the gate of the Court in Peking. These filial actions won the admiration of the Emperor, who ordered Fang's father released. See Peterson, pp. 22–23, for a fuller account of this incident. [39]Chou, *Tu-hua-lu*, chüan II, p. 23. [40]See above, Mo Shih-lung's picture, cat. 32.

Three More Nanking Painters
by Patricia Berger

Three painters working in or near Nanking in the early and mid-seventeenth century are forerunners of a larger group of individualist artists and intellectuals in Nanking in the early Ch'ing period, of whom the central figure was Chou Liang-kung (1612–1672), and the leading painter Kung Hsien (died 1689). These three were Hu Yü-k'un, Yün Hsiang, and Tsou Chih-lin.

Hu Yü-k'un came from an old Nanking family of painters,[1] a family which had in recent generations taken no part in official life. His uncle was Hu Tsung-jen, a painter of some renown in his own day, nearly forgotten now. Five other members of the family were painters. Hu Yü-k'un met Chou Liang-kung in 1641, and Chou remains the best source of information on him.[2] An individualist who is placed by Chinese critics in the "untrammeled class" of painters, Hu is represented in the exhibition by an album of twelve leaves, probably painted in 1614–1615 (cat. no. 59). The compositional inventiveness of all the leaves, coupled with a purposeful naiveté, makes them a delight. The second leaf provides a bird's-eye view over an expanse of blossoming peach trees and water, making daring use of ambiguities of mass and void. The composition, that is, can be read either as solid and void or as pattern and non-pattern; there is little sense of real mass. Hu's fondness for patternization becomes more obvious as the album continues. The third leaf, after Li Ch'eng, turns the classic motif of gnarled and twisted trees into another tangle of pattern. In the fourth, Hu pushes almost all the matter of the painting to the bottom of the page and only hints at the continuance of the mass into the center, where it is pinned down by a tiny building. This odd compositional trick is used also by Kung Hsien in a few of his small pictures. Chou Liang-kung wrote of Hu's talent for using voids in his paintings:

> Li Chün-shih (Jih-hua) used to say: In painting, only the areas of void are really difficult. As far as I have seen, the only painter good at using void is . . . Hu Yü-k'un, Ch'ang-pai's (Tsung-jen's) nephew. He was untrammeled by nature and so was his painting. In his brushwork and use of colors he loved to depict diffuse, formless voids. As a result, within a fraction of an inch, one could imagine a thousand miles of distance.[3]

Several of the leaves are devoid of form, with only textured space. Hu Yü-k'un's methods were simple and his aims modest and playful. As Kung Hsien wrote in a letter to Hu: "Brush and ink as you use them have a special flavor, outside the orthodox paths. Everything is achieved smoothly and spontaneously. You can transcend the commonplace and escape from vulgarity."[4]

Yün Hsiang, whose original name was Yün Pen-ch'u, lived in Wu-chin near Wu-hsi on the Grand Canal, but seems to have been well known in Nan-ing intellectual circles as well. He was born in 1586 and died in 1655. Endowed with a classical education, he held a post in the Secretariat for a time. Critics say that in his early years he followed the traditions of Tung Yüan and Chü-jan, but later in life turned to the Yüan masters Ni Tsan and Huang Kung-wang as models, and used ink only sparingly. He was an independent artist with no school affiliations.[5] He is represented in the exhibition by a hanging scroll, painted in ink on paper, from the collection of Mr. and Mrs. C. D. Carter (cat. no. 60). His stylistic debts to Chü-jan, Ni Tsan, and Huang Kung-wang are clearly apparent. The soft *t'u-shan* or "earth mountains" from Chü-jan's repertory are built up in intervals to flat-topped plateaus in a manner reminiscent of Huang Kung-wang. He uses his ink in a dry manner, like Ni Tsan, relying chiefly on outlines, rarely indulging in washes. What is more interesting than his indebtedness to the past is his anticipation of certain later painters such as the Anhui masters Hung-jen, Yao Sung, and even Tai Pen-hsiao. Like them, he creates a monumental, towering, substantial landscape structure within a very limited format and with very limited materials. His approach is an extension of the formalism of Tung Ch'i-ch'ang. His structures, precipitous mountains connected by linear waterfalls, anticipate also Kung Hsien; but where Kung heightens the complexity of his compositions with wet, dense brushwork, Yün Hsiang's compositions retail qualities of lucidity and transparence through his very restrained use of ink. Even Kung Hsien admired this element of his painting, saying: "Most painters are controlled by their brush and ink, but Tao-sheng [Yün Hsiang] is one who is in control of his brush and ink. He has what may be called an 'unattainable simple-mindedness.'"[6]

Tsou Chih-lin was also from Wu-chin. He took his *chin-shih* degree in 1610 and was given a post, according to one source, as an assistant in the Board of Punishments; another source says it was in the Board of Works.[7] He later left the capital, having been unable to govern his quarrelsome temperament, and went to Nanking. In his painting he followed Huang Kung-wang, a fact amply attested by an album of landscapes in the collection of Mr. H. C. Weng (cat. no. 61). The album is remarkable in its spareness. All textures, save those of a few unmodulated washes, are eliminated. The design is blocked out by thick, wet, smooth lines, of which slight variations in breadth provide intellectual clues to differences in surface and form. Kung Hsien in his *Hua-chüeh* discussed this sort of painting: "In literati painting, there is one variety that has no texture strokes *(ts'un)*. In this, one only repeats (builds up) the contours. If this repetition of contour is done in a slightly dry manner, the result resembles texture strokes. In going over the contours, you mustn't muddy up the prior drawing. It must be deliberate and yet as if careless, so that it naturally isn't muddy and naturally doesn't depart. On the one hand, this doesn't detract from broadness of manner; on the other hand, the drawing seems all the more fine (detailed). It appears confused but isn't confused; it has both strength and spirit."[8] In this manner, Tsou Chih-lin paints nine leaves that are intellectualizations of motifs familiar from Huang Kung-wang's "Fu-ch'un Mountains" scroll. The traditional relationships of flat-topped mass to rounded mass, of dynamic solid to precipitous void, of foliage to rock, all these are *a priori* assumptions taken by the artist. He need only delineate roughly the direction of his thinking. Since his audience is inculcated into the same restricted set of expectations as he is, his work is readily understandable as a sort of minimized coded exchange. By partaking to such a full extent of the clique-ish restrictions of his day, Tsou Chih-lin exemplifies the artist in the late Ming, whose object was not to have any sort of universal appeal, but rather to establish himself within a small, exclusive and impenetrable social sphere. ■

Notes

[1]*Tu-hua lu*, in *Hua-shih ts'ung-shu*, chüan II, pp. 20–22, for information on Hu Yü-k'un; see also chüan II, pp. 19–20, for Hu's uncle Hu Tsung-jen. [2]In Chou Liang-kung's *Tu-hua lu*; see *Hua-shih ts'ung-shu*. [3]*Tu-hua lu*, chüan II, p. 20. Translation by John Hay from unpublished manuscript. [4]*T'an-i lu*, in *Mei-shu ts'ung-shu*, III, 10.15a. [5]*Kuo-ch'ao hua-cheng lu*, A, p. 6, and *Wu-sheng-shih shih*, chüan IV, p. 24. [6]*T'an-i lu*, p. 15a. Translated by James Cahill, "The Early Styles of Kung Hsien," *Oriental Art*, XVI:1 (1970), 56. [7]*Kuo-ch'ao hua-cheng lu*, A, p. 7; and *Wu-sheng-shih shih*, chüan IV, p. 11. [8]*Ch'ai-chang-jen hua chüeh*, in *Hua-yüan pi-chi* edition, p. 4a–b. Translated by James Cahill, *op. cit.*, p. 59.

51. Hsü Wei (1521–1593). *Bamboo, Flowers, Vegetables and Fishes:* handscroll section. H. 11-5/8″. Collection J. T. Tai, New York.

52. Mi Wan-chung (before 1575–1628). *The Paradise Landscape of Yang-so.* Dated 1625. 135-5/8 x 40-1/8″. Stanford University Museum of Art; Gift of the Committee for Art at Stanford.

53. Chang Jui-t'u (1576–1641). *Mountains and Misty Forest.* Dated 1633. 48 x 15-3/4″. Collection Mr. and Mrs. Henry Brandon, Washington, D. C.

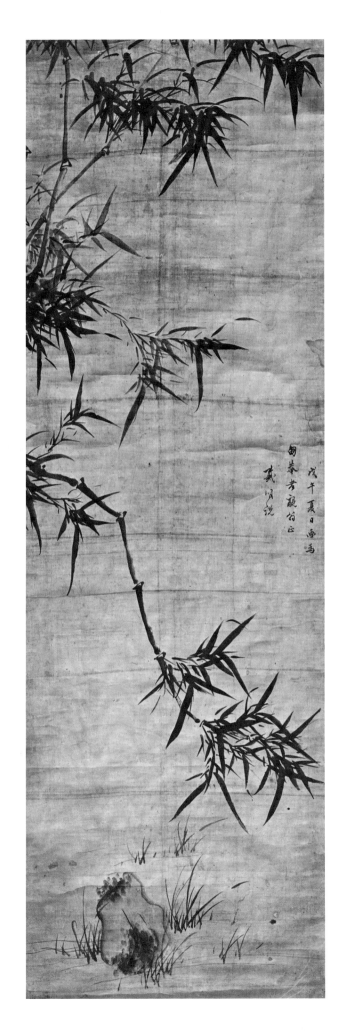

55. Wang To (1592–1652). *Mountain Landscape.*
    69-3/4 x 17-1/8″. Collection Cheng Chi, Tokyo.

56. Tai Ming-yüeh (ca. 1600–after 1656). *Bamboo Bending
    Over a Rock.* Dated 1618. 66-1/4 x 19-3/8″. Ching Yüan
    Chai Collection.

54. Chang Jui-t'u (1576–1641). *Mountains Along River Banks.*
    65-1/4 x 20-1/2″. The Art Museum, Princeton University.

58. Fang I-chih (ca. 1607–1671). *Mountains by a River.* Dated 1642. 17-7/16 x 11-1/2″. Ching Yüan Chai Collection.

57. Yang Wen-ts'ung (1597–1646). *Solitary Pavilion by Mountain and Stream.* Dated 1643. 14-3/4 x 7″. Nelson-Atkins Gallery, Kansas City, Missouri (Nelson Fund).

60. Yün Hsiang (1586–1655). *Landscape.* 1624 or before.
65 x 20″. Mr. and Mrs. C. D. Carter Collection, Scarsdale,
New York.

Huang Tao-chou (1585–1646). *Three Scenes of Pines and Rocks:* handscroll section. H. 10-4/5″ (entire scroll 91-2/5″ long). Osaka Municipal Museum. (Not in exhibition.)

130

59. Hu Yü-k'un (active early to mid-17th century). *Album of Landscapes:* leaf j. Dated 1614–1615 (?). 8-7/8 x 6-11/16″. Ching Yüan Chai Collection.

61. Tsou Chih-lin (active 1610–1651). *Album of Landscapes:*
leaf c. 11-1/8 x 8-1/2″. Wango H. C. Weng Collection,
New York.

132

Lan Ying and the Chekiang Masters

by Patricia Berger

Painting as an expressive language is capable of conveying both the discrete intention of the artist and his position relative to other artists. But just as the nearly infinite possibilities of language are limited in practice to socially and semantically acceptable speech, so all possible forms of artistic expression are limited by time, place, and society. Artists are judged as much on their acceptability and expectability as on their aesthetic merit. The stance of Chinese connoisseurs has always been restricted by considerations of location, lineage, and social hierarchy. It is this restricted stance which has colored the reputations of all Chinese artists but especially that of Lan Ying.

Lan Ying (*tzu* T'ien-shu, *hao* Tieh-sou) lived from 1585 to after 1660. He was born and lived in Ch'ien-t'ang in Chekiang Province, and because of this has always been considered to be the last representative of the Che School, a notion which has tinged his memory with overtones of mediocrity and professionalism.[1] The Che School was founded in the early Ming dynasty by Tai Chin after his banishment from the Ming Court and his subsequent residence in Hang-chou, a city also located in Chekiang Province. The works of Tai Chin and his immediate follower Wu Wei, especially their more formal and decorative landscapes, derive closely from those of the Southern Sung masters Ma Yüan and Hsia Kuei. This stylistic affiliation, which bypassed in part the art of the more recent Yüan masters, placed the Che School in opposition to the Wu School, which felt its closest kinship to be with the Yüan. After Wu Wei, the Che School disintegrated into a group of unimaginative imitators and producers of hard, sterile pictures. No new impetus for stylistic innovation was forthcoming within the school; a creative artist such as Lan Ying was forced to look beyond the confines of the established tradition.

Lan Ying's position is unique because he was a professional whose concerns as an artist were dispassionately formal. While the rapid facility of his brushwork, his textures, and his rock and tree types are taken from the Che School, and ultimately from Tai Chin, they are arranged within frameworks or compositions which are taken from masters established as orthodox by literati painters, such as Wang Wei and Li Ch'eng, Huang Kung-wang and Ni Tsan, as well as from masters well beyond what was considered orthodox, such as Fan K'uan, Li T'ang, Ma Yüan and Hsia Kuei. Thus, while Lan Ying's vocabulary is typical of the Che School, the structures by which this vocabulary is integrated are multiple and mutually exclusive. This confusion of categories is symptomatic of the heterogeneous artistic and social situation in the late Ming. Lan Ying, lacking an acceptable established medium within which to express his formal intentions, developed a style which cannot be called either eclectic or synthetic. There is no felicitous blending of diverse stylistic elements. Instead, his methods can be seen as agglutinative, taking appropriate parts from many wholes but abstaining from any final melding or synthesis.

The earliest work in this group of paintings by Lan Ying is the "View of Mount Sung" (cat. no. 62), a landscape in ink and color on silk in the Boston Museum of Fine Arts, which is dated to the seventh year of T'ien-ch'i or 1628. The composition as it presently exists has been cropped at the bottom, and consequently our view of it is distorted. In its original state it must have resembled even more than it does now Fan K'uan's famous "Travelers Among Streams and Mountains." The mountain rises abruptly out of a bank of mist and a grove of heavily foliated trees. It is built up, as in the Fan K'uan picture, of a parallel series of vertically frontal planes, each one stepping back to the next and creating a shallow recession into space. Interestingly, Lan Ying confuses the foreground and background in a way foreign to the Northern Sung master Fan K'uan by stretching one exceptionally tall pine up the left side of the painting. Thus, he emphasizes the corner of the composition, a device derived from Tai Chin's more academic works, which in turn are indebted to the Southern Sung master Ma Yüan. Lan Ying's composition, though related in structure to Fan K'uan, shares its ambiance with Ma Yüan. The two scholars chatting comfortably in the leafy grove below seem unaware of the forbidding mountain behind them. They are oblivious, as was Lan Ying, to what can be seen in the light of late Ming painting theory as an incongruous juxtaposition of elements.

A painting which relates very well to the "View of Mount Sung" is the "Winter Landscape in the Manner of Wang Wei," dated by the artist to 1638 (cat. no. 63). Here, the same abrupt mountain is pushed to the side. Almost all sense of spatial recession is eliminated with only a small peninsula of snow-capped hills holding down the background. The whole composition hangs from the left edge of the picture plane. The trees clawing out to the opposite side establish the dramatic precipitousness of the mountain and the urgency of circumstance of a group of travelers on the road below. Lan Ying interests himself in a Southern Sung device which had been revived by the early Che School, the play of rough solid against blank void. His use of these two elements, however, produces a feeling of ominousness rather than of elegance. The tree, which is the focus of the composition, is curious in its dramatic contrast of light and shadow, a technique that may betray Western influence. This is in marked opposition to the summarily rendered cliff, and the roughly sketched background. Once again, Lan Ying has gathered together elements from disparate sources and juxtaposed them without attempting to modify each in relation to the others.

An album of twelve leaves in The Metropolitan Museum of Art is represented here by four leaves in the manners of Fan K'uan, Li Ch'eng, Wang Meng, and Mi Fu (cat. no. 64). Both the Li Ch'eng leaf and the Mi Fu leaf are dated 1642. All are rendered in a brush style which, except in the case of the Mi Fu leaf, makes little reference to the masters in question. In the leaf after Fan K'uan, especially, there is an eccentric reduction of a monumental motif to an intimate format. The typical Fan K'uan mountain, as it is still seen in "View of Mount Sung," is diminished in both actual and relative size to the point of bucolic docility. Moreover, it is pushed far to the side so it no longer forms a plug in a narrow space. The newly liberated background is established by two-dimensional jagged peaks. The mountain is pivoted around several degrees, so one is no longer forced to encounter it abruptly. This slight pivoting allows the space to flow smoothly past what might have been no more than a flimsy prop. But with proper lighting and positioning, the prop takes on a real formal function, that of channeling space, a function which is the exact antithesis of that intended by Fan K'uan. Neither the Li Ch'eng nor the Wang Meng leaf makes more than a passing reference to its supposed model. The Wang Meng leaf lacks the complication and dynamism of texture characteristic of Wang and instead, like the Li Ch'eng leaf, maintains Lan Ying's own quick, flashy facility of brushwork, that over-fluency of style that the Chinese critics deplore.

A large hanging scroll in ink and light color on paper in the Ching Yüan Chai Collection is a winter landscape after Fan K'uan (cat. no. 65). It is dated by the artist to 1655. This painting forms the third member of a trio of works we have seen by Lan Ying in which he alludes compositionally to Fan K'uan. From a fairly straightforward presentation of his style, modified only by one reference to Ma Yüan, to an intimate reduction of the monumental motif, Lan Ying arrives at a version of the master in which the allusion is only in the narrow, towering, bifurcated peak. The bilithic character of the main mass is distorted in a number of ways. First, its relative size is reduced by making the elements of human occupation in the landscape larger. The mountain, as in the Metropolitan album leaf, no longer plugs the space. Instead, all of the foreground and newly developed middle ground elements are made to serve the function of pointing to the mass of the mountain, and also, by means of the slanting flat-topped rock which echoes the middle ground tree, beyond the mountain mass through a narrow pass to the background. The main masses are broken up into small, identical but discrete units which provide texture and form. This tendency toward divisionism and articulation of the major masses recalls developments in the later Ch'ing dynasty, a tendency already bemoaned by Tung Ch'i-ch'ang. This painting, in fact, belongs chronologically to the Ch'ing dynasty. Lan Ying here sacrifices integrity of form to the necessity for space, a tendency which is increasingly apparent in his works.

One of the most lyrical of this group of works by Lan Ying is an undated handscroll in ink and color on paper in the collection of C. C. Wang (cat. no. 66). It is a work of composite allusion done in the styles of Yüan dynasty masters. It probably dates from around 1650. Lan Ying moves in a series of transitions from the style of Wang Meng through that of Huang Kung-wang and Wu Chen, ending in the style of Ni Tsan. Short introductory and concluding passages frame these visual quotes. A winding river relates each section to the next and erases any sense of abrupt transition. Once again the void, the area occupied by the river, forms the central motif, eventually and classically triumphing at the end of the scroll. The composition is a recital of the formal concerns proper to an artist of the late Ming. Launching the viewer into the picture via a leaning tree, Lan Ying first discusses, in the medium of Wang Meng, the relationship of texture to form and dynamic motion. Next, using motifs taken from Huang Kung-wang, he divides and rebuilds a mountain mass. In the Wu Chen and Ni Tsan sections, he tests the possibilities of a basic background-foreground relationship, only subtly varying his brushwork from one section to the next. It is the relationship of forms and voids which interests Lan Ying, as well as the virtuoso display of calligraphic brushmanners that evoked masters of the past.

Lan Ying's association with his pupil Ch'en Hung-shou, and his affinities in style with Ts'ui Tzu-chung (both painters to be discussed below), bring out his own somewhat anomalous position as an artist. While those painters searched for subject matter among the popular stories of their time, affiliating themselves in spirit as in style with the tastes of the rising middle class, Lan Ying, a man of similar background and a professional painter, sought to deny his own origins by adopting the modes of the literati painters. While his brushwork is clearly derived from the Che School artists, in its consistency it becomes an almost anonymous medium for what was for him a larger concern, that of formal allusion to the styles of early masters. Whether he took this direction out of personal choice or because paintings in old manners were popular in his day is an unanswerable question.

Lan Ying had a number of followers including Lan Meng, Lan Shen, and Ch'en Hung-shou. One painter who claimed him as a teacher was Liu Tu. Liu Tu also lived in Ch'ien-t'ang[2] and must have been only slightly younger than Lan Ying himself. He is represented here by "Landscape with Figures" from the Stanford University Art Museum, dated 1642 (cat. no. 67). This work is divided into three parts, a finely detailed foreground with assorted tree types, a middle ground of tree tops interlaced with mist, and a background of heavily colored, flat mountains. The foreground trees are subtly arranged and create a nicely graded recession into space. The use of line and color adheres to that of Lan Ying's academic, decorative pieces, although Liu Tu's brushwork is more delicate and less exciting than Lan Ying's.

Lan Ying's most distinguished pupil, of course, was Ch'en Hung-shou; but Ch'en depended on his teacher only for his landscape style, and perhaps some elements of his bird-and-flower painting; the figure style for which he is best known, and for which he will be discussed in the next chapter, is entirely his own creation. Even in landscapes, he soon left his teacher behind to move on to an individual style. The fan painting "Autumn Landscape" (cat. no. 68) appears to be an early work, judging from its close derivation from Lan Ying, the names Ch'en uses in his signature and seal, and the cautious calligraphy in which the inscription is written. The trees, with heavily shaded trunks, may be compared to those in Lan Ying's "Winter Landscape" of 1638 (cat. no. 63); the rocks, with dotted texture strokes and distinctive contours, and the mouth of the stream (shui-k'ou) in upper right, belong closely to the school repertory, as can be seen in comparing them with the Liu Tu picture (cat. no. 67). Already Ch'en reveals a sensitivity of touch that distinguishes him from his teacher; the red leaves fallen on the rocks, the touches of bright color in the leafy bushes, suggest somehow that the picture was more deeply felt than were most of Lan's landscapes.

The painting of "Mt. Wu-hsieh" in the Cleveland Museum of Art (cat. no. 69) must be a later work, largely free of residual influences from Lan Ying.

The landscape style of T'ang Yin (1470–1523) and his later imitators underlies the sleek, angular drawing of rocks and the sudden contrasts in ink value caused by dark outcroppings that appear unexpectedly on a cliff or a slope. The tortuous convolutions of the terrain remind us of Wu Pin, whose work Ch'en may have encountered in Nanking. In his use of smooth, fairly heavy shading on some of the forms, Ch'en appears to be experimenting with this new technique, which the Chinese learned from European paintings and prints. It makes the rock formations in the upper and lower portions of the composition almost excessively voluminous and heavy, and emphasizes their activation, for an effect not unlike that of Tung Ch'i-ch'ang's paintings. This unnatural activity in the landscape is relieved somewhat in the center by an expanse of foliage, but this too is dynamically charged with a network of white branches. There is little depth anywhere; every passage in the picture meets the viewer's eyes at the same speed. Typically for late Ming, the representation of landscape becomes a matter of composing graphic forms in an assigned space.

A bird-and-flower painting in ink and color on silk in the Ching Yüan Chai Collection (cat. no. 70) is by the painter Chiang Hung about whom little is known. However, his rendering of the large rock and his oversized green and black *tien* affiliate him with Lan Ying. The birds are painted in a manner reminiscent of Lan Ying and of Pien Wen-chin, a painter of the early Ming who in turn recalls the bird painters of the Southern Sung Academy. Here, the contrasts between the finely rendered sharp leaves, the rough textured rock, and the delicately arching branch, provide an iconic balance.

The most curious of this group of paintings in subject is a lovely hanging scroll in ink and colors on silk in the Ching Yüan Chai Collection (cat. no. 71) by an artist named Ch'en Ch'üan. Ch'en Ch'üan is unknown as a painter, this work being the only document of his in existence, but from the inscription at the top of the painting it may be inferred that he was probably a Ch'an (Zen) adherent, as the painting was presented to "Ch'an master Tzu-weng for his correction." There is also a long inscription by a monk named Tung-ming Yüeh-feng, who is not recorded in biographical compilations of monks of the later dynasties. However, we know that the Tung-ming Temple was located in Hang-chou,[3] a fact which limits the geographic location of the painting to the area under the stylistic influence of the Che School. The treatment of far distance might be seen by Chinese viewers as an archaizing spatial arrangement derived from Tung Yüan, but the interest in the darkened sky, the extreme flatness of the ground plane, the grouping of the trees in isolated, space-defining clumps, and the perspective of the arching bridge, all suggest some influence from the West. The groups of scholars, each appreciating its own reflection of the moon in the river, suggest a dream within which one recurrent theme, the moon, unites an otherwise fragmented scene. The inscription reads: "I have depicted: 'All the moons in the water are held by a single moon; / One single moon can thus hold all the lakes and rivers.'" The allusion is to a couplet in an old Ch'an Buddhist poem:

"The moon imprints itself on a thousand rivers, /
And yet, in reality, is a single moon." ∎

Notes

[1] *Kuo-ch'ao hua-cheng lu* (*Hua-shih ts'ung-shu* edition) p. 12.
[2] *Wu-sheng-shih shih*, chüan VII, p. 18. [3] *Hsin-hsü kao-seng-chuan ssu-chi* lists a number of monks from the Tung-ming Temple, but does not mention the writer of this inscription, Tung-ming Yüeh-feng. The location of the temple is given as Hang-chou.

62. Lan Ying (1585–after 1660). *View of Mount Sung.*
Dated 1628. 76-1/4 x 38-5/8″. Museum of Fine Arts,
Boston, James Fund.

63. Lan Ying (1585–after 1660). *Winter Landscape in the
Manner of Wang Wei.* 69-5/8 x 20″. Dated 1638. Ching
Yüan Chai Collection.

64. Lan Ying (1585–after 1660). *Album of Landscapes:* leaf e.
Dated 1642. 12-7/16 x 9-3/4″. The Metropolitan Museum
of Art, New York, The Sackler Fund, 1970.

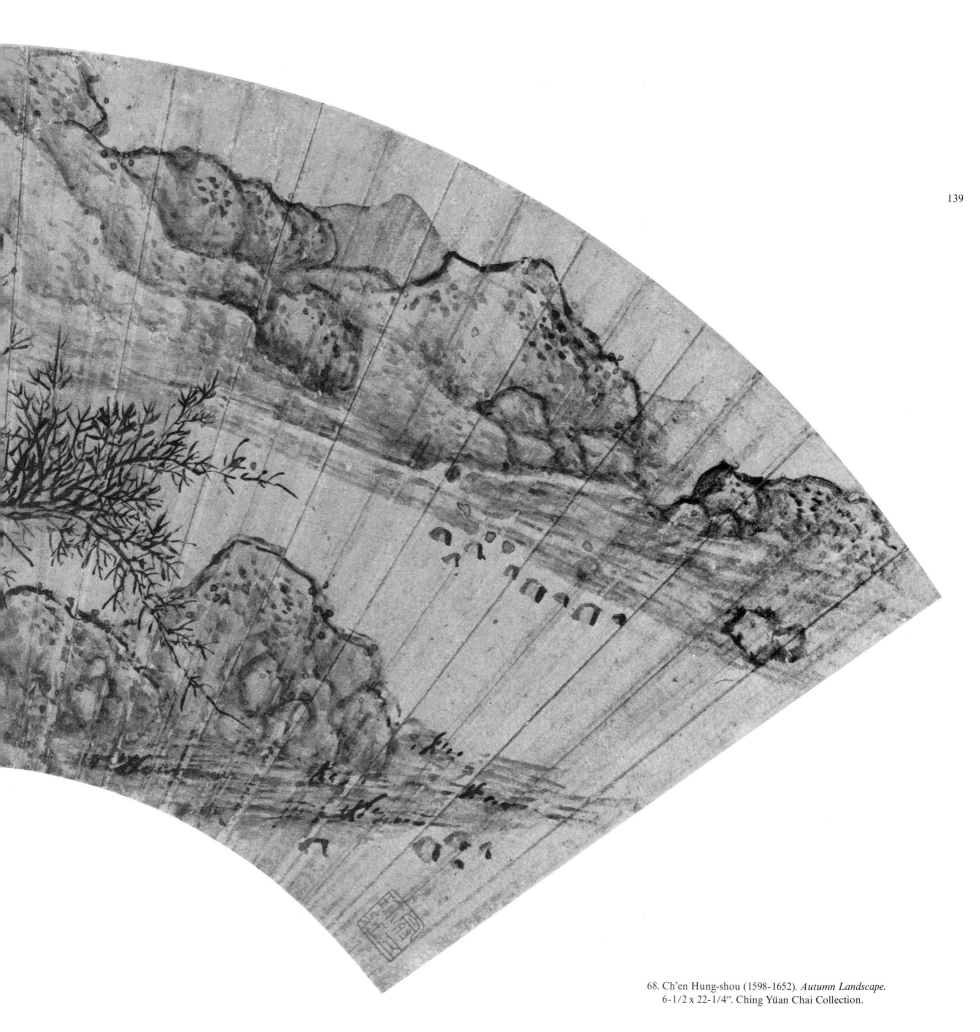

68. Ch'en Hung-shou (1598-1652). *Autumn Landscape.*
6-1/2 x 22-1/4". Ching Yüan Chai Collection.

65. Lan Ying (1585–after 1660). *Cold Mountains and Snowy Peaks, in the Manner of Fan K'uan.* Dated 1655. 55-1/4 x 23-1/4″. Ching Yüan Chai Collection.

66. Lan Ying (1585–after 1660). *Handscroll in the Manner of Yüan Masters:* section. H. 11-1/8″. C. C. Wang Collection, New York.

142

69. Ch'en Hung-shou (1598–1652). *The Wu Hsieh Mountain.*
46-9/16 x 20-15/16″. Cleveland Museum of Art: Purchase,
John L. Severance Fund.

67. Liu Tu (active late Ming). *Landscape with Figures.* Dated 1636. 35-13/16 x 15-1/8″. Stanford University Museum of Art; Gift of the Committee for Art at Stanford.

70. Chiang Hung (dated works 1674–1690). *Birds in a Tree; Narcissus and Rock.* 49-3/4 x 18-7/8″. Ching Yüan Chai Collection.

144

71. Ch'en Ch'üan (late Ming). *Landscape with Reflections of the Moon*. 43-1/2 x 17-3/4″. Ching Yüan Chai Collection.

Figure Painters of Late Ming

by Stella Lee

Figure painting has a long history in Chinese art. From early times, specialists in figure subjects such as Ku K'ai-chih (ca. 344–406) and Wu Tao-tzu (ca. 720–760) had already established a tradition of drawing in fine lineament. Later, Chou Fang (ca. 780–810) and Li Kung-lin (ca. 1049–1106) brought this branch of painting to a climax, the former doing pictures of court ladies and the latter paintings in *pai-miao* style (pure line-drawing). There were not many important innovations in the following centuries; most of the artists either imitated the past or emulated the accomplishments of their forerunners. It was only in the second half of the Ming dynasty that portrait painting once again reached a high point. Late Ming figure painting, as seen in the present exhibition, can be divided into two main groups: portraits of scholars, and religious figures. In both groups the artists are able not only to carry on the previous tradition of drawing in fine lineament, but also to respond to outside stimuli and work in new styles. On a pictorial level, these stimuli came with the introduction of European styles of painting, which were responsible for new tendencies toward realism. On an ideological ground, the social and political convulsions of late Ming engendered a new humanism in their presentation of human images, in which the artists revealed their feelings toward both men and society.

Ch'en Hung-shou was born in 1598, into a declining gentry family in Chekiang. It is recorded in Chu I-tsun's biography of him that when Ch'en was four years old he painted a ten-foot-tall portrait of Kuan-tzu. His father-in-law is said to have been stunned by its power.[1] The story is surely exaggerated, but indicates Ch'en's early talent in figure painting. At the age of ten he met Lan Ying in Hang-chou. Lan Ying was similarly impressed by young Ch'en's talent, and from then on, it is said, overawed by his pupil, "did not paint flower and bird pictures for the rest of his life."[2] Lan Ying became Ch'en's teacher in landscape painting, and the influence of the older master on the younger is clearly visible in the landscapes by Ch'en Hung-shou in this exhibition.

The twelve leaves of the small album in the Ching Yüan Chai Collection (cat. no. 72) include land-scapes as well as bird and flower paintings, but the landscapes, fascinating as they are in their extreme formalization, will not occupy us here. They demonstrate, as does the Cleveland Museum picture (cat. no. 69), Ch'en's ability to step outside the confines of Lan Ying's style through conscious, highly sophisticated distortions of form and scale as a manifestation of stylistic virtuosity.

The other leaves in the album attest to the same originality, ostensibly following very old traditions but in fact achieving ironic commentary on those traditions through calculated distortions. In these the artist singles out a subject and depicts it with extreme, almost obsessive concentration on eccentrically refined qualities. In two leaves, for example, one representing a peony and the other a butterfly perching on a flower, delicately drawn lines spread out from the base of each flower petal and disappear at its outer edge. These lines then continue on, but in different directions, on other petals. Within the form of each flower the delicate, refined, systematic lines flow in each assigned area. The textural movement of each area is associated with that of the neighboring areas, constituting a flat major pattern with decorative sub-patterns, and building up a well-adorned substantiality, a finished work, in empty space; the *shih* (substantiality) counter-balances the *hsü* (void). The formation of each object is basically realistic, yet the deliberate twist of balance and harmony, as well as the play on ambiguous scale, carry reality beyond into the realm of unreality and almost to surrealism. The artist's intention is clear: in distorting objects into curious shapes, as if using a magnifying glass, he aims at an "unpleasantly" pleasant and "ugly" beautiful vision.

The decorative intent of Ch'en Hung-shou is clear as well in other leaves of the same album, in which the subjects themselves belong to a decorative art such as one might see in designs on ceramics. Too much concentration on decoration is the decadent side of Ch'en Hung-shou. In addition to flowers and butterflies, he was fond of portraying languishing ladies and illustrating sentimental sections of the melodramas popular in his time, such as the "Story of the Western Chamber." Personally, he was at-tached to singing girls and famous prostitutes, and led a Bohemian life. The local gazetteer of Chu-chi, his native place, comments: "His calligraphic style was untrammeled and seductive, like that of calligraphers of the late T'ang period."[3] The Chinese word for "seductive," *mei,* used in characterizing his calligraphy, is often applied to the extreme state of femininity, while the late T'ang period was the golden age of decadent poetry. This adjective is applicable as well to his painting style, since his calligraphic and painting styles bear the same spirit.

Nevertheless, the fall of the Ming regime must have awakened the decadent Ch'en Hung-shou; after 1644 he became a monk and used the names Hui-ch'ih (Belated Repentance), Lao-ch'ih (Old and Late), Yün-men-seng (Monk of the Cloud Gate Mountains), and Hui-seng (The Repentant Monk). As a matter of fact, this conversion to Buddhism was only a disguise, an attempt to escape from chaotic reality, as he confessed in a passage included in the anthology of his writings, *Pao-lun-t'ang chi:* "In the summer of 1646, I, the Repentant, ran into the mountains to save my life. At places where monkeys and birds gathered, I then cut off my hair and put on a monk's robe. How could I become a monk? It was only a matter of borrowing the monk's form for the sake of staying alive."[4]

The hanging scroll, "A Scholar Instructing Girl Pupils in the Arts" (cat. no. 73), in the University Art Museum, Berkeley, bears the signature Lao-ch'ih, and thus can be dated after 1646 when he adopted this name. This picture exemplifies his habitual dwelling on details and design, as seen in the sashes of the girl students, the cloth cover of the zither, and the leaf pattern on the surface of the chair. Ch'en also likes to represent another painting within a painting. In this hanging scroll, the small bamboo and rock picture on the desk in front of the girl student is a finished painting in itself, although parts of it are concealed. There is even an indistinct lotus flower drawn on the fan that the girl is holding. In one of his illustrations for "Story of the Western Chamber"[5] a painting within a painting becomes an important feature of the style. This outstanding treatment of texture in space is familiar to us through

146 the Ching Yüan Chai album discussed above. Like the magnified flowers and butterflies, the richly drawn sub-painting substantiates an assigned area in insubstantiated space.

The "Homecoming" handscroll (cat. no. 74) in the Honolulu Academy of Arts represents eleven scenes from the life of T'ao Yüan-ming (372–427?), to each of which two lines of poetry by Ch'en Hung-shou are attached. T'ao Yüan-ming was a poor scholar-official and poet in the Six Dynasties, a period of political intrigues and moral destruction. He retired from political office and became a hermit in the later stages of his life. His poetry is distinguished by plainness and simplicity in style, and by intimate contact with nature in concept.

Written at the end of this handscroll, the artist's own inscription reads: "In 1650, in mid-summer, my old friend Chou Li-yüan (Chou Liang-kung) asked me for a painting. This summer Lin Chung-ch'ing had Hsiao Su-ch'ing (a singer) attend me with ink and brushes at the Ting-hsiang bridge. In mid-winter I posted the painting to my old friend Chou. Please show this painting to our friend Hsü Yu (native of Fukien, known for his flower and landscape paintings). [Signed] Lao-ch'ih, Hung-shou, who painted this scroll; Ming-ju (his fourth son) applied the color."[6]

In the *Lai-ku-t'ang shu-hua-pa*, Chou Liang-kung himself wrote:

> Chang-hou (Ch'en Hung-shou) and I have been friends for twenty years. A hanging scroll depicting T'ao Yüan-ming was the only painting he did for me fifteen years ago at the capital. I requested another one from him.... He never responded. In 1650, on my way to the north (from Fukien), I met him at the West Lake. He was still firmly set against painting for me. In the following year, I returned to my duties in Fukien. It was at the Ting-hsiang bridge (at the West Lake in Hang-chou) that he became inspired. 'Now, this is the time to do more paintings for you' he announced. We rushed painting silk to him. He chewed on salted cabbage, and sipped Shao-hsing wine. Sometimes he asked the singer Hsiao Su-ch'ing to stand against the railing and sing. After only a few sentences of a song he stopped him, either raising one

hand to scratch his head, or with two fingers stroking his feet. He stared in silence, or held a brush, teasing children. There was not a quiet moment. From the Ting-hsiang bridge we moved to my house, from my house to the lakeshore, then to a Taoist temple, then onto a houseboat, then to the temple Chao-ch'ing. He had painting materials with him wherever he went. This went on for eleven days. He painted large and small, hanging scrolls and handscrolls, altogether forty-two paintings. This unexpected generosity greatly puzzled my guests and myself. Did he then have a premonition of his death in the following year?[7]

The "Homecoming" handscroll painted during this occasion in 1652 is one of the last paintings Ch'en Hung-shou ever did. T'ao Yüan-ming appears in each of the eleven scenes that make up the scroll, often larger than the other figures. Making the hero of the story appear repeatedly on stage had long been a presentational convention. In Ku K'ai-chih's "Nymph of the Lo River,"[8] for instance, the nymph appears eleven times with her flowing robe, leading the story onward. Another painting attributed to Ku, the "Admonitions of Ladies in the Court,"[9] provides another ancient example of interspersing the procession of the story with inscriptions. The form, then, was antique.

The linear quality of Ch'en Hung-shou's figure drawing, best exemplified in this handscroll by the drawing of the flowing robes, sleeves, and hands, is no less fluid, yet firmer, than that featured in the handscrolls of the Six Dynasties period, the age of the flowing line. Whimsicality achieved by a conscious distortion of form distinguishes Ch'en Hung-shou's work. In the late Ming dynasty it was not only Ch'en Hung-shou but also his contemporaries Ts'ui Tzu-chung and Wu Pin who shared in the stylistic devices of distortion, of twisting the normal features of the figures for specific effects. But while Ts'ui attained an air of insubstantiality by making his figures excessively slender, and Wu Pin a bizarre vision by stylistic extremism, only Ch'en Hung-shou arrived at an expression of wit.

The drawing of the sedan-chair in which T'ao Yüan-ming sits, and of the baskets, shows his love of design. The two fans placed on the rock desk in front

of the meditative T'ao have a well-drawn donkey on one of them and two figures on the other, again indicating his propensity for treating paintings within paintings. Both passages are manifestations of his attachment to detail. Yet compared to his early works, the witty, sensitive world of Ch'en Hung-shou was much deepened. At the end of his life his prime concern was with men and men only; he was not only humorous but humane. T'ang Chui-ching, his friend and a critic, observed Ch'en's stylistic change as a consequence of experiences in his life: "Chang-hou (Ch'en Hung-shou) lived for less than sixty years, but his brush and ink underwent four (three?) changes: wonderfully clever in his youthful days, inspired in his middle period, and transcending ordinary standards in his old age."[10] By the time he was in his fifties he had suffered from personal misfortunes and the political and moral degeneration of late Ming society. Life to him had been a succession of disasters from both sides. Like a silkworm spinning out its silk, the tender, fluid, yet strenuous brush lines were exuded from the substance and essence of his own being. Living in equally troubled times, Ch'en Hung-shou was much like T'ao Yüan-ming. While the latter laments in his "Homecoming" poem: "How long shall I stay in the world? Why do they not leave my heart in peace? Why do I torment myself so vainly? Shall I stay, shall I go?"[11] Ch'en Hung-shou bemoans: "Since May of 1646, whenever I passed the place where I used to study, a guilty conscience, a sense of unfaithfulness, was aroused, and my face flushed and my ears turned red out of shame."[12]

To stay or not to stay, to be or not to be, the choice agonized the intellectuals. T'ao Yüan-ming found a way out by escaping into pastoral life, which must have been Ch'en Hung-shou's wish as well. Yet Ch'en Hung-shou was not so fortunate; he was torn by the tension of choice, which split him between his true nature and his sense of Confucian duty inculcated by education. At the fall of Ming, Ch'en witnessed the martyrdom of friends and contemporaries such as Ts'ui Tzu-chung, Wen Chen-heng,[13] Yang Wen-ts'ung, Ni Yüan-lu, and his teacher Huang Tao-chou. Some joined the resistance, fighting in the underground. At this crucial moment,

Ch'en Hung-shou lost his nerve, and he was afterward very conscious of this loss. From then on he never forgave himself. He was aware of his failure in commitment to the country and was tortured by his sense of guilt.

The chanting of T'ao Yüan-ming from the beginning to the end of the "Homecoming" poem is the moaning of the distressed Ch'en Hung-shou. The portrait of T'ao Yüan-ming is Ch'en Hung-shou's own portrait, and is the portrait of the late Ming scholar. Disguised as T'ao Yüan-ming, through spiritual projection into remote history, Ch'en Hung-shou exposed allegorically the psychological complexity of the scholar, the contemporary social situation, and the relationship between the two. On this level, Ch'en Hung-shou's portrait of the scholar, put into the context of the chaotic late Ming environment, can be likened to the neo-figuration of postwar Europe. Both concepts of figuration are "a way of revealing the world of the subject in the object. It deals with a subjective reality; metamorphosis of the real by the act of spiritual projection." [14] While Francis Bacon's (born 1909) work "is a reflection of our times, or, more precisely expressed, the reflection of a man who contemplates our times with clear eyes," [15] Ch'en Hung-shou likewise represents "the spirit of the epoch." [16] His portrait of the scholar testifies to the facts of late Ming history.

While Ch'en Hung-shou gained his reputation in the region south of the Yangtze River, Ts'ui Tzu-chung was considered to be his Northern rival. They were paired in the saying: *Nan-Ch'en-pei-Ts'ui* (Ch'en of the south and Ts'ui of the north). The short biographical note in the *Ming-hua lu* mentions that Ts'ui Tzu-chung's paintings were never available for money, but were only done for friends, and that he was very secluded by nature. [17]

The "Entertaining a Guest in the Apricot Garden" by Ts'ui Tzu-chung dated 1638 in the Ching Yüan Chai Collection (cat. no. 75) is one of the most exquisite paintings in the entire exhibition. One can easily recognize the subtlety in linear drawing and color, in the sparse trees dotted with a few flowers, and in the rocks entwined with vines like spider webs. Ch'en Hung-shou's line forever flows; Ts'ui Tzu-chung's, as seen in this painting, pivots and turns angularly en route. As a result, Ch'en of the south features fluid lineament, Ts'ui of the north presents brisker drawing, yet both have equally forceful and assured hands. Nevertheless, where Ch'en Hung-shou's figures still retain some reminder of the body, Ts'ui Tzu-chung's figures are completely deprived of substantiality. They all have bony, tapering faces, and long "phoenix" eyes. Although they actually are images of Ts'ui Tzu-chung himself and his friends, they look more like elves or some other beings existing only in legends. The foreground rock further screens the viewer from the already remote actions of the figure groups. Drawn with a split-tipped brush in double lineament, [18] the peculiar rock shimmers across the air like a ghost.

Another work by Ts'ui Tzu-chung, in the Cleveland Museum of Art, represents a third century Taoist: "Hsü Cheng-yang Moving His Family" (cat. no. 76). Here again Ts'ui plays on archaic styles, in both the figures and the setting. The landscape evokes—and is meant to evoke—memories of paintings ascribed to the T'ang and Five Dynasties periods, in which individual forms were delineated in continuous fine line that has the effect of flattening them, and filled with even washes of ink or color with only minimal texture-strokes that give no sense of natural roughness. The drawing of the trees, with knotty trunks and masses of individually outlined leaves as decorative patterns, is also an archaism. The bizarre line drawing used for the figures and animals is a whimsical, art-historical allusion to a manner of drawing called "tremulous brushline" *(chan-pi)* used in some early figure paintings. All this removes the event to the status of an old anecdote, perceived over an expanse of history, as the main group of figures is removed to the middle ground in the composition and seen beyond trees and water. This is a painting for antiquarians, of more cultural than pictorial value.

Ts'ui Tzu-chung seeks the subject matter of painting primarily in legends, history, and religion. In 1644 when the Ming empire was finally destroyed Ts'ui locked himself in a clay room and committed suicide by fasting. [19] In fact, this idea of remoteness in painting, associated with that of archaism as a common stylistic feature in portraiture during this time, reveals the artists' discontent with their environment. In search of utopia in a bygone world, as a subtle protest, were Ch'en Hung-shou and Ts'ui Tzu-chung, as well as Wu Pin.

Wu Pin (fl. 1568–1626) was a painter active in Nanking, whom we have already discussed as a landscapist. His figure painting in his own time was considered peculiar and weird; he was said to have "departed from the ways of old masters." [20] Faced with the "Five Hundred Arhats" handscroll in the Cleveland Museum of Art (cat. no. 77), the modern viewer is no less surprised by the strange forms of the Arhats. Wu Pin in this long handscroll exaggerated all animals, figures, and landscape elements in such a way that the final expressiveness is truly beyond the viewer's expectation. Each of the five hundred quasi-religious images is distinguished by his specific eccentricity. Awkwardness, normally a presentational vice, is here consciously manifested to the effective point where it becomes an idiosyncratic virtue. All the immortals have well-delineated heads, complete with facial features and gestures, and with distinct pupils in their eyes. Piercing glances are psychologically interrelated, as if some events unknown to us were occurring before them. Although concerned with religious subjects, Wu Pin does not avoid subjective emotional attachment. He projects himself into the world of Buddhism and captures the instantaneous moment of the Arhats' everlasting life. As far as emotional content is concerned, Wu Pin is the most overt among all the artists treated in this discussion.

Wu Pin spent part of his life as a monk. At the end of the handscroll, he signed: "The Chih-yin Monk Wu Pin painted this with austere heart." The Chih-yin monks were untonsured monks, an order that existed from the fourteenth century. They were allowed to wear regular clothes, and did not adhere to any doctrinal sect. Only in this kind of free religion could Wu Pin's heterodox spirit feel release.

The "Five Hundred Arhats" in landscape settings, originally a series of twenty-five (?) hanging scrolls of which three are in the exhibition (cat. no. 78), were painted by Ting Yün-p'eng together with another painter, Sheng Mao-yeh, and are dated 1594. Ting Yün-p'eng's treatment of Arhats is as amusing as that of his contemporary Wu Pin; the religious figures similarly have staring pupils in their eyes, focusing at some point in front of them. Their facial expressions indicate deep concentration in the affairs in which they are engaged. Some are fishing, some painting; others, with wide-open eyes, watch other Arhats taming wild animals. These are the whimsical "still-shots" of the Arhats' immortal lives. In catching the momentary feeling of the figures' actions, both painters manifest their skill. However, where Wu Pin by means of extreme distortion is able to exalt his images to the unearthly realm, Ting Yün-p'eng's rather stay on earth. This is due to the realistic tendencies in Ting's facial drawing: the Arhats' faces are based on human visages, so that they seem almost human, portrait-like. Eventually, Ting Yün-p'eng's exaggeration or twisting of style is effective only to show the individual personality of the depicted images.

Extensive information on Ting Yün-p'eng's life is lacking. Judging from his numerous works with religious themes, such as "Washing the Elephant" paintings in the Palace Museum and other collections, one would assume that Ting was a professional painter of Buddhist subjects. This discloses another facet of late Ming religious painting; many of the artists may have produced pictures on commission for use, for instance, in temples. For this reason, the point of view is different from the casual and individualistic style used by painters more self-motivated. Indeed, whether the "Five Forms of Kuan-yin" by Ting Yün-p'eng in the Nelson-Atkins Gallery (cat. no. 79) was for a specific Buddhist purpose or not, compared to the eccentric views of the two "Five Hundred Arhats," it certainly appears reserved, severe, and conventional. What catches the viewer's attention is primarily the line drawing and tonal contrast. The cool and warm colors, usually white against red, contrast with each other in almost every figure of the handscroll. The soft lines

and the white color only give an outline of Kuan-yin's body, of which the incorporeal feeling is enhanced by the opaque red on the elements of her apparel. The end of the handscroll is perhaps a climax of presentation, in which the white-robed Kuan-yin, seated in a cave, is supported and worshipped by supernatural figures.[21] By virtue of the fantastic rocks, water demons, and waves all depicted in tumbling, rhythmic strokes, this last scene is as if in a state of constant flux. The bluish-gray ink sets the general air of gloominess.

The "Portrait of a Scholar" dated 1639 in the University Art Museum, Berkeley (cat. no. 80), is another work done as a collaboration: Tseng Ch'ing (1568–1650) did the figure, and a certain Ts'ao Hsi-chih the landscape setting. Tseng Ch'ing was the most famous portraitist of the late Ming, active during the second quarter of the seventeenth century. The *Wu-sheng-shih shih* says of him: "His portraiture could be compared to taking images from a mirror, wonderfully obtaining both the spirit and the appearance [of the subject]. His coloring was dense and moist. The application of pupils to the eyes produced [a sense of] movement…The turning of the head, the glance of the eyes, and the smiling expressions were forceful and realistic…When he painted a portrait, he used overlaid washes [of ink and color], applying them in many layers. Until he had fulfilled his skill, he would not stop." [22]

The landscape setting in the picture is conventional, done in the style of Sung Hsü, which by this time was old-fashioned. The scholar's image by Tseng Ch'ing, however, denotes a new, realistic approach to portraiture, as we would expect from the above-quoted passage. The entire face of the scholar is shaded for a three-dimensional effect, a technique influenced by European painting which had become known in China by this time, especially in the Nanking area, through the Christian missionaries. In the eighteenth-century *Kuo-ch'ao hua-cheng-lu*, Chang Keng stated that there were two different modes of portraiture at this time: "The first kind emphasizes the ink framework [literally "ink-bones"], in which one first finished the ink structure, then added colors to it, in order to differentiate

physical age, yet the spirit [of the figure] is already transmitted through the ink framework. This is the method of Tseng Po-ch'en [Tseng Ch'ing] in Fukien. In the other mode, one uses light ink to delineate the general nature of the facial features, and then colors them with powdered pigments. This mode formed the traditional method of the southern painters. Tseng Ch'ing was also very good at it."

Still another collaborative work in the exhibition is a handscroll in ink and colors on paper, dated 1648, done by Lan Ying and Hsieh Pin (cat. no. 81). Hsieh was a pupil of Tseng Ch'ing, a portraitist scarcely remembered today and represented by only a few works. The portraits in this scroll are all of the same person, a gentleman named Tz'u-weng who belonged to the same literary and social club as Hsieh. He appears five times in the scroll. As in other joint productions, such as the collaboration of Tseng Ch'ing and Ts'ao Hsi-chih discussed above, the tendencies toward realism seen in the figures, which are painted with very fine shading and precise outlines, did not extend to the depiction of the landscape setting, which is in Lan Ying's typically rough style. This discrepancy between the two styles, here as elsewhere, evidently did not disturb the Chinese, as it may disturb us; the setting, and the placing of the figures in it, were only intended to provide an idealized picture of the subject's daily activities. If we are to believe the painting, that is, he strolled beside the river, read books in a secluded cottage, relaxed in a boat with his family, his facial expression never changing in the slightest.

The "Portrait of Madame Ho-tung" in the Fogg Art Museum (cat. no. 82) was painted in 1643 by Wu Cho, a minor figure-painter and perhaps a writer. Madame Ho-tung, whose family name was Liu, began as a singing girl. She determined, however, to form an alliance with a learned man, and in 1641 she became the mistress of Ch'ien Chien-i, famous poet, scholar, and official. In the library where Ch'ien kept his great collection of books, the two studied and composed poems together. Madame Ho-tung helped Ch'ien to edit the section on women in his anthology of Ming poets, and her own poems appeared in various anthologies. After the library was destroyed by fire in 1650, the couple devoted themselves to Buddhist studies. Harassed by blackmailers after Ch'ien's death in 1664, she hanged herself.[23]

Clarity and a frontal flatness are two stylistic features of this hanging scroll, which in composition can be easily divided into two parts: the figure, placed in a partly recumbent, zig-zag posture, and a background divided into horizontal bands, of which the central, textured or figural ones are parts of a broad bench or *k'ang*. A stone panel, cut so that its natural markings resemble a misty landscape painting of the Mi School, is set into the backrest. Typically for Ming, the drawing of the figure is less concerned with volume than with the descriptive feeling of line on surface. But the proportions and gesture are extremely realistic; paradoxically, the patternization of the figure and its robes through stylized lineament and designs seems to be consciously done as a device of descriptive realism. In keeping with this is the three-dimensional treatment of the drapery, which, as in so much other figure drawing of this period, especially that of professional and specialist artists, betrays some acquaintance with Occidental art.

The face is impassive. With the brushwork, ink, and colors, it gives an effect that is on the whole low-keyed, portraying the decadent world of the withering scholar-gentry class. Nevertheless, one is inclined to speculate that Madame Ho-tung might have led a life as romantic and nearly as creative as did Ch'en Hung-shou, on the basis of her biography, and of the manner in which she sits on the bench, with one leg bent in a very casual way, a gesture unwelcome to "high-class" Chinese women with traditional moral sense, yet compositionally balancing well her diagonally slanting body.

A remarkable painting by an unknown artist named Ch'eng I, "Confucius and His Disciples on the Apricot Terrace Enjoying the Music of Moderation" (cat. no. 83), concludes our exhibition. Ch'eng I was once identified with a painter active in the Yung-lo era (1403–1425), but this identification was certainly mistaken, as the style of the painting places it se-

curely in the late Ming period. The similarity of the rocks in the foreground, with spidery patterns of tree branches set against them, to similar passages in the painting of Ts'ui Tzu-chung (cat. no. 75) is a first clue; the portrait-like faces, and the realism with which the tables and screen are painted (the latter, like the seat in the preceding painting by Wu Cho, inlaid with a slab of white marble with darker markings), preclude any dating earlier than late Ming. Confucius sits in a dignified but not stiff posture in the center; before him are two disciples playing the "music of moderation" on *ch'in* (psalteries). The other disciples stand loosely grouped in a semi-circle around them, some between the trees behind. The apricot trees, which have put forth only a few blossoms (the season is presumably early spring), are in perfect harmony with the Confucian subject: a bit severe in aspect (heavily blossoming trees would be quite wrong), their branches and twigs forming precise patterns. In contrast to some of the Buddhist paintings considered earlier, this one is wholly serious, by an artist of great skill and cool, objective approach, who succeeds in his own way in the aim of so much late Ming painting, the evocation of the past. ■

Notes

[1]Chu I-tsun, "Ch'en Hung-shou ch'uan." This passage is reprinted in the collection of Ch'en Hung-shou's writings, *Pao-lun-t'ang chi*, of which the preface by Ch'en himself is dated 1635. However, another preface by Hu Ch'i-i dated 1705 states that this collection was actually edited over thirty years after Ch'en's death in 1652. [2]Mao Ch'i-ling, "Ch'en Hung-shou chüan," also in *Pao-lun-t'ang chi*. [3]Huang Yung-ch'üan, *Ch'en Hung-shou nien p'u*, Peking, 1960, p. 92. [4]Ch'en Hung-shou, *Pao-lung-t'ang chi*. [5]Reproduced in Huang Yung-ch'üan's *Ch'en Hung-shou*, Peking, 1958, pls. 7, 8, and 9; also in his *Ch'en Lao-lien pan-hua hsüan-chi*, Peking, 1957. [6]Tseng Yu-ho's translation; see "A Report on Ch'en Hung-shou," *Archives of the Chinese Art Society of America*, Vol. XIII (1959), pp. 75–88. [7]*Ibid.*, pp. 79–80. Slightly altered from Tseng's translation. [8]Reproduced in Siren, *Chinese Painting*, Vol. III, pls. 9–10 (Freer version) and 9A–B (Peking version). [9]*Ibid.*, pls. 11–14. [10]Wai-kam Ho, "Nan-Ch'en Pei-Ts'ui," *Bulletin of the Cleveland Museum of Fine Arts*, Vol. 49, no. 1, 1962, p. 7. [11]Translation in Robert Payne, *The White Pony*, New York and Toronto, 1947, p. 144. [12]*Pao-lun t'ang chi*. [13]Wen Cheng-heng (1585–1645) was Wen Cheng-ming's great-grandson. [14]Aldo Pellegrini, *New Tendencies in Art*, New York, 1966, p. 198. [15]*Ibid.*, p. 200. [16]*Ibid.*, p. 197. [17]Hsü Ch'in, *Ming hua-lu*, colophon dated 1673. [18]Cf. James Cahill, *Fantastics and Eccentrics in Chinese Painting*, New York, 1967, p. 41. [19]The circumstances of the death of Ts'ui Tzu-chung were recorded differently by Ch'ien Chien-i, who writes that after 1644 Ts'ui lived with one of his friends and finally died of starvation through poverty. See Fu Pao-shih, *Ming-mo min-tsui-jen chuan*, 1939, p. 75. [20]*T'u-hui-pao-chien hsü-tsuan*, edited by Lan Ying and others, published in the early Ch'ing dynasty. [21]The tradition of representing the white-robed Kuan-yin, perhaps said to have begun with Li Kung-lin, was continued by Mu-ch'i, Fan-lung, and others. The device of ending the scroll with Kuan-yin in a cave has its predecessors in Fan-lung's picture in the Freer Gallery of Art. [22]Chiang Shao-shu, *Wu-sheng-shih shih*, compiled at the end of Ming, published in early Ch'ing, postface dated 1720, Vol. IV. [23]Information taken from the Fogg Museum's label for the picture.

150

74. Ch'en Hung-shou (1598–1652). *The Homecoming of T'ao Yüan-ming:* handscroll section. Dated 1650. H. 12″. Honolulu Academy of Arts.

151

152

73. Ch'en Hung-shou (1598–1652). *A Scholar Instructing Girl Pupils in the Arts.* 35-3/4 x 18″. University Art Museum, Berkeley. Gift of Mrs. Elizabeth Hay Bechtel, University of California, Berkeley, Class 1925.

75. Ts'ui Tzu-chung (died 1644). *Entertaining a Guest in the Apricot Garden.* Dated 1638. 60-3/4 x 20-1/4″. Ching Yüan Chai Collection.

76. Ts'ui Tzu-chung (died 1644). *Hsü Cheng-yang Moving his Family.* 65-3/16 x 25-1/4″. Cleveland Museum of Art: Mr. and Mrs. William H. Marlatt Fund.

78. Ting Yün-p'eng (ca. 1575–1638), and Sheng Mao-yeh
(active 1574–1637). *Five Hundred Arhats in a Landscape:*
scroll a. Dated 1594. 81-7/8 x 40-3/16''. Private Collection,
Kyoto.

77. Wu Pin (ca. 1568–1626). *The Five Hundred Arhats:*
handscroll section. H. 13-1/4″. Cleveland Museum of Art:
Purchase, John L. Severance Fund.

156

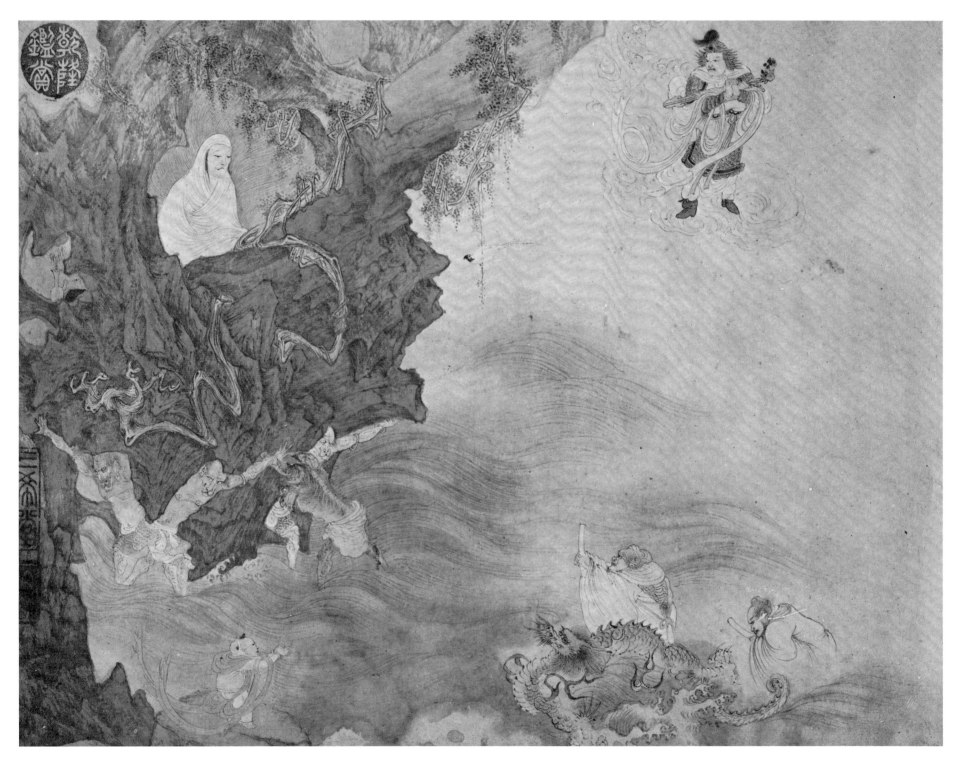

81. Lan Ying (1585–after 1660), and Hsieh Pin (active mid-17th century). *Landscape with Scholars:* handscroll section. Dated 1648. H. 11-7/16″. Ching Yüan Chai Collection.

82. Wu Cho (17th century). *Portrait of Madame Ho-tung.* Dated 1643. 47 x 24-1/2″. Fogg Art Museum, Harvard University.

159

83. Ch'eng I (early to mid-17th century?). *Confucius and His Disciples on the Apricot Terrace Enjoying the Music of Moderation.* 57-1/2 x 41″. Collection Shogoro Yabumoto, Amagasaki, Japan.

Catalogue to the Exhibition

Dimensions are in inches, height preceding width. All works are illustrated, with page of illustration noted in brackets at the end of each entry. All works are in both showings of the exhibition. Works are catalogued, generally and as much as possible, in the order in which they appear in the text section:

1. Chang Fu (1546–after 1631). *Landscape with Waterfalls.* Dated 1596. Hanging scroll, ink and light colors on paper. 40-1/4 x 12-1/4″. Ching Yüan Chai Collection. [Ill. p. 47].
Inscription by artist: On an autumn day in the *ping-shen* [year] of the Wan-li [era, 1596], Chang Fu painted this in the "Listening to Bushwarbler's Study" (Ting-ying Hsien). Two seals of the artist (Contag and Wang, nos. 2 and 3).

2. Ch'en Huan (dated works 1605–1615). *Landscape in the Manner of Wang Meng.* Dated 1605. Hanging scroll, ink and light colors on silk. 44-5/8 x 18-1/2″. University Art Museum, Berkeley. [Ill. p. 47].
Inscription by artist: *I-ssu* [year, 1605], fifteenth day of the tenth month, done in the manner of Huang-hao Shan-ch'iao [Wang Meng]. Ch'en Huan. One seal of the artist, reading *Ch'en Tzu-wen Shih.* Two collectors' seals, unidentified. Published: *Selection 1968: Recent Accessions to the University Art Collections,* Berkeley, 1968, no. 14. Former Nü Wa Chai Collection.

3. Ch'en Huan. *Landscape.* Handscroll, ink and light colors on paper. 8 x 62-5/8″. Wango H. C. Weng Collection, New York, [Ill. p. 48].
Signed by artist: Ku-wu Ch'en Huan. Seal of the artist, reading *Wu-ho.* Colophon (collection of pastiche poems) by Huang Tao-chieh, dated 1903, with two seals. Colophon by Weng T'ung-ho (1830–1904), dated 1897, with one seal.

4. Yüan Shang-t'ung (1570–1661). *The Road to Shu.* Dated 1631. Hanging scroll, ink on paper. 52-7/8 x 23-3/4″. Ching Yüan Chai Collection. [Ill. p. 49].
Inscription by artist: Fragrant trees line the Ch'in mountain path, / The long flowing [river] encircles the city of Shu. / An autumn day in the *hsin-wei* [year, 1631]. / Yüan Shang-t'ung. Two seals of the artist. One collector's seal, unidentified.

5. Li Shih-ta (active late 16th–early 17th century). *Landscape with Figures: Men Seated in a Bamboo Grove.* Hanging scroll, ink and light colors on silk. 57-1/4 x 39″. Collection Mr. Yuji Eda, Tokyo. [Ill. p. 50].
Inscription by artist: In the midst of the fog, colors of trees, filled with a thousand blossoms; / In the bamboo grove, the sound of a stream spraying in a hundred directions. / Li Shih-ta. Two seals of the artist (Contag and Wang, nos. 3 and 4). Published: (1) *Kyuka Inshitsu Meiga Mokuroku,* I; and (2) Harada, *Pageant of Chinese Painting,* pl. 654. Former Kuwana Tetsujo Collection, Kyoto.

6. Li Shih-ta. *T'ao Yüan-ming Appreciating Chrysanthemums.* Dated 1619. Hanging scroll, ink and colors on silk. 62-9/16 x 22-11/16″. University of Michigan Museum of Art, Ann Arbor. [Ill. p. 49].
Inscription by artist: Painted in autumn of the *chi-wei* [year, 1619], Li Shih-ta. Two seals of the artist. One

collector's seal (faded). Published: J. D. Ch'en, *Chinese Paintings from the King Kwei Collection,* Vol. I, Kyoto, 1956, pl. 38. Former collection of J. D. Ch'en, Hong Kong.

7. Anonymous. *The Lan-t'ing Gathering.* Handscroll, ink and colors on paper. 13 x 120″. Ching Yüan Chai Collection. [Ill. p. 51].
Spurious signature reading "Cheng-ming" [Wen Cheng-ming]. Three spurious seals of Wen Cheng-ming. Seven collectors' seals, all spurious: Liang Ch'ing-piao (1620–1691), An Ch'i (1683–after 1742), and the Chien-lung Emperor (reigned 1736–1796).

8. Ch'en Kuan (active 1610–1640). *Landscape with Cranes.* Dated 1638. Hanging scroll, ink and colors on silk. 78 x 38-3/4″. Ching Yüan Chai Collection. [Ill. p. 52].
Inscription by artist: Cranes nesting in the pine trees everywhere, / People visiting the wicker gate are few. / On an auspicious day in the first month of the *mou-yin* [year, 1638], / Ch'en Kuan painted this as a present for Mr. Ming-tai. Two seals of the artist. Former Nü Wa Chai Collection.

9. Ku Ning-yüan (active ca. 1636). *Landscape in the Style of Chao Meng-fu.* Hanging scroll, ink and colors on paper. 21-1/4 x 12-1/4″. Ching Yüan Chai Collection. [Ill. p. 54].
Inscription by artist: Quiet and calm, with the spirit of high antiquity, / Free and expansive, going beyond the dusty world, / In [my] leisure time, whistling a song, / In the midst of rivers and mountains, observing autumn colors. / Ning-yüan. Two seals of the artist. Seven collectors' seals: Chu Chih-ch'ih (dated 1652, Contag and Wang nos. 3, 5, 6, 7, 10, and 12), and Chang Hsiao-ssu (late Ming period).

10. Hsiang Sheng-mo (1597–1658). *Meditative Visit to a Mountain Retreat.* Dated 1648. Handscroll, ink on paper. 12 x 107-1/2″. Cleveland Museum of Art: Purchase from the J. H. Wade Fund. [Ill. p. 53].
Inscription by artist of a poem in the *tz'u* form. Eight seals of the artist (Contag and Wang, nos. 9, 18, 54, 71, 74, 76, 77, and 78). Thirteen collectors' seals, including those of Chang Heng (Ts'ung-yü, modern).

11. Hsiang Sheng-mo. *Album of Landscapes.* Dated 1649. Album of eight leaves on paper, four leaves in color, four in ink wash. Each leaf 10-1/4 x 13″. Collection J. T. Tai, New York. [Ill. p. 56].
Each leaf inscribed by the artist with a short poem describing the scene. Each leaf signed and with seals of the artist. Three leaves dated: Leaf D: 1649 summer, fifth moon; Leaf E: 1649, on the day the frost falls, at age fifty-three; Leaf H: 1649, summer solstice. Many collectors' seals, including Lu Yün Lou, Pai Ching Chai, T'an Ch'ing (modern), Chang Heng (Ts'ung-yü, modern), and others. Published: *Chugoku Meigashu,* Tokyo, 1935, Vol. IV.

12. Sheng Mao-yeh (active 1594–1637). *Waterfall on Mt. Lu.* Hanging scroll, ink and colors on silk. 81-1/2 x 39-1/4″. University Art Museum, Berkeley. [Ill. p. 64].
Inscription by artist: Waterfall on [Mt.] K'uang-lu. Wu-yüan Sheng Mao-yeh. Three seals of the artist. One collector's seal, unidentified.

13. Sheng Mao-yeh. *Album of Landscapes.* Three leaves from an album of eight. Ink and light colors on paper. 11-1/4 x 18-5/8″. Private Collection, New York. [Ill. p. 65].
The remaining five leaves in the Center of Asian Art and Culture, San Francisco, are not in the exhibition. One of the leaves not included bears a couplet, the signature, and one seal of the artist (see Sirén, *Chinese Painting*, Vol. VI, pl. 279A). The three leaves in the exhibition are without signature or seals. Published: Osvald Sirén, *Chinese Painting*, Vol. VI, pl. 275B (Leaf A).

14. Sheng Mao-yeh. *Album of Landscapes.* Two leaves from an album of six. Ink and light colors on silk. Each leaf 11 x 11-7/8″. The Metropolitan Museum of Art, New York, The Sackler Fund, 1969. [Ill. p. 68].
Each leaf bears a verse couplet by the artist (for translations, see p. 58), signature, and one seal. Five collectors' seals, unidentified.

15. Sheng Mao-yeh. *Moonlit Landscape.* Dated 1632. Fan painting, mounted as a hanging scroll, ink and colors on gold-surfaced paper. 9-1/8 x 20-1/2″. Ching Yüan Chai Collection. [Ill. p. 66].
Inscription by artist of a verse couplet (for translations, see p. 58, signed, with one seal. A long poem written on the painting by Wu Yün-hao, unidentified, is dated to the same year as the painting, 1632.

16. Chang Hung (1577–after 1660). *The Chih Garden.* Dated 1627. Eight leaves from an album of twenty, ink and colors on paper. Each leaf 32 x 34-1/2″. Vannotti Collection, Lugano. [Ill. p. 70].
Inscription by artist on Leaf A: A complete view of the Chih Garden, painted by Chang Hung of Wu-men. Two seals of the artist on each leaf.

17. Chang Hung. *Album of Landscapes in Old Manners.* Dated 1636. Eleven leaves from an album originally of twelve, ink and colors on silk. Each leaf 12-5/8 x 7-7/8″. Ching Yüan Chai Collection. [Ill. p. 69].
Inscription by artist: In the summer of the *ping-tzu* [year] of the Ch'ung-chen [era, 1636], Jen-weng ("Stammering Old Man") asked me to paint these twelve leaves. But the refined spirit of a thousand ages in the works of the old masters is not easy to recapture. I pursued it in my painting, but the result is extremely rude and disorderly. I am ashamed that I have not been able to emulate their brush-tips. Still, it is good for a laugh, isn't it? [Signed] Chang Hung of Wu-men. Published: *I-tan* (Fine Arts), no. 1, Taipei, 1968 (four leaves).

18. Chang Hung. *Album of Figure Compositions.* Dated 1649. Album of fourteen leaves, ink and colors on silk. Each leaf 11-1/4 x 8″. George J. Schlenker Collection, Piedmont, California. [Ill. p. 71].
Inscription by artist: On summer days in the *chi-ch'ou* [year, 1649], in leisure time in my mountain dwelling, whenever my friends recounted stories of the unconventional people of the past—those who were idle and untrammeled, or heroic, or hermetical, or eccentric—I couldn't help applauding....I copied(?) these fourteen leaves [portraying them]. The style is simple and awkward, but lively and pleasant....Chang Hung, at the age of seventy-three.

19. Shao Mi (active 1620–1640). *Album of Landscapes.* Dated 1638. Five leaves from an album of ten. Each leaf 11-1/4 x 16-9/16″. Seattle Art Museum. [Ill. p. 72].
Inscription by artist of a poetic couplet on Leaf J: A divine place, where immortals are concealed; / I came once in a dream to these shores. / Fourth month of the *mou-yin* [year] of the *Ch'ung-chen* [era, 1638], Shao Mi. Two seals of the artist. Inscription by artist on a separate leaf: To take the old masters as your teachers is certainly good, but in order to make further progress it is necessary to take Heaven and Earth as teachers. I often returned to the mountains and observed the changing clouds and mist in the mornings, and also the singular trees and springs. In gathering it all on the plain silk, I sometimes went forward and sometimes backward; such are the pleasant diversions of hermits. I painted this album after drinking wine by lamplight; it is not worth examining by critical eyes. (Translation from Sirén, *Chinese Painting*, Vol. V, p. 33.) A colophon by an unidentified wrtier on another leaf copies a passage concerning Shao Mi from *Mei-tsun chi*, the literary works of Wu Wei-yeh (1609–1671). It speaks of his refinement of character, his learning and talent in the arts, his imitation of Sung and Yüan masters in painting, his achievements in calligraphy; it ends with the statement that people who owned even small paintings by him during his lifetime treasured them, and sold them for high prices if at all; this, Wu concludes, indicates how highly he was valued in his time. Four seals of the writer, and four collectors' seals on this leaf.

20. Shao Mi. *The Waterfall on Mt. Lu.* Double album leaf, ink and colors on silk, accompanied by a separate leaf of calligraphy. Each leaf 14-1/8 x 13-7/8″. The University of Michigan Museum of Art, Ann Arbor: Margaret Watson Parker Art Collection. [Ill. p. 73].
Title and signature of the artist, with two of his seals.

21. Shao Mi. *The Hsiang-li Dwelling.* Handscroll, ink and light colors on paper. 10-9/16 x 66-7/8″. Wango H. C. Weng Collection, New York. [Ill. p. 74].
Inscription by artist, giving the title and a dedication to a Mr. Chin-p'ing; signature and one seal of the artist.

An oval seal at the beginning of the scroll reading *Hsiang-li Kuan* is presumably that of the recipient of the scroll. Inscription on the painting by the calligrapher and painter Wan Shou-ch'i (1603–1652) with one seal; a colophon following the painting by another contemporary artist, Chou Ch'üan, written at the request of the same Mr. Chin-p'ing, with two seals.

22. Sung Hsü (1525–1605). *Album of Scenes of Famous Places.* Album of twelve leaves, ink and light colors on silk. Each leaf 10-1/2 x 10-1/4″. Ching Yüan Chai Collection. [Ill. p. 80].
Each leaf inscribed with a title identifying the scene, followed by signature and one or two seals of the artist: Leaf A: The Sung-liang long bridge; Leaf B: The Hsiao-hsia (Passing the Summer) Bay; Leaf C: T'ai-tsung [Peak on T'ai-shan, in Shantung Province]; Leaf D: The T'eng-wang pavilion [at Nan-ch'ang in Kiangsi Province]; Leaf E: Shao-shih (Bodhidarma's cave of meditation) [on Sung-shan in Honan Province]; Leaf F: T'ien-t'i (Heavenly Stairs) [on Hua-shan]; Leaf G: The Old Buddhist Monastery (at?) Yün-yüan; Leaf H: Yen-(tzu)-chi (Swallow Jetty) [on the Yangtze River near Nanking]; Leaf I: Hills by the Lake at Wu-lin [on the West Lake near Hang-chou]; Leaf J: Hsiao Pai-hua Yen (The Small White Flower Cliff); Leaf K: Huang-hao Lou (The Yellow Crane Pavilion) [at Wu-ch'ang in Hopei Province]; Leaf L: Yo-yang [a tower on the Yangtze River in Honan Province]. Seals on some leaves of the collector Liang Jui-shan, unidentified.

23. Sung Hsü. *Autumn Mountains and Waterfall.* Dated 1587. Hanging scroll, ink on paper. 51 x 31″. Collection J. T. Tai, New York. [Ill. p. 81].
Inscription by artist: On the twentieth day of the ninth month in autumn of the *ting-hai* [year] of the Wan-li [era, 1587], Shih-men Shan-jen Sung Hsü drew this "Autumn Mountains and Waterfall." Two seals of the artist (Contag and Wang, nos. 4 and 8). One collector's seal on mounting, unidentified.

24. Sung Hsü. *Landscape with Waterfall.* Dated 1589. Hanging scroll, ink and light colors on paper. 74-1/4 x 16-3/8″. Ching Yüan Chai Collection. [Ill. p. 81].
Inscription by artist: Drawn in the tenth month in winter of the *chi-ch'ou* [year] of the Wan-li [era, 1589]. Shih-men Shan-jen Sung Hsü. Two seals of the artist (Contag and Wang, nos. 6 and 8). Two inscriptions on the mounting, with seals: (1) P'u Ju (P'u Hsin-yü, 1887-ca. 1960); and (2) Chang Yüan (Chang Ta-ch'ien, born 1899). Published: *T'ien-yin-t'ang ming-hua hsüan*, I, pl. 32.

25. Sung Hsü. *Thousand Peaks and Myriad Gulleys.* Dated 1604. Hanging scroll, ink and colors on silk. 60 x 27-1/8″. Collection Walter Hochstadter, Hong Kong. [Ill. p. 82].
Inscription by artist: On a winter day in the *chia-ch'en* [year] of the Wan-li [era, 1604], I painted, in the manner

of the Northern Sung master Tung Pei-yüan [Tung Yüan], this "Thousand Peaks and Myriad Gulleys" picture. The eighty-year-old Shih-men Shan-jen Sung Hsü. Two seals of the artist.

26. Sung Hsü. *Album of Twelve Landscapes.* Dated 1605. Album of twelve leaves, ink and light colors on paper. Each leaf 9-7/8 x 7-1/2". Wango H. C. Weng Collection, New York. [Ill. p. 83].
Inscription by artist on Leaf L: On an autumn day in the *i-ssu* [year, 1605], painted by Shih-men Sung Hsü. Each leaf bears one seal of the artist (Contag and Wang, no. 5 or 6). Leaf A bears three additional seals: (1) Weng T'ung-ho (1830–1904); (2) H. C. Weng (modern); (3) Seal reading *Chien-ch'ing shen-ting* (perhaps belonging to the eighteenth-century painter, Chang Shih-ying).

27. Sung Mou-chin (active late 16–early 17th century). *Pair of Landscapes.* Two album leaves mounted as hanging scrolls, ink and light colors on paper. Each leaf 12-1/4 x 15-1/2". Collection Mrs. Paul A. Bissinger, San Francisco. [Ill. p. 89].
Leaf A signed Mou-chin, with seal reading *Ming-chih.* Leaf B signed Sung Mou-chin, with double seal reading *Ming-chih.* One collector's seal on each leaf reading *Hui-chang chien-ting*, unidentified. Former Nü Wa Chai Collection.

28. Chao Tso (active 1600–1630). *Lofty Recluses Among Mountains and Streams.* Dated 1609–1610. Handscroll, ink on paper. 12-1/2 x 179". Ching Yüan Chai Collection. [Ill. p. 84].
Inscription by artist: "Lofty Recluses Among Streams and Mountains" picture. In the ninth month of the *chi-yu* [year, 1609], I first applied the brush; on the fifteenth day of the first month of the *keng-hsü* [year, 1610], I finished it. Chao Tso of Hua-t'ing. Two seals of the artist (Contag and Wang, no. 1 and another). Seals of the artist also on the paper joins. Label on outside written by Nagao Uzan (early twentieth century). Title written by Li Jui-ch'ing (Ch'ing Tao-jen), dated 1918. One seal of Tung Ch'i-ch'ang (1555–1636). One seal of Sung Pao-shun (1747–after 1817). Two collectors' seals, unidentified.

29. Chao Tso. *Winter Landscape.* Hanging scroll, ink and light colors on silk. 69-1/4 x 37". Collection Mr. and Mrs. Allen D. Christensen, Atherton, California. [Ill. p. 85].
Inscription by artist: Against the paper windows the wind strikes bamboo, / Opening the door, [I see] the snow filling the mountains. / Chao Tso drew the scenery. Two seals of the artist. Former Nü Wa Chai Collection.

30. Shen Shih-ch'ung (active 1610–1640). *Album of Landscapes.* Dated 1619. Album of twelve leaves, ink and light colors on paper. Each leaf 13 x 8-3/4". Collection Walter Hochstadter, Hong Kong. [Ill. p. 86–87].
Inscription by artist on Leaf L: In the first month in spring of the *chi-wei* [year] of the Wan-li [era, 1619], Shen

Shih-ch'ung of Yün-chien drew these twelve small scenes. Each leaf bears two seals of the artist (Contag and Wang, no. 7, and another reading *Shen Shih-ch'ung yin*).

31. Shen Shih-ch'ung. *Landscape.* Dated 1622. Handscroll, ink and light colors on paper. 9-1/4 x 53-1/8". Stanford University Museum of Art: Gift of the Committee for Art at Stanford. [Ill. p. 88].
Inscription by artist: In the spring of the *jen-hsü* [year, 1622], Shen Shih-ch'ung drew this in the I-chiao Dwelling. One seal of the artist. Title by Shen Ch'üan (Ch'ing calligrapher, 1624–1684): "Cleansing Emotions and Regarding the Tao." Colophon by unidentified writer, with two seals. Published: Michael Sullivan, "The Nü-wa-chai Collection," *Stanford Today*, Summer 1967, p. 1. Former Nü Wa Chai Collection.

32. Mo Shih-lung (ca. 1550–ca. 1585). *Landscape after Huang Kung-wang.* Dated 1581. Hanging scroll, ink and light colors on paper. 46-7/8 x 16-1/8". Collection Ernest Erickson, New York. [Ill. p. 96].
Inscription by artist: In the autumn of the *hsin-ssu* [year, 1581], painted in the Shih Hsiu Chai [Mo Shih-lung's studio, signed] Yün-ch'ing. Two seals of the artist (Contag and Wang, nos. 9 and 17). Inscription by Ch'en Chi-ju (1558–1639): The calligraphy and painting of Mo T'ing-wei [Shih-lung] are indeed the marvels of our prefecture. Even Hsüan-tsai [Tung Ch'i-ch'ang] followed in his footsteps. This painting is in the manner of Ta-chih [Huang Kung-wang]; the layered mountain peaks, piled cliffs, and vigorous brushstrokes would cause a wanderer to perceive it as though hearing the [sad tunes] of the Yang Mountain Pass played on a flute. Seal of Ch'en Chi-ju (Contag and Wang, no. 16). Published: *Chinese Paintings from the Chiang Er-shih Collection*, Parke Bernet Galleries, Inc., New York, 1971, no. 21.

33. Tung Ch'i-ch'ang (1555–1636). *Landscape Painted for Ch'en Chi-ju.* Dated 1599. Handscroll, ink on paper. 12-3/4 x 141-1/2". Wango H. C. Weng Collection, New York. [Ill. p. 95].
First inscription by artist: Mountain mists zig-zagging and paths crossing, shadows floating on huts narrow and dark. The pines I planted are full grown. For a whole year I have not set foot on the district magistrate's street [i.e., I have been out of political life]. Followed by one seal of the artist. Second inscription by artist: In the first month of the *ssu-hai* [year, 1599], we were sailing on the Ch'un Shen River [the Whangpoo River, near Shanghai], following the wind from east to west, meeting with clouds morning and evening, gathering close friends, and riding freely in our boat. Chung-shun [Ch'en Chi-ju] and I were drinking to each other and painting with brush and ink to absorb into our breasts [the scenery] of Chü-ch'ü, and gazing at the Milky Way. We then became aware of the tediousness of the cares of the world, and the carefree pleasures of boating with lighted candles. I was asked to

do this scroll. As an artist, I did it to honor our old friendship. [Signed] Ch'i-ch'ang. Inscription by Weng T'ung-ho, dated 1901. Seal of Chu Chih-ch'ih (Ming Dynasty, died 1652). Three seals of Weng T'ung-ho (1830–1904). Seal of H. C. Weng. Seal reading *Erh-fang Hsien-ju*, unidentified, and three others.

34. Tung Ch'i-ch'ang. *Calling on the Hermit at Ching-hsi.* Dated 1611. Handscroll, ink on paper. 11-1/8 x 47-1/2". Wango H. C. Weng Collection, New York. [Ill. p. 97].
First inscription by artist: "Calling on the Hermit at Ching-hsi" picture, painted on the "birthday of mankind" [seventh day of the first month] of *hsin-hai* [year, 1611], by Tung Hsüan-tsai at the Pao-ting Studio. Seal of the artist (Contag and Wang, no. 8). Second inscription by artist: In 1611 I did this scroll for Ch'e-ju [Wu Cheng-chih, see below], the *Kuang-lu* [an official post]. The year before that, I was conscripted from the country into the government, and I and Ch'e-ju served at the same time. I had already made an ancestral vow not to serve, and Ch'e-ju also wanted to be free like flying geese. I took a poem which I had presented to a friend, and inscribed it on this scroll: "I am like distant mountain clouds; you are like the rising sun. The aspirations of each has its own logic; why must one be with the crane and plum [in seclusion]? I only want to be allowed to retire from the world, and end my days in the Peach Blossom Spring." Ch'e-ju carried this with him when he toured the Chiang-men [region in Kuang-tung] and from time to time looked at it and knew that I was not as excessive as K'ung Chih-kuei [a famous Six Dynasties recluse]. 1611, eighth month, after the fall full moon, third day, your "younger brother" of Hua-t'ing, Tung Ch'i-ch'ang, written while in a boat to I-ch'ang. Three seals of the artist (Contag and Wang, nos. 21, 39, and another). Colophon by Wu Cheng-chih (Ch'e-ju), dated 1617. The colophon states that Tung Ch'i-ch'ang and Ch'e-ju knew each other early in life and took their *chin-shih* degrees together. Tung Ch'i-ch'ang fell behind in later examinations and Ch'e-ju fell into disfavor, so that both were exiled to fill frontier outposts. Although they were six hundred *li* (about two hundred miles) apart, they were in constant communication. Later they both met further reverses by offending a powerful man named Ch'en Chih-tse; Ch'e-ju was further demoted and Tung came to visit him. At that time Tung painted this picture, then they went their separate ways. The theme of the painting [about being in retirement] forecast Ch'e-ju's life to come, and he spent long days in the mountains and in the company of life-long friends in refined pursuits away from the world. Ch'e-ju is pleased with his retirement and no longer interested in an official post. The colophon is signed: 1617, summer solstice, at leisure, Wu Cheng-chih. Two seals of Wu Cheng-chih. Inscription by Weng T'ung-ho, dated 1877, and three seals. Two seals of H. C. Weng (modern). Two seals of Chun-chai, unidentified. Published: Nelson Wu,

"Tung Ch'i-ch'ang, Apathy in Government and Fervor in Art," in Arthur Wright, editor, *Confucian Personalities,* Stanford, 1962, pl. III.

35. Tung Ch'i-ch'ang. *Landscape.* Dated 1617. Hanging scroll, ink on paper. 65-3/8 x 20-5/8". C. C. Wang Collection, New York. [Ill. p. 96].
Inscription by artist: In the *ting-ssu* [year, 1617], the fifteenth day of the ninth month, I painted this as a gift for the Envoy Hsüan-yin in the Lo-chih garden at Wu Lin. Tung Hsüan-tsai. Three seals of the artist. Six collectors' seals, unidentified. Published: (1) Osvald Siren, *Chinese Painting,* Vol. VI, pl. 263B; and (2) *Exhibition of Paintings of the Ming and Ch'ing Period,* Hong Kong City Museum and Art Gallery, 1970, no. 22.

36. Tung Ch'i-ch'ang. *Album of Landscapes.* Dated 1630. Album of eight leaves, ink on paper. Each leaf 9-3/4 x 6-3/8". The Art Museum, Princeton University. [Ill. p. 98]. Each leaf bears the seal of the artist, and some bear inscriptions and signatures. Inscription on Leaf H: On the ninth day of the ninth month of the *keng-wu* [year, 1630], I painted these eight scenes. The seventy-six-year-old-man. Inscription by artist facing Leaf H: Since the fourth month of the *ting-chou* [year, 1577] when I started to learn to paint, until the *keng-wu* [year, 1630], fifty-two years have passed. Although the quality of my painting is not yet fixed, still the time I have spent is long, longer than any other painter. In ancient times they said that after forty-nine years the Wheel of the Law is still not turned [i.e., one has not really mastered the art]. Am I like this? If so, then there are no real criteria. [Signed] Hsüan-tsai. Colophon by Lu Keng, dated 1796, with two of his seals. Colophon by Weng Wen-chih (1730–1802), with one seal. Nine other collectors' seals, on title sheets and colophons.

37. Li Liu-fang (active 1537–1619). *Snow-Gazing Along River Banks.* Dated 1616. Handscroll, ink on gold paper. 11-1/8 x 84-1/2". George J. Schlenker Collection, Piedmont, California. [Ill. p. 99].
Inscription by artist: In the *ping-ch'en* [year, 1619], five days before the summer solstice, I stopped my boat at T'ang-hsi [in Chekiang Province]. The rain was cold; it was about to snow. I had these pieces of gold paper sent by my friend Pu-yuan, so I used them to paint this picture of "Snow-Gazing Along a River Bank." Li Liu-fang. One seal of the artist. One seal of Wu Yün (1811–1883). Six collectors' seals, unidentified.

38. Ku I-te (active ca. 1620–1633). *Enjoying the Moon from a Bridge Over the Brook.* (Landscape in the Manner of Wang Meng). Dated 1628. Hanging scroll, ink and light colors on paper. 60-3/4 x 19-1/4". The Metropolitan Museum of Art, New York, Gift of John C. Ferguson, 1913. [Ill. p. 100].
Inscription by artist: On a spring day in the *mou-chen* [year, 1628], I painted this imitating the brush-manner

of Wang Shu-ming [Wang Meng], as a gift for my old master Ch'ang-weng [perhaps Ku Cheng-i]. Two seals of the artist. Inscription by Tung Ch'i-ch'ang saying the painting is after Wang Meng's *Ch'i-ch'iao nan-yüeh-t'u* (Enjoying the Moon on a Bridge over a Stream), and that it surpasses the original. Two seals of Tung Ch'i-ch'ang. Two seals of Liang Ch'ing-pao (1620–1691). One collector's seal, unidentified. Published: (1) Sherman Lee, *Chinese Landscape Painting,* Cleveland Museum of Art, second edition, 1962, no. 76; and (2) Aschwin Lippe, "Enjoying the Moon," *Metropolitan Museum of Art Bulletin,* May, 1951.

39. Wang Shih-min (1592–1680). *Landscape After Huang Kung-wang.* Dated 1636. Handscroll, ink and light colors on paper. 12-1/2 x 254-3/4". Wango H. C. Weng Collection, New York. [Ill. p. 102].
Inscription by artist: There is a long handscroll in ink by Tzu-chiu [Huang Kung-wang] which captures the insight of Chü-jan. In the summer of the *ping-wu* [year, 1636], I did this playfully, following the conception [of Huang's scroll] as a present for the old gentleman Mr. Meng-han, for his inspection. Colophon by Weng T'ung-ho, dated 1902. Seal of H. C. Weng. Two collectors' seals, unidentified.

40. Pien Wen-yü (active ca. 1620–1670). *Landscape.* Dated 1648. Hanging scroll, ink on paper. 38 x 10-3/4". Collection Pihan C. K. Chang, Hong Kong. [Ill. p. 100].
Inscription by artist: In the *mou-tzu* [year, 1648], at the time of the Ch'ing-ming festival, painted in the Tung-yen Ts'ao-t'ang (East Cliff Thatched Cottage). Seal of the artist (Contag and Wang, no. 3).

41. Ku T'ien-chih (active mid-17th century). *River Landscape.* Dated 1649. Handscroll, ink and light colors on paper. 10-1/8 x 167". Cleveland Museum of Art: Purchase, John L. Severance Fund. [Ill. p. 101].
Inscription by artist: Wu Li-fu [probably Wu Lai, Yüan period philosopher] once said, "Unless one has a myriad books stored in the mind, and all the strange mountains and rivers of the world stored in his eyes, he cannot produce literature." I say it is the same for painting. I studied the Tao for the past ten years, in solitude like a monk in retreat, never travelling beyond Chin-ling [Nanking] in the north, or Ch'ien-t'ang [the region of Hang-chou] in the south. Still, I do not tire of thinking of the beautiful places in the world, and after I finish this scroll, I will carry my brush to seek mountains, carefree, and will then be like a wandering monk. Fifteenth day of the tenth month of the *chi-ch'ou* [year, 1649], recorded by Tung-lu. Three seals of the artist. Inscription by Ku T'ien-chih's teacher, Ku Yin-kuang (nephew of Ku Cheng-i): Huang Kung-wang's paintings of the *Fu-chun Mountains* and *Floating Mountain Mists and Warm Green Colors* have been the treasures of the ages. Once I saw these paintings in the collection of Mr. Hsiang of Ho-chung [Hsiang

Yüan-pien, 1525–1590]. Although they are done in color, the quality of the ink is clear and deep as if new, and is very similar to the quality of the brush [in this painting]. This is because Tung-lu [Ku T'ien-chih] has a refined and wide-ranging spirit. In painting he learns from the heart, so naturally he can recreate the subtleties of the ancients. On a clear day by the window, at leisure, I unrolled this scroll and wrote a few words. Twenty-sixth day, twelfth month, on the *chi-chou* [year, 1649], Chi-yüan. Seal of Ku Yin-kuang. Inscription by Ch'ang Hsün-man dated 1650, tracing the lineage of painters in the Ku family from Ku K'ai-chih onward, and praising Ku Yin-kuang and Ku T'ien-chih. Signed, and with two seals. Six collectors' seals, unidentified.

42. Wu Pin (ca. 1568–1626). *Scenery on Mount T'ien-t'ai.* Dated 1607. Handscroll, ink and light colors on silk. 11-3/4 x 57". Honolulu Academy of Arts, Honolulu, Hawaii: Purchase, 1970; opening section given by Miss Renee Halbedl in memory of Mrs. Theodore A. Cooke. [Ill. p. 108].
Inscription by artist: Picture of (Mt.) T'ien-t'ai. *Ting-wu* [year, 1607], painted by Wu Pin. Two seals of the artist. Colophon by Huang Hao-ao, dated *mou-shen* or 1608? Three collectors' seals; one pair, the upper of which reads *T'ien-mu Shan-jen* (probably Ku Ta-chung, late Ming calligrapher from Kiangsu); the other unidentified. Published: James Cahill, "Wu Pin and His Landscape Paintings," *International Symposium in Chinese Painting,* Taipei, Taiwan, 1971 (in press), fig. 25.

43. Wu Pin. *Landscape.* Hanging scroll, ink and light colors on silk. 84-5/16 x 34-1/4". Ching Yüan Chai Collection. [Ill. p. 109].
Inscription by artist: In Fang-hu [one of the Taoist Isles of the Immortals], the scenery is unlike the Three-thousand Worlds [of Buddhism]; In Yüan-chiao [another of the Isles], a feeling of spring is engendered in the Twelve Towers [of the Taoist fairyland]. Wu Pin. Four seals of the artist. Published: James Cahill, "Wu Pin ahd His Landscape Paintings," *International Symposium in Chinese Painting,* Taipei, Taiwan, 1971 (in press), fig. 34.

44. Kao Yang (active early 17th century). *Landscape with Waterfall.* Dated 1608. Hanging scroll, ink and light color on paper. 79-1/4 x 17-3/4". Ching Yüan Chai Collection. [Ill. p. 110].
Inscription by artist: Summer of the *mou-shen* [year] of the Wan-li [era, 1608], painted by Kao Yang. Two seals of the artist.

45. Kao Yang. *Rocky Landscape.* Dated 1609. Hanging scroll, ink and light color on silk. 69-1/2 x 26-5/8". Ching Yüan Chai Collection. [Ill. p. 110].
Inscription by artist: Winter of the *chi-yu* [year] of the Wan-li [era, 1609], Kao Yang. Two seals of the artist. Spurious signature of Tung Yüan, tenth century. Twelve

collectors' seals, including spurious seals of Hsiang Yüan-pien (1525–1590), and other famous collectors, presumably added at the time the painting was re-attributed to Tung Yüan. Former collection of Senator Francis Green, Rhode Island.

46. Kao Yang. *Strange Rocks*. Hanging scroll, ink on paper. 52 x 22-1/4″. Collection Walter Hochstadter, Hong Kong. [Ill. p. 111].
Signature and two seals of the artist. One collector's seal, unidentified. Published: *The Famous Chinese Paintings of the Tsin*, etc. (Nanking exhibition catalogue), Commercial Press, 1943, pl. 177.

47. Wang Chien-chang (active 1628–1644). *Searching for a Poem in the Mountain Shade*. Hanging scroll, ink and light color on silk. 60-7/8 x 19-3/8″. Ching Yüan Chai Collection. [Ill. p. 112].
Quatrain inscribed by the artist: After the rain, the sound of water falling in a hundred streams; / The glitter of rivers, color of mountains, are plays of clear brightness. / Seeking a poem, I chance to turn to where mountains' shadows fleet; / Sitting alone on a bridge, I let night come without returning home. A dedication (?) and signature have been erased. Three seals of the artist. Published: *Nanju Meigaen* 12. Former Kumagai Naoyuki Collection, Kyoto; Yamanaka Shinten Collection; Hattori Kojuro Collection.

48. Wang Chien-chang. *Returning Home from Gathering Fungus*. Dated 1628. Hanging scroll, ink and light colors on silk. 33-1/2 x 20″. Private Collection, Chicago. [Ill. p. 112].
Inscription by artist: Trees on the cliff cage clouds, half moist; / The brushwood gate beside a stream is newly opened. / Facing the dawn I seek for a poem, all alone; / As I gather fungus the sun sets, and I return. / *Mou-ch'en* [year, 1628], the *tuan-yang* day [fifth of the fifth month], painted and inscribed by Wang Chien-chang. Two seals of the artist.

49. Wang Chien-chang. *The Isles of the Immortals on a Spring Morning*. Dated 1638. Handscroll, ink and color on gold-flecked paper. 7-11/16 x 38-1/4″. Seattle Art Museum. [Ill. p. 113].
Inscription by artist: Spring morning in *P'eng-ying* [two Isles of the Immortals], *mou-yin* [year] of the Ch'ung-chen [era, 1638], the retired Scholar of the Yen-t'ien Cottage, Wang Chien-chang. Three seals of the artist. Two collectors' seals on painting, unidentified. Seventeen collectors' seals on mounting, unidentified. Published: (1) *Kyuka Inshitsu Kanzo Garoku* (catalogue of the Kuwana Tetsujo Collection), I; (2) Osvald Siren, *Later Chinese Painting*, I, p. 237; (3) Detroit Institute of Arts catalogue, *Arts of the Ming Dynasty*, 1952, no. 61; (4) Cleveland Museum of Art, *Chinese Landscape Painting*, 1954, no. 78; and (5) *Ars Orientalis* II, 1957, pp. 478–479 (there attributed by

Sherman Lee to Lu Chih). Former Kuwana Tetsujo Collection, Kyoto.

50. Cheng Chung (active ca. 1610–1644). *Landscape*. Dated 1632. Handscroll, ink and colors on paper. 11 x 160-3/4″. Collection Cheng Chi, Tokyo. [Ill. p. 114].
Inscription by artist with a dedication to Liu-weng, or Hsü Hung-chi (Wei-kuo Kung). Colophon by artist: In the *mou-wu* [year] of the Wan-li [era, 1618], my friend Wang Ju-k'ai was a guest at my Chia-shan Library. In the leisure time between our studies, we calmly reminisced about the several decades we have spent learning the ancient masters' methods of formulating their [pictorial] ideas and using the brush [executing the pictures]. I summarized my understanding in this scroll. Several years passed, and I still hadn't finished it; it was just then that things were happening on all sides. In accordance with the advice of my teacher P'u-men, I chose a place [of refuge] and fled to it; I was living for a long time at Po-men [Nanking]. Since the autumn of the *jen-shen* [year, 1632], I have been residing at T'ao-yeh-ch'i (Peachleaf Stream), teaching my son, cultivating my garden, enjoying my remaining years. Now I have managed to take up this old project and finish it, as a repository for my whole life's conceptions of landscape. The Grand Tutor Liu-weng, Duke Wei, has been my protector since I came to stay in the South [the Yangtze River region]. Seeing this painting, he loved and enjoyed it beyond measure, so I have gladly presented it to him. Since there are several thousands of scrolls by earlier painters in the Duke's collection, I don't know how this scroll will stand up to those of the old masters. I only know that the destiny of half my life's brush-and-ink has truly found its proper owner. Fourth month of the *mou-yin* [year, 1638], recorded by Cheng Chung of T'ien-tu. Four seals of the artist. Colophon by Cheng Chi and seven of his seals. Two seals of Hsü Hung-chi. Five seals of Wu Yüan-hui (nineteenth-century Cantonese collector).

51. Hsü Wei (1521–1593). *Bamboo, Flowers, Vegetables, and Fishes*. Handscroll, ink on paper. 11-5/8 x 208-5/8″. Collection J. T. Tai, New York. [Ill. p. 124].
Inscription by artist accompanying each section; most inscriptions concern the subjects of the painting. The inscription on one section illustrated reads: Fish, crabs, melons, vegetables, bamboo shoots, peas, all smell so good….But, after all, they suit a poor man's taste. Nevertheless, one can only get food like this in Chiang-nan. A title and colophon written by the artist are also on this scroll. The colophon, and several of the poems accompanying the painting, are identical with those on the scroll now in the Freer Gallery of Art (see Tseng Yu-ho, "A Study on Hsü Wei," *Ars Orientalis* V, 1962, figs. 5, 6, 8). Sixty-five seals on the painting, many of them the artist's, the remainder collectors' seals.

52. Mi Wan-chung (before 1575–1628). *The Paradise Land-*

scape of Yang-so. Dated 1625. Hanging scroll, ink and light colors on paper. 135-5/8 x 40-1/8″. Stanford University Museum of Art: Gift of the Committee for Art at Stanford. [Ill. p. 125].
Inscription by artist consisting of a poem, partly damaged, the date and signature with two seals (Contag and Wang, nos. 9 and 14). Published: (1) Michael Sullivan, "The Nü Wa Chai Collection, 'They Speak of Eternal Things,'" *Stanford Today*, Summer 1967, p. 4; and (2) Osvald Siren, *Chinese Painting*, VII, 305A. Former Nü Wa Chai Collection.

53. Chang Jui-t'u (1576–1641). *Mountains and Misty Forest*. Dated 1633. Hanging scroll, ink on silk. 48 x 15-3/4″. Collection Mr. and Mrs. Henry Brandon, Washington, D.C. [Ill. p. 125].
Inscription by artist of poem in the *fu* (prose-poem) genre, followed by: *Kuei-yu* [year, 1633], fifth month in summer. Po-hao-an Jui-t'u. Four seals of the artist. Two collectors' seals, unidentified. Published: (1) Charles McSherry, *Chinese Art*, exhibition catalogue, Smith College Museum of Art, Northampton, Massachusetts, 1962, no. 24; and (2) *1000 Jahre Chinesische Malerei*, Munich, 1959, pl. 69. Former Richard Hobart Collection.

54. Chang Jui-t'u. *Mountains Along River Banks*. Hanging scroll, ink on silk. 65-1/4 x 20-1/2″. The Art Museum, Princeton University. [Ill. p. 127].
Inscription by artist: A boat moves from the city wall into the forest; / The river banks are far apart, and the water reflects the sky. / Po-hao-an Jui-t'u. Two seals of the artist.

55. Wang To (1592–1652). *Mountain Landscape*. Hanging scroll, ink on paper. 69-3/4 x 17-1/8″. Collection Cheng Chi, Tokyo. [Ill. p. 126].
Inscription by artist; signed with one seal (Contag and Wang, no. 9). Three collectors' seals. Published: *Chugoku bijutsu ten*, Kumamoto, Japan, 1961, no. 29.

56. Tai Ming-yüeh (ca. 1600–after 1656). *Bamboo Bending Over a Rock*. Dated 1618. Hanging scroll, ink on satin. 66-1/4 x 19-3/8″. Ching Yüan Chai Collection. [Ill. p. 126].
Inscription by artist: On a summer day in the *mou-wu* [year, 1618], I painted this for old Tien-an (the term of address for Tien-an, *ch'in-weng*, indicates that he may have been the father-in-law of one of Tai Ming-yüeh's children). Three seals of the artist, all faded.

57. Yang Wen-ts'ung (1597–1646). *Solitary Pavilion by Mountain and Stream*. Dated 1643. Hanging scroll, ink on satin. 14-3/4 x 7″. Nelson-Atkins Gallery, Kansas City, Missouri (Nelson Fund). [Ill. p. 129].
Inscription by artist which states that in the autumn of 1643 he looked at one of Shen Chou's paintings in the collection of a friend and was impressed by the sparse use of the brush and the extremely untrammeled style.

[Signed] Chi-chou Yang Wen-ts'ung. Two seals of the artist (Contag and Wang, no. 6 and another). One collector's seal, unidentified. Published: Harada, *Pageant of Chinese Painting,* p. 696.

58. Fang I-chih (ca. 1607–1671). *Mountains by a River.* Dated 1642. Hanging scroll, ink on paper. 17-7/16 x 11-1/2″. Ching Yüan Chai Collection. [Ill. p. 128]. Inscription by artist: Painted in the summer of the *jen-wu* [year,1642], for my "elder brother" Ch'iu-yü. Two seals of the artist. Three collectors' seals, one of which bears the date 1697, possibly the year the collector acquired the painting. One paper seal in the center of the painting: *Chin-su-shan ts'ang-ching shih* (Sutra paper kept in the Chin-su Mountain [Temple]—this paper, made in the Sung period and preserved in that temple, was used by calligraphers and occasionally painters in the late Ming period and after; see Chang Yen-ch'ang, "Chin-su ch'ien shuo" [A Discussion of the Chin-su Paper], *Mei-shu ts'ung-shu,* part II, no. 6).

59. Hu Yü-kun (active early to mid-17th century). *Album of Landscapes.* Dated 1614–1615 (?). Album of twelve leaves, ink and color on paper. Each leaf 8-7/8 x 6-11/16″. Ching Yüan Chai Collection. [Ill. p. 131]. Inscription by the artist on each leaf; according to the last, the album was painted in the *chia* and *i* years (1614–1615?). Accompanying inscriptions by friends dated 1614, 1615, and 1622. Each leaf bears one or more seals of the artist. The leaves of calligraphy bear the seals of the calligraphers.

60. Yün Hsiang (1586–1655). *Landscape.* 1624 or before. Hanging scroll, ink on paper. 65 x 20″. Mr. and Mrs. C. D. Carter Collection, Scarsdale, New York. [Ill. p. 129]. Inscription by artist consisting of a quatrain, signed, "Hsiang-shan Yün Hsiang." Two seals of the artist. Inscription by Ch'eng Chia-sui (1565–1643), with three of his seals (Contag and Wang, nos. 13, 15, and another); two others, one giving the cyclical date *chia-tzu* or 1624.

61. Tsou Chih-lin (active 1610–1651). *Album of Landscapes.* Album of nine leaves, with four leaves of calligraphy, ink on paper. Each leaf 11-1/8 x 8-1/2″. Wango H. C. Weng Collection, New York. [Ill. p. 132]. Inscription of artist on a separate leaf: Ten small scenes I did at idle moments to amuse myself. Chün-cheng came by my Yang-hsien Hall, saw them and loved them. He brought some paintings by [Liu] Sung-nien, Po-hu [T'ang Yin], and Shun-chü [Ch'ien Hsüan]…. He said to me, "How about trading old [paintings] for new? Is this a fair trade?" Out of conscience and gratitude, I added two or three more small leaves. Chün-cheng thanked me happily, laughed, and went away. [Signed] Chih-lin. One seal of the artist on each leaf. Two inscriptions by Weng T'ung-ho, one dated 1894. One seal of H. C. Weng. One collector's seal, unidentified.

62. Lan Ying (1585–after 1660). *View of Mount Sung.* Dated 1628. Hanging scroll, ink and colors on silk. 76-1/4 x 38-5/8″ (cropped at bottom). Museum of Fine Arts, Boston: James Fund. [Ill. p. 136]. Inscription by artist: a *fu* (prose-poem) in praise of Mount Sung (translated in the Portfolio, see below). [Signed] Ch'ien-t'ang Chiao-min Lan Ying. Two seals of the artist. Published: *Portfolio of Chinese Painting, Yüan to Ch'ing Period,* Museum of Fine Arts, Boston, pl. 84.

63. Lan Ying. *Winter Landscape in the Manner of Wang Wei.* Dated 1638. Hanging scroll, ink and colors on silk. 69-5/8 x 20″ (portion missing at bottom, restored). Ching Yüan Chai Collection. [Ill. p. 136]. Inscription by the artist stating that he did the painting in imitation of a handscroll by Wang Wei (699–759) titled "Flying Snow Over the Long River," which he saw in 1638. [Signed] Lan Ying, with two seals (Contag and Wang, nos. 23 and 26).

64. Lan Ying. *Album of Landscapes.* Dated 1642. Four leaves from an album of twelve, ink and colors on paper. Each leaf 12-7/16 x 9-3/4″. The Metropolitan Museum of Art, New York: The Sackler Fund, 1970. [Ill. p. 137]. Four leaves only included in the exhibition. Inscription on each leaf identifying the artist whose manner he is following: Leaf A: after Fan K'uan; Leaf C: after Mi Fei; Leaf E: after Wang Meng; Leaf L: after Li Ch'eng (?). Signed, with seals of the artist, Leaf C dated 1642. Published: (1) *Ran Denchiku hoko sanzui-satsu,* Bunseido, Kyoto, 1920; and (2) *1000 Jahre Chinesische Malerei,* Munich, 1960, pl. 78. Former Richard Hobart Collection.

65. Lan Ying. *Cold Mountains and Snowy Peaks, in the Manner of Fan K'uan.* Dated 1655. Hanging scroll, ink and light colors on paper. 55-1/4 x 23-1/4″. Ching Yüan Chai Collection. [Ill. p. 140]. Inscription by the artist giving the title, date, and dedication to Tz'u-weng. [Signed] Lan Ying at age of seventy-one. Two seals of the artist. Published: Joseph R. Levenson, *Modern China and Its Confucian Past,* New York, 1964, pl. 3.

66. Lan Ying. *Handscroll in the Manner of Yüan Masters.* Handscroll, ink and color on paper. 11-1/8 x 113-3/8″. C. C. Wang Collection, New York. [Ill. p. 141]. Inscription by artist: Following the 'brush conception' of the Yüan masters, done in the Shih-wu Mountain Cottage, T'ieh-sou Lan Ying. Two seals of the artist (Contag and Wang, nos. 19 and 20). Four collectors' seals, unidentified.

67. Liu Tu (active late Ming, died 1628). *Landscape with Figures.* Dated 1636. Hanging scroll, ink and colors on silk. 35-13/16 x 15-1/8″. Stanford University Museum of Art: Gift of the Committee for Art at Stanford. [Ill. p. 143]. Inscription by artist: On the day before the solstice in the *ping-tzu* [year, 1636], following the style of Li Ch'eng's

"Searching for a Line of Poetry in the Cold Forest." Liu Tu. Two seals of the artist. Former Nü Wa Chai Collection.

68. Ch'en Hung-shou (1598–1652). *Autumn Landscape.* Fan painting, ink and colors on gold-surfaced paper. 6-1/2 x 22-1/4″. Ching Yüan Chai Collection. [Ill. p. 138]. Inscription by artist: Hung-shou painted this for his "younger brother" in the [poetry?] club Tzu-shih. Double seal of the artist reading Chang-hou. Seal of Ho Kuan-wu, modern collector.

69. Ch'en Hung-shou. *The Wu Hsieh Mountain.* Hanging scroll, ink on silk. 46-9/16 x 20-15/16″. Cleveland Museum of Art: Purchase, John L. Severance Fund. [Ill. p. 142]. One seal of the artist. Inscription by Kao Shih-ch'i (1645–1704), dated 1699, describing the scenery of the Wu Hsieh mountain. Three seals of Kao Shih-ch'i. Published: (1) Osvald Siren, *Chinese Painting,* Vol. V, p. 64, and Vol. VI, pl. 315; (2) *Masterpieces of Asian Art,* Asia House Gallery, New York, 1970, pl. 45; and (3) *Toso Gen-min Meiga Taikan,* Tokyo, 1929, pl. 373.

70. Chiang Hung (dated works 1674–1690). *Birds in a Tree; Narcissus and Rock.* Hanging scroll, ink and colors on silk. 49-3/4 x 18-7/8″ Ching Yüan Chai Collection. [Ill. p. 143]. Inscription by artist dedicating the painting as a birthday gift for Mr. Hua-kuo (probably Chang P'an-kuei, Ch'ing Dynasty calligrapher). [Signed] Hsi-leng Chiang Hung. with two seals.

71. Ch'en Ch'üan (late Ming). *Landscape with Reflections of the Moon.* Hanging scroll, ink and colors on silk. 43-1/2 x 17-3/4″. Ching Yüan Chai Collection. [Ill. p. 144]. Inscription by artist: verse couplet (for translation, see p. 135), followed by the dedication: Presented to the Ch'an Master Tz'u-weng for his correction. [Signed] Ch'uan-ch'ien Ch'en Ch'üan from T'ai-yüan [in Shansi Province]. Two seals of the artist. Long inscription by the monk Tung-ming Yüeh-feng, originally mounted above the painting, now mounted as a separate scroll. Two collectors' seals, unidentified.

72. Ch'en Hung-shou. *Album of Flowers, Birds, and Landscapes.* Album of twelve leaves, ink and colors on silk. Each leaf 8-1/4 x 6″. Ching Yüan Chai Collection. [Ill. p. 150]. Leaf L is signed by the artist: Hung-shou. Each leaf bears the artist's seal: Hung-shou. Opposite Leaf A are two seals: (1) Preciously owned by Lai-cho Hua-tzu [unidentified]; and (2) Do not (let) fall into vulgar hands. Opposite Leaf L are three more collectors' seals, unidentified.

73. Ch'en Hung-shou. *A Scholar Instructing Girl Pupils in the Arts.* Hanging scroll, ink and light colors on silk. 35-3/4 x 18″. University Art Museum, Berkeley: Gift of

Mrs. Elizabeth Hay Bechtel, University of California, Berkeley, Class 1925. [Ill. p. 152].

Inscription by artist: Old and Late, Hung-shou painted this at the Willow Bridge. (The painting was presumably done after 1646, since Ch'en Hung-shou adopted the *hao* "Old and Late" in that year.) Two seals of the artist. Published: (1) James Cahill, *Fantastics and Eccentrics in Chinese Painting,* Asia Society, New York, 1967, pl. 9; (2) Victoria Contag, *Chinese Masters of the Seventeenth Century,* 1969, pl. 82; (3) Sickman and Soper, *Art and Architecture of China,* Baltimore, 1956, pl. 147; and (4) *Selection 1968: Recent Accessions to the University Art Collections,* Berkeley, 1968, no. 15.

74. Ch'en Hung-shou. *The Homecoming of T'ao Yüan-ming.* Dated 1650. Handscroll, ink and light colors on silk. 12 x 127-3/4″. Honolulu Academy of Arts, Honolulu, Hawaii. [Ill. p. 151].

The scroll consists of eleven scenes from T'ao Yüan-ming's life. There are two poetic lines composed by Ch'en Hung-shou attached to each scene, and also an inscription at the end of the handscroll, with the artist's signature (translated by Tseng Yu-ho, see below). Two collectors' seals on painting, two on mounting. Eight colophons by later artists and collectors. Published: (1) James Cahill, *Chinese Painting,* Skira, 1960, fig. 157; (2) Tseng Yu-ho, "A Report on Ch'en Hung-shou," *Archives of the Chinese Art Society of America,* Vol. XIII, 1959, pp. 82-84; (3) Osvald Siren, *Chinese Painting,* Vol. VI, pl. 319; and (4) Chung-hua Press Album Shanghai, 1933.

75. Ts'ui Tzu-chung (died 1644). *Entertaining a Guest in the Apricot Garden.* Dated 1638. Hanging scroll, ink and colors on silk. 60-3/4 x 20-1/4″. Ching Yüan Chai Collection. [Ill. p. 153].

Inscription by artist stating that the painting was done in the autumn of 1638 for Mr. Yü-chung. Seal of the artist. Published: James Cahill, *Fantastics and Eccentrics in Chinese Painting,* Asia Society, New York, 1967, pl. 11.

76. Ts'ui Tzu-chung. *Hsü Cheng-yang Moving His Family.* Hanging scroll, ink and colors on silk. 65-3/16 x 25-1/4″. Cleveland Museum of Art: Mr. and Mrs. William H. Marlatt Fund. [Ill. p. 153].

Two seals of the artist. Two seals of a son of Hsiang Yüan-pien (1525-1590); two seals of T'ang Yü-ch'ao. Published: Wai-Kam Ho, "Nan-Ch'en Pei-Ts'ui: Ch'en of the South and Ts'ui of the North," *Bulletin of the Cleveland Museum of Art,* January 1962, pp. 1-11.

77. Wu Pin. *The Five Hundred Arhats.* Handscroll, ink and colors on paper. 13-1/4 x 816-13/16″. Cleveland Museum of Art: Purchase, John L. Severance Fund. [Ill. p. 155].

Short inscription by artist (for translation, see p. 147). Signature and seal of the artist at the end of the scroll. Seal of the Ch'ien-lung Emperor (reigned 1736-1796). Five seals of Cheng Chi. Former collections of J. D.

Ch'en, Hong Kong; and Cheng Chi, Tokyo.

78. Ting Yün-p'eng (ca. 1575-1638) and Sheng Mao-yeh (active 1594-1637). *Five Hundred Arhats in Landscape.* Dated 1594. Three hanging scrolls, from a set (of twenty-five?), ink and colors on paper. Private Collection, Kyoto, Japan. [Ill. p. 154].

The faces are by Ting Yün-p'eng; the remainder of the figures and the landscape setting are by Sheng Mao-yeh. All three paintings bear the seals of both artists; painting C (presumably the last painting in the series) bears inscriptions by both. Ting Yün-p'eng's reads: "Complete portraits of the Five Hundred Reverend Arhats, respectfully painted in the spring of the *chia-wu* [year, 1594] by the Buddhist disciple Ting Yün-p'eng." Sheng Mao-yeh adds: "Sheng Mao-yeh painted the pictures" [i.e., all but the portrait faces].

79. Ting Yün-p'eng. *Five Forms of Kuan-yin.* Handscroll, ink and colors on paper. 11 x 52-13/16″. Nelson-Atkins Gallery, Kansas City, Missouri (Nelson Fund). [Ill. p. 156]. An inscription by Tung Ch'i-ch'ang at the beginning of the scroll states that Ting Yün-p'eng painted this picture when he was in his thirties, but became pedantic later and could no longer return to this "skillful and wonderful" state. Imperial seals of the Ch'ien-lung, Chia-ch'ing, and Hsüan-ts'ung Emperors. Attached to the scroll is a copy of the *Ta-fo-ting Leng-yen ching,* a sutra, written in minute characters. Published: Osvald Siren, *Chinese Painting,* Vol. VI, pl. 309.

80. Tseng Ch'ing (1568-1650). *Portrait of a Scholar.* Dated 1639. Hanging scroll, ink and colors on paper. 46-3/4 x 16-1/4″. University Art Museum, Berkeley. [Ill. p. 157]. Inscription by Tseng Ch'ing: *Chi-mao* [year, 1639], seventh month in autumn, painted by Tseng Ch'ing in the P'ing-hsiu-ko. Two seals of the artist. Inscription by Ts'ao Hsi-chih: Chen-ch'ih Tao-jen Ts'ao Hsi-chih painted the [background] scenery. Two seals of Ts'ao Hsi-chih. Inscription by Chin Hsing-hua, dated 1641, the first two lines of which read: Most people, in painting portraits, depict the appearance; only Mr. Tseng searches for the spirit. Seal of the modern collector P'ei Ching-fu of Wu-hsi. Published: *Selection 1968: Recent Accessions to the University Art Collections,* Berkeley, 1968, no. 19. Former Nü Wa Chai Collection.

81. Lan Ying and Hsieh Pin (active mid-17th century). *Landscape with Scholars.* Dated 1648. Handscroll, ink and colors on paper. 11-7/16 x 167″. Ching Yüan Chai Collection. [Ill. p. 158].

Inscription by Lan Ying: Done by Hsieh Wen-hou [Pin], a member of the [poetry?] club, for old Shih-jen of the club; Lan Ying added the scenery and inscribed it. Seventh month in autumn of the *mou-tzu* [year, 1648]. Two seals of the artist.

82. Wu Cho (17th century). *Portrait of Madame Ho-tung.*

Dated 1643. Hanging scroll, ink and colors on silk. 47 x 24-1/2″. Fogg Art Museum, Harvard University. [Ill. p. 159].

Inscription by artist: In the autumn of 1643, Wu Cho of Hua-t'ing painted this for Madame Ho-tung at the Fu-shui Mountain Villa. Two seals of the artist.

83. Ch'eng I (early to mid-17th century?). *Confucius and His Disciples on the Apricot Terrace Enjoying the Music of Moderation.* Hanging scroll, ink and colors on silk. 57-1/2 x 41″. Collection Shogoro Yabumoto, Amagasaki, Japan. [Ill. p. 160].

Inscription by artist: Painted by the Ku-Yüeh Ti-tzu ("Disciple of Old Yüeh") Ch'eng I. (The "Ku-Yüeh" indicates that he was a native of the Chekiang-Fukien area.) Published: *Shimbi Taikan,* III; *Toso Genmin meiga taikan,* 255. Former collections: Hiranoya Gohei; Prince Fushimi. The painting has been in Japan at least from the early nineteenth century, as it was copied by Tanomura Chikuden (1777-1835), Okada Hanko (1782-1846), and other Japanese painters.

84 (addendum). Li Shih-ta. *A Gathering of the Keng-she Literary Club.* Accompanied by an inscription dated 1589. Handscroll, ink and colors on paper flecked with gold and mica. 11-5/8 x 55-1/2″. Collection J. T. Tai, New York. [Ill. p. 55].

Signed by the artist with two of his seals. Title ("United Voices [or Chorus of Compositions] of the Keng-she Literary Club") and inscriptions by seven members of the Keng-she Literary Club: Yang T'ing-yin; Tseng Yung-chih; Liu Erh; K'ung Chen-yüan; Liu Hsüeh-chih; K'ung Chen-ming; last inscription unidentified. Each inscription accompanied by two or three seals of the writer. Five other seals on title and painting, one probably that of the Keng-she Club, one (perhaps spurious) of An Ch'i (1683-after 1742), the others unidentified. The inscriptions are poems composed in honor of the fortieth birthday of one of the members of the club. The fourth in the series, by K'ung Chen-yüan, reads: "The season was early autumn, the taste of *pai-chu* [a party dessert made with white potatoes] became cool / We entered the grove and sat in a circle, the chanting at mid-day was long / The gentlemen [of the Club] were all of exquisite taste and refined manner / But I, shamefully dumb, (should have) turned to face the wall [allusion to a recalcitrant pupil of Confucius] / We decided to set up the *ch'in* [Chinese zither] and let it follow the untrammeled spirit / Appreciating the flowers and birds, we wandered carefree (among them) / Year after year I will remember this day / Abstractedly, while holding a colorful cup, I present the wine of longevity (the Birthday toast)."

Selected Bibliography

Busch, Heinrich, "The Tung-lin Academy and its Political and Philosophical Significance," *Monumenta Serica* 14 (1949–1955).

Cahill, James, *Fantastics and Eccentrics in Chinese Painting*, Asia House Gallery, New York, 1967.

Cahill, James, "Wu Pin and His Landscape Paintings," paper for the International Symposium on Chinese Painting, Taipei, 1970.

Chan Ching-feng, *Tung-t'u hsüan-lan pien*, late sixteenth century, in *Mei-shu ts'ung-shu*, V, 1.

Chang Ch'ou (1577–1633), *Ch'ing-ho shu-hua fang*, preface 1616.

Chang Keng, *Kuo-ch'ao hua-cheng lu*, preface 1739, in *Hua-shih ts'ung-shu*.

Chao Tso, "Lun hua," in *Hua-hsüeh hsin-yin*, III.

Ch'en Chi-ju, *Ni-ku lu*, in *Mei-shu ts'ung-shu*, I, 10.

Ch'en Hung-shou, "Lao-lien lun-hua," in *Hua-lun lei-pien*, I, 139–140.

Chiang Shao-shu, *Wu-sheng-shih shih*, compiled at the end of Ming; first published in 1720?

Chou Liang-kung (1613–1672), *Tu-hua lu*, preface 1673, in *Hua-shih ts'ung-shu*.

Chu Mou-yin, *Hua-shih hui-yao*, preface 1631.

deBary, William Theodore, ed., *Self and Society in Ming Thought*, New York, 1970.

Fairbank, John and Ssu-yü Teng, *China's Response to the West*, Cambridge, 1954.

Fan Yün-lin, "Yü-liao-kuan lun-hua," in *Hua-lun lei-pien*, I, 126.

Fong Wen, "Tung Ch'i-ch'ang and the Orthodox Theory of Painting," *National Palace Museum Quarterly*, vol. II, no. 3 (January 1968).

Fu Pao-shih, *Ming-mo min-tsu i-jen chuan*, 1911.

Fu Shen, "A Study of the Authorship of the So-called 'Hua-shuo'," paper for the International Symposium on Chinese Painting, Taipei, 1970.

Ho Ping-ti, *The Ladder of Success in Imperial China*, New York, 1962.

Ho Wai-kam, "Nan-Ch'en Pei-Ts'ui: Ch'en of the South and Ts'ui of the North," *Bulletin of the Cleveland Museum of Art*, vol. XLIX, no. 1 (January 1962).

Ho Wai-kam, "Tung Ch'i-ch'ang's New Orthodoxy and the Southern School Theory," in *Artists and Traditions: A Colloquium on Chinese Art*, Princeton, 1969.

Hsiao, K. C., "Li Chih: An Iconoclast of the Sixteenth Century," *T'ien Hsia Monthly*, vol. VI, no. 4 (April 1938).

Hsieh Chao-chih, *Wu-tsa-tsu*, ca. 1600.

Hsü Ch'in, *Ming-hua lu*, colophon dated 1673, in *Mei-shu ts'ung-shu*, III, 7.

Huang, Ray, *The Grand Canal During the Ming Dynasty*, doctoral dissertation, University of Michigan, 1964.

Hucker, Charles, *The Censorial System of Ming China*, Stanford, 1966.

Hucker, Charles, ed., *Chinese Government in Ming Times*, New York, 1969.

Hucker, Charles, "Su-chou and the Agents of Wei Chung-hsien," *Silver Jubilee Volume of the Zinbun Kagaku Kenkusyo of Kyoto University*, Kyoto, 1954.

Hucker, Charles, "The Tung-lin Movement of the Late Ming Period," in John Fairbank, ed., *Chinese Thought and Institutions*, Chicago, 1957.

Ku Ning-yüan, *Hua yin*, late sixteenth century, in *Mei-shu ts'ung-shu*, I, 4.

Lan Ying, Hsieh Pin, *et.al.*, *T'u-hui pao-chien hsü-tsuan*, compiled in the early Ch'ing period, in *Hua-shih ts'ung-shu*.

Levenson, Joseph, *Modern China and Its Confucian Past*, New York, 1964.

Li Chu-tsing, "The Development of Painting in Soochow During the Yüan Dynasty," paper for the International Symposium on Chinese Painting, Taipei, 1970.

Li Liu-fang (1575–1629), "Lun hua," in *Hua-hsüeh hsin-yin*, II.

Mote, Frederick, "The Transformation of Nanking," paper for the Conference on Urban Society in Traditional China, Portsmouth, New Hampshire, 1968.

Nivison, David, "The Problem of 'Knowledge' and 'Action' in Chinese Thought since Wang Yang-ming," in A. Wright, ed., *Studies in Chinese Thought*, Chicago, 1953.

Shen Hao (active ca. 1630–1650), *Hua chu*, in *Hua-lun ts'ung-k'an*.

Siren, Osvald, *Chinese Painting: Leading Masters and Principles*, London, 1958.

Sullivan, Michael, "Some Probable Sources of European Influence on Late Ming and Early Ch'ing Painting," paper for the International Symposium on Chinese Painting, Taipei, 1970.

T'ang Chih-ch'i (1579–1651), *Hui-shih wei-yen*, in *Mei-shu ts'ung-shu*, V, 6.

Tseng Yu-ho, "A Study on Hsü Wei," *Ars Orientalis*, V, 1963.

Tseng Yu-ho, "A Report on Ch'en Hung-shou," *Archives of the Chinese Art Society*, XIII, 1959.

T'u Lung, *Hua ch'ien*, ca. 1600, in *Mei-shu ts'ung-shu*, I, 6.

Tung Ch'i-ch'ang, *Hui-shih so-yen*, composed in 1590?, published in 1627.

Tung Ch'i-ch'ang, *Jung-t'ai chi*, collected literary works, preface 1630.

Tung Ch'i-ch'ang, *Hua-ch'an shih sui-pi*, compiled in 1720.

Tung Ch'i-ch'ang, *Hua yen*, in *Mei-shu ts'ung-shu*, I, 3.

Wang Lo-yü, *Shan-hu-wang hua-lu*, preface dated 1643.

Wang Yang-ming, *Ch'uan-hsi lu*, translated by Wing Tsit-chan, *Instructions for Practical Living and Other Neo-Confucian Writings*, New York, 1963.

Wen Chen-heng (1585–1645), *Ch'ang-wu chih*, in *Mei-shu tsung-shu*, III, 9.

Wu, Nelson, "Tung Ch'i-ch'ang: Apathy in Government and Fervor in Art," in A. Wright, ed., *Confucian Personalities*, Stanford, 1962.

Yonezawa, Yoshiho, *Painting in the Ming Dynasty*, Tokyo, 1956.

Yüan Hung-tao (1568–1610), "P'ing-hua-chai lun-hua," in *Hua-lun lei-pien*, I, 129.

Chinese Names and Terms

An Ch'i	安岐	Chao Ling-jang	趙令穰	Chiang-nan	江南
Anhui	安徽	Chao Tso	趙左	Chiang Shao-shu	姜紹書
Bijutsu kenkyū	美術研究	Che (School)	浙	Chiang Yüan-tsu	江元祚
Chang Ch'ou	張丑	Chekiang	浙江	Chiao-mo	焦墨
Chang Chü-cheng	張居正	Ch'e-ju	澈如	Chiao Ping-ch'en	焦秉貞
Chang Fu	張復	Ch'en-ch'ih tao-jen	真癡道人	Chien-ch'ing Shen-ting	建卿審定
Chang Heng	張珩	Ch'en Chi-ju	陳繼儒	Ch'ien Ku	錢穀
Chang-hou	章侯	Ch'en Chih-tse	陳治則	Ch'ien-lung	錢隆
Chang Hsiao-ssu	張孝思	Ch'en Ch'üan	陳銓	Ch'ien-t'ang	錢塘
Chang Hung	張宏	Ch'en Huan	陳煥	Chih	寘
Chang Jui-t'u	張瑞圖	Ch'en Hung-shou	陳洪綬	Chih-yüan	止圜
Chang Keng	張庚	*Ch'en Hung-shou chuan*	陳洪綬傳	Chin Hsing-hua	金星曄
Chang P'an-kuei	章攀桂	*Ch'en Hung-shou nien-p'u*	陳洪綬年譜	Chin-ling	金陵
Chang Seng-yu	張僧繇	Ch'en Kuan	陳祼	Chin-p'ing	錦屏
Chang Shih-ch'eng	張士誠	Ch'en Shun	陳淳	Chin-shih	進士
Chang Shih-ying	張士英	Cheng Ch'ao-tsung	鄭超宗	"Chin-su ch'ien shou"	金粟箋說
Chang Ta-ch'ien	張大千	Cheng Chung	鄭重	Ch'in Tsu-yung	秦祖永
Chang Ts'ung-yü	張蔥玉	Cheng Mou	鄭鄤	Ching Yüan Chai	景元齋
Chang Yen-ch'ang	張燕昌	Ch'eng Chih-sui	程嘉燧	Ching Hao	荊浩
Chang Yüan	張爰	Ch'eng I	誠意	*Ch'ing-ho shu-hua fang*	清河書畫舫
Ch'ang-kung	長公	Chi-chou	吉州	Ch'ing-liu	清流
Ch'ang-pai	長白	Chi-she	幾社	Ch'ing tao-jen	清道人
Ch'ang Weng	長翁	Chi-yüan	寄園	Ch'ing-t'eng	青藤
Ch'ai-chang-jen Hua-chüeh	柴丈人畫訣	Chia-ching	嘉靖	Ch'iu Ying	仇英
Chan Ching-feng	詹景鳳	Chia-shan Shu-wu	家山書屋	Ch'iu-yü	求玉
Chan-pi	戰筆	Chia-ting	嘉定	Chou Ch'en	周臣
Ch'an Hsün-man	單惆漫	Chiang Hung	姜泓	Chou Ch'üan	周荃
Chao Ch'ien-li	趙千里	Chiang-men	江門	Chou Liang-kung	周亮工

Chu Chih-ch'ih	朱之赤	Fa	法	Hsia Kuei	夏珪
Chu-lan mo-chün t'i-yü	竹嬾墨君題語	Fan Ch'i	樊圻	Hsia Yün-i	夏允彝
Chu Hsi	朱熹	Fan K'uan	范寬	Hsiang-li kuan	香里館
Chu I-tsun	朱彝尊	Fan-lung	梵隆	Hsiang Sheng-mo	項聖謨
Chu Yu-sung	朱由崧	Fan Yün-lin	范允臨	Hsiang Yüan-pien	項元汴
Chu Yüan-chang	朱元章	Fang-hu	方壺	Hsiao-hsia wan	消夏灣
Chü-ho-t'ang	聚和堂	Fang I-chih	方以智	*Hsiao-hsin chai cha chi*	小心齋劄記
Chü-jan	巨然	Fang K'ung-chao	方孔炤	Hsiao Pai-hua yen	小白花岩
Ch'uan-hsi lu	传習録	Fen-shu	焚書	Hsieh Chao-chih	謝肇淛
Ch'üan-ch'ien	權倩	Fu	賦	Hsieh Chih-liu	謝稚柳
Ch'üan-chou	泉州	Fu Pao-shih	傅抱石	Hsieh-i	寫意
Chüeh-ssu	覺斯	Fukien	福建	Hsieh Kuo-chen	謝国楨
Chūgoku Bijutsu ten	中国美術展	Fu-kung	福公	Hsieh Pin	謝賓
Chūgoku meiga shū	中国名畫集	Fu-she	復社	*Hsieh-shan-shui chüeh*	寫山水訣
Chün-shih	君實	Fushimi, Prince	伏見宮	Hsin	心
Ch'un Shen	春申	Fu Shui	拂水	Hsin-hsüeh	心学
Ch'un-she t'u	春社圖	Han-lin Academy	翰林院	Hsin T'ung	邢侗
Chung-chao	仲詔	Hang-chou	杭州	Hsü	虛
Chung-kuo hua-lun lei-pien	中国畫論類編	Hao	號	Hsü Ch'in	徐沁
Chung-shu she-jen	中書舍人	Hattori Kōjūrō	服部小十郎	Hsü Hung-chi	徐弘基
Chung-shu-sheng	中書省	Hiranoya Gohei	平野屋五兵衞	Hsü Pang-ta	徐邦達
Chung-shun	仲醇	Hou Fang-yü	侯方域	Hsü Wei	徐渭
Ch'ung An	崇安	Ho Hsin-yin	何心隱	Hsüan-t'ung	宣統
Ch'ung-ch'en	崇禎	Ho Kuan-wu	何冠五	Hsüan-wu men	宣武門
Dai Kan-wa jiten	大漢和辭典	Ho-kung	褐公	Hu Tsung-hsien	胡崇憲
Erh-fang Hsien-ju (seal)	而放閑入	Ho-tung	河東	Hu Tsung-jen	胡宗仁
Erh-shih	二實	*Hsi-hu wo-yu t'i-pa*	西湖卧遊題跋	Hu Wei-yung	胡惟庸
Erh-shui	二水	Hsi Leng	西冷	Hu Yü-k'un	胡玉昆

Hua-ch'an-shih sui-pi	畫禪室隨筆	I-ch'eng ssu	一乘寺	Kung Hsien	龔賢
Hua-chih	畫旨	I-t'ang	怡堂	K'ung Chih-kuei	孔稚圭
Hua-chu	畫塵	*I-shu ts'ung-pien*	艺术叢編	K'ung Shang-jen	孔尚任
Hua-chung chiu yu	畫中九友	Jen	仁	*Kuo-ch'ao hua-cheng-lu*	国朝畫徵録
Hua-chüeh	畫訣	Juan Ta-ch'eng	阮大誠	Kuwana Tetsujō	桑名鉄城
Hua-hsüeh hsin-yin	畫学心印	*Jung-t'ai chi*	容台集	Lan-t'ing	蘭亭
Hua-kuo	華国	K'ang	炕	Lan Ying	藍瑛
Hua shan	華山	K'ang Chin Wang	康親王	Lao-chih	老遲
Hua-shih hui-yao	畫史会要	Kao Lien	高濂	Leng Mei	冷枚
Hua-shih ts'ung-shu	畫史叢書	Kao P'an-lung	高攀龍	Li	理
Hua-t'ing	華亭	Kao Shih-ch'i	高士奇	Li	禮
Hua-yin	畫引	Kao Yang	高陽	Li Chao-tao	李昭道
Huang Hao-ao	黃鶴翶	*K'ao-p'an yü-shih*	考槃餘事	Li Ch'eng	李成
Huang-hao lou	黃鶴樓	Keng-she	庚社	Li Chih	李贄
Huang Kung-wang	黃公望	*K'o-tso chui-yü*	客座贅語	Li Jih-hua	李日華
Huang-hao shan-ch'iao	黃鶴山樵	Ku Cheng-i	顧正誼	Li Jui-ch'ing	李瑞清
Huang Tao-chieh	黃濤楷	Ku Hsien-ch'eng	顧憲成	Li Kung-lin	李公麟
Huang Tao-chou	黃道周	Ku I-te	顧懿德	Li Liu-fang	李流芳
Huang Yung-ch'üan	黃湧泉	Ku K'ai-chih	顧愷之	Li Shih-ta	李士達
Hui-chang chien-t'ing	惠璋鑑史	Ku Ning-yüan	顧凝遠	Li Ssu-hsün	李思訓
Hui-ch'ih	悔遲	Ku Ta-chung	顧大仲	Li T'ang	李唐
Hui-seng	悔僧	Ku T'ien-chih	顧天植	*Li-tai hua-shih hui-chuan*	歷代畫史彙傳
Hui-shih wei-yen	絵事微言	Ku Yin-kuang	顧胤光	Li Tsai	李在
Hui-tsung	徽宗	Kuan T'ung	關同	Liang-chih	良知
Hung-jen	弘仁	Kuan Yin	觀音	Liang Ch'ing-piao	梁清標
Hung-wu	洪武	K'uang-lu pao	匡盧瀑	Liang Jui-shan	梁瑞山
Hung Yeh	洪業	Kuang-tsung	光宗	Liang K'ai	梁楷
I Chang	宜昌	Kumagai Naoyuki	熊谷直行	Liu Ju-shih	柳如是

Wang Wen-chih 王文治
Wang Yang-ming 王陽明
Wei-chung-hsien 魏忠賢
Wei-kuo-kung 魏国公
Wei Shang-kung 魏上公
Wen 文
Wen-chang 文長
Wen Chen-heng 文震亨
Wen Cheng-ming 文徵明
Wen Chia 文嘉
Wen-ch'ing 文清
Wen-hou 文侯
Wen-tu lun-hua 文度論畫
Wu 吳
Wu-ch'ang 武昌
Wu Chen 吳鎮
Wu Cheng-chih 吳正志
Wu Chin 武進
Wu Cho 吳焯
Wu hsieh shan 五洩山
Wu-ho 五河
Wu-lin hu-shan 武林湖山
Wu Li-fu 吳立夫
Wu Pin 吳彬
Wu-sheng-shih shih 無声詩史
Wu Tao-tzu 吳道子
Wu-tsa-tsu 五雜組
Wu Wei 吳偉
Wu Yüan-hui 伍元蕙
Wu Yün 吳雲
Yamanaka Shinten 山中信天
Yang-so 陽朔
Yang Wen-tsung 楊文驄
Yang Wu-pu 楊無補
Yao Sung 姚宋
Yao-t'u hua 凹凸畫
Yeh Hsin 葉欣
Yen-an 研菴
Yen-an 硯菴
Yen-hsien ch'ing-shang ch'ien 燕閒清賞箋
Yen Sung 嚴嵩
Yen-t'ien 硯田
Yen-tsung 嚴犖
Yen (tzu) chi 燕(子)磯
Ying-she 應社
Yo-yang 岳陽
Yonezawa, Yoshiho 米澤嘉圃
Yu-shih 友石
Yü Chien-hua 俞劍華
Yü-chi shan fang hua wai-lu 玉几山房畫外錄
Yü-chung 魚仲
Yü I-cheng 于奕正
Yü-kang-chai pi-chu 鬱岡齋筆塵
Yüan-chiao 員嶠
Yüan Chung-lang chi 袁中郎集
Yüan Hung-tao 袁宏道
Yüan-jun 元潤
Yüan Shang-t'ung 袁尚統
Yün-chien 雲間
Yün-ch'ing 雲卿
Yün Hsiang 惲向
Yün-lin shih-p'u 雲林石譜
Yün-men-seng 雲門僧
Yün-lin 雲林
Yün-yüan ku ch'a 雲源古刹
Yung-lo 永樂

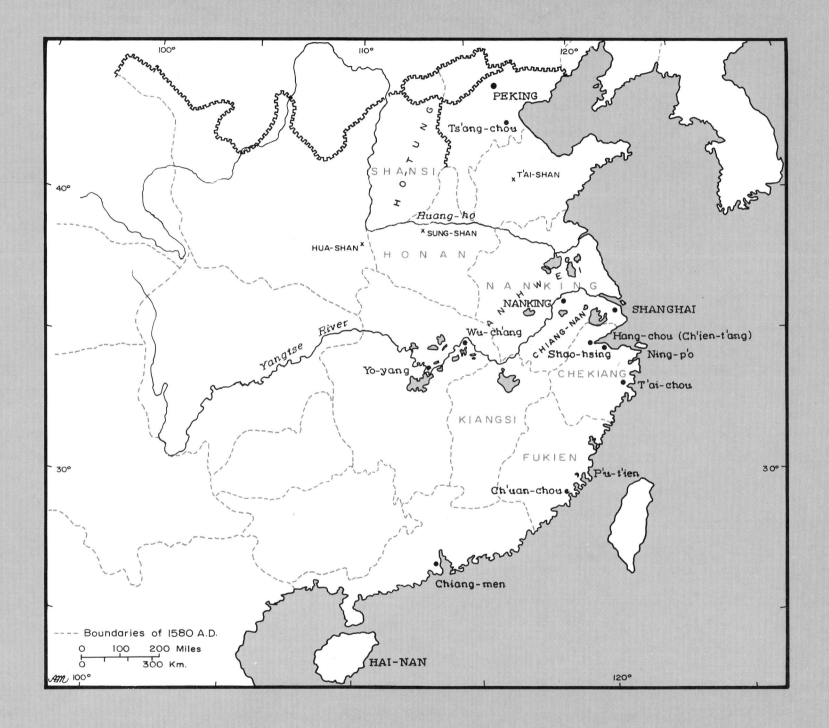

100°
110°
120°

PEKING

Ts'ang-chou

H O T U N G

S H A N S I

× T'AI-SHAN

40°

Huang-ho

× SUNG-SHAN

HUA-SHAN ×

H O N A N

N A N K I N G

A N H W E I

NANKING

SHANGHAI

Wu-ch'ang

C H I A N G - N A N

Hang-chou (Ch'ien-t'ang)

Shao-hsing

Ning-p'o

Yo-yang

C H E K I A N G

T'ai-chou

Yangtse River

K I A N G S I

F U K I E N

30°

P'u-t'ien

Ch'uan-chou

30°

Chiang-men

— — Boundaries of 1580 A.D.

0   100   200 Miles

0   300 Km.

100°

HAI-NAN

120°

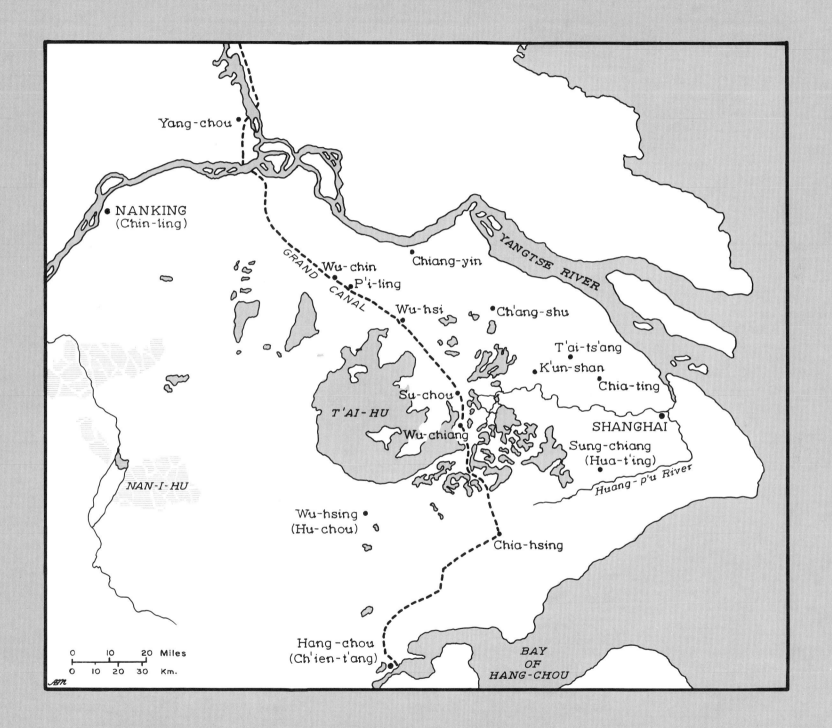

Yang-chou

NANKING
(Chin-ling)

GRAND CANAL

Wu-chin
P'i-ling

Chiang-yin

YANGTSE RIVER

Wu-hsi

Ch'ang-shu

T'ai-ts'ang

K'un-shan

Chia-ting

Su-chou

T'AI-HU

SHANGHAI

Wu-chiang

Sung-chiang
(Hua-t'ing)

Huang-p'u River

NAN-I-HU

Wu-hsing
(Hu-chou)

Chia-hsing

Hang-chou
(Ch'ien-t'ang)

BAY
OF
HANG-CHOU

0   10   20 Miles

0   10 20   30 Km.

Lenders to the Exhibition

Schedule of the Exhibition

Mrs. Paul A. Bissinger, San Francisco
Mr. and Mrs. Henry Brandon, Washington, D.C.
Mr. and Mrs. C. D. Carter Collection, Scarsdale, New York
Pihan C. K. Chang, Hong Kong
Cheng Chi, Tokyo
Ching Yüan Chai Collection
Mr. and Mrs. Allen D. Christensen, Atherton, California
Yuji Eda, Tokyo
Ernest Erickson, New York
Walter Hochstadter, Hong Kong
George J. Schlenker, Piedmont, California
J. T. Tai, New York
Vannotti Collection, Lugano, Switzerland
C. C. Wang Collection, New York
Wango H. C. Weng Collection, New York
Shogoro Yabumoto, Amagasaki, Japan

University Art Museum, Berkeley
Museum of Fine Arts, Boston
Cleveland Museum of Art
Fogg Art Museum, Harvard University
Honolulu Academy of Arts
The University of Michigan Museum of Art, Ann Arbor
Nelson-Atkins Gallery, Kansas City, Missouri
The Metropolitan Museum of Art, New York
The Art Museum, Princeton University
Seattle Art Museum
Stanford University Museum of Art

University Art Museum, Berkeley
November 9, 1971–January 2, 1972

Fogg Art Museum, Harvard University
February 12–April 2, 1972

180

2500 copies of this catalogue designed by Bruce Montgomery, San Francisco, have been printed in October 1971 on the occasion of the exhibition *The Restless Landscape: Chinese Painting of the Late Ming Period.* Typography is Times Roman, set by Spartan Typographers, Oakland. Offset Lithography is by Cardinal Printing Company, San Francisco. Reproductions are printed in 200 line screen and spot varnished. Cover paper is Champion's Kromekote. Text paper is Warren's Cameo Dull book.